HAWAII
A NATURAL HISTORY

The Natural History Press, publisher for The American Museum of Natural History, is a division of Doubleday & Company, Inc. Directed by a joint editorial board made up of members of the staff of both the Museum and Doubleday, the Natural History Press publishes books in all branches of the life and earth sciences, including anthropology and astronomy. The Natural History Press has its editorial offices at Doubleday & Company, Inc., 277 Park Avenue, New York 10017, and its business offices at 501 Franklin Avenue, Garden City, New York.

HAWAII
A NATURAL HISTORY

Geology, Climate,

Native Flora and Fauna Above the Shoreline

Sherwin Carlquist

Illustrations by Sherwin Carlquist and Jeanne R. Janish

Published for The American Museum of Natural History

The Natural History Press/Garden City, New York

1970

PREFACE

Like a great museum of geology and island plant and animal life, the Hawaiian Islands lie isolated in the mid-Pacific. Over millions of years this isolation has permitted unique animal and plant phenomena to develop. Natural crossings of vast stretches of ocean by plants and animals in prehuman times are amazing feats of dispersal. After arrival, these organisms, isolated from mainland areas, have taken curious and unexpected courses of evolution, have presented us with the most exciting and astonishing flora and fauna to be found on an archipelago of oceanic islands. About 95 per cent of native Hawaiian plants and animals occur nowhere else in the world—a higher percentage than in any comparable area in the world.

This book is devoted to phenomena of these uniquely Hawaiian matters. Man has introduced numerous plants and animals, but they are not really Hawaiian, they are only plants and animals of other regions living as weeds or ornamentals in the Hawaiian Islands. Unfortunately, these "weeds" are conspicuous in many places in the Islands, so the visitor who sees an area of man-introduced plants and animals and attempts to identify them in this book will be disappointed. There was not enough space to include both the native and the man-introduced plants and animals, so I chose to tell the story of the natives. These provide many interesting stories, whereas the man-introduced species could only be a catalog of sorts.

The land, the climate, the native flora and fauna form a natural unit with many interlocking aspects. Space did not permit addition of marine biology to these aspects, but marine biology does not relate as directly, so drawing a line at the shore makes for a minimally awkward demarcation. Likewise, anthropology, traditionally included in the concept of natural history, could not be included. I could not have presented Hawaiian marine biology and Hawaiian anthropology adequately or effectively in any case: I, like other biologists, have my limitations even within the fields of biology I know best.

My scheme of design for this book stresses several features not available, or not readily available, elsewhere. Photographs of Hawaiian flora and fauna, or even scenes, have been infrequent and scattered, and many of these are now long out of print. Photographs present much information in a condensed fashion, and are useful for identification and browsing.

The use of numerous chapters is a deliberate way of placing in relief numerous interesting "stories" which might have been buried by the use of long, unillustrated chapters. By "stories" I mean explorations of the significance of features. What is unusual about the Hawaiian climate, what special interest does Hawaiian geology have? Why do we see particular beak shape in Hawaiian birds, why do we see particular forms and colors in Hawaiian flowers? Adaptations such as these are not easy to discuss, but the attempt should be made. Too much scientific literature omits such discussions, or presents flora and fauna as a catalog of scientific names and complicated descriptions.

Most of the drawings and photographs are mine (these are indicated by absence of credit line), but I could not have produced this book without photographs and drawings from other sources. I wish especially to mention the habit drawings of plants, all of which are the work of Mrs. Jeanne R. Janish. Credit lines for various photographs indicate the help of a number of individuals, for which I would like to offer my thanks.

In addition to tangible materials, much assistance of an intangible nature made this book possible. These individuals extended hospitality to me, took me on field trips, and gave me useful information—and tangible materials as well in some cases. For kindness in such ways, appreciation is extended to: Mr. and Mrs. Roy M. Bauer, Dr. Andrew J. Berger, Mrs. Mary Ann Bigelow, Mr. Edwin H. Bryan, Jr., Mr. Norman Carlson, Mr. Charles Christianson, Mr. Ralph Daehler, Dr. Roland Force, Dr. and Mrs. George W. Gillett, Dr. William A. Gosline, Dr. J. Linsey Gressitt, Dr. H. Elmo Hardy, Mr. Ronald Hurov, Mr. and Mrs. Tadayuki Kato, Mr. Karl Kenyon, Mr. and Mrs. Eugene Kridler, Dr. Charles H. Lamoureux, Mr. Libert Landgraf, Mr. and Mrs. James W. Larson, Mr. David B. Marshall, Dr. H. A. Powers, Mr. and Mrs. Ernest Ross, Dr. Harold St. John, Mr. Herbert Shipman, Dr. and Mrs. A. C. Smith, Dr. and Mrs. William L. Stern, Dr. and Mrs. Frank Tabrah, Dr. and Mrs. Robert F. Thorne, Mr. Bunichi Usagawa, Dr. and Mrs. Warren H. Wagner, and Mr. Ronald Walker.

CONTENTS

Preface   vii

The Hawaiian Setting   1

   1. Geology   1
   2. Climate   63

Hawaiian Biological Phenomena   81

   3. Dispersal to the Hawaiian Islands   81
   4. Problems of Island Existence   111
   5. Adaptive Radiation and Unique Adaptations   122
   6. Arborescence   139
   7. Flightlessness in Insects and Birds   157
   8. Loss of Dispersibility in Plants   163
   9. Loss of Competitiveness and Other Changes   173

Special Hawaiian Groups   180

   10. The Land Shells   180
   11. The Honeycreepers and Other Birds   190
   12. The Lobelioids   222
   13. The Silverswords and Their Relatives   250

Biological Regions of the Main Islands   267

   14. The Coast   267
   15. The Dry Forest   275
   16. The Wet Forest   300
   17. The Epiphytic Vegetation   333
   18. The Bogs   345
   19. The Alpine Zone   358

The Leeward Chain 375

 20. Nihoa 376

 21. Necker 381

 22. French Frigate Shoal 389

 23. Gardner Pinnacles 395

 24. Laysan 398

 25. Lisianski 410

 26. Pearl and Hermes Reef 413

 27. Midway Islands and Kure 425

For Your Information 429

 28. Field Trips 429

 29. References 436

 30. Hawaiian Names and Words 447

Index 449

HAWAII
A NATURAL HISTORY

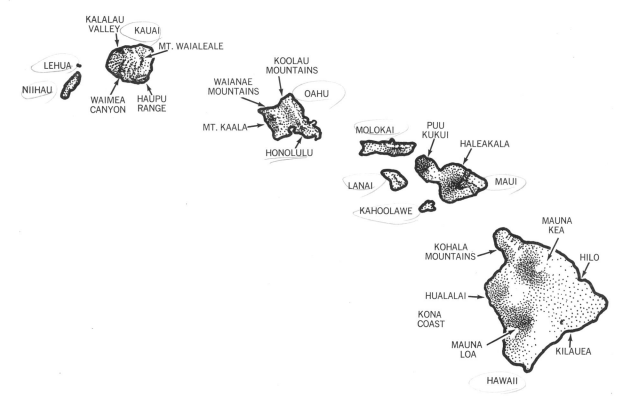

The major Hawaiian Islands

THE HAWAIIAN SETTING

Chapter 1 ❦ GEOLOGY

HAWAIIAN volcanoes would be interesting if only because of the ways in which their forms and histories have guided animals and plants into diverse and curious destinies. These geological formations are, however, compelling in their own right. Hawaiian volcanoes form an unusually complete and exceptionally graphic story. To convert the Islands into a three-dimensional self-explanatory history book, one need only look at them.

The history of these Islands reads from west to east. Beginning at Kure and Midway, the sequence of eruptions has continued to the island of Hawaii, which is still quite active. Underlying these Islands is a fault, or zone of weakness, in the ocean floor, and like a crack in a pane of glass, it has lengthened. Small short rifts contribute to this fault, but the west-to-east pattern is remarkably consistent. Even within each island, the western portion is almost unexceptionably the oldest, the eastern part the newest. Currently the easternmost tip in the Islands is a lava flow which occurred in 1960, at Kapoho on the island of Hawaii.

Most of the sixteen-hundred-mile length of the Hawaiian chain today is composed of small islands; the high islands cluster at the eastern end. Because of the clear sequence and because we know the stages by which high volcanoes are worn down into low, sandy atolls, we can hypothesize that the atolls of the western Hawaiian chain, the so-called Leeward Islands, were once high volcanoes. Just how large and how high we cannot say with any degree of certainty. The last vestiges of an island—a submerged reef or even a sandy atoll—gives no evidence of what former volcanic cones once were there. We only know that there once were volcanic cones. However, the sizes of the present-day high islands of the Hawaiian chain probably simulate the former masses of the Leeward Islands. Many of the Leeward Islands are surrounded by banks, some of them shallow. And, like icebergs, the vast bulk of all of the Hawaiian Islands is underwater. These Islands rise from ocean depths of

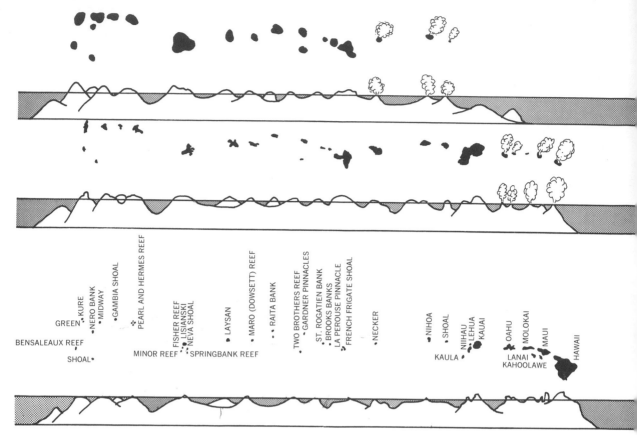

The history of the Hawaiian chain encompasses not merely that of eight major islands, but of a chain which extends from Hawaii to Midway and Kure. Island building proceeded from west to east, as these three stages suggest. The western islands are now reduced to low atolls or submerged reefs; the westernmost island which still has lava rock above the sea surface is Gardner Pinnacles. Sizes and shapes of now-vanished land areas in the first two stages are hypothetical. The third map shows the present-day Hawaiian chain; the first stage represents how the chain might have looked about ten million years ago, the second perhaps five million years ago or less.

more than fifteen thousand feet. Consequently, an island which now is merely a reef is still a volcano at least fifteen thousand feet high. The larger of the Leeward Islands, such as Nihoa and Necker, give a few hints as to their former extent. The slope of existing lava beds suggests how large an island might have been. Steeply inclined beds indicate a more precipitous former cone, and thus a smaller island. More level flows suggest a broad dome. Still, an island such as Nihoa might have had several cones, and a smaller cone might be the only remnant. Even on a single volcanic cone, some lava flows are steeper, some more nearly level. Very likely some of the Leeward Islands were once high enough to have supported some or most of the plants and animals characteristic of today's major Hawaiian volcanoes. We can be certain that the Hawaiian chain was never a continuous strip of land, nor was it connected to any continent. It was surely, as it is today, a chain of islands separated from mainland areas by approximately the same distance as it is today, and with climates very similar to those today.

How old is the Hawaiian chain? If we cannot estimate with certainty the age of any of the Leeward Islands, any statement about the antiquity of the entire chain will be a guess. We do know that the stages from high volcano to low atoll take place rather rapidly in geological terms, however. With the aid of paleontology, geologists are now able to date some atolls and many prove relatively recent. Compared with the slow changes of vast continental masses, the emergence, erosion, and disappearance of a volcano in an ocean area is a brisk geological sequence. The most probable hypotheses say that the rift in the Pacific floor through which volcanoes emerged opened about 25 million years ago, but the islands we see are much more recent than that. The Leeward Islands probably formed between five and ten million years ago.[1] Recent chemical tests (potassium—argon ratio) of rocks from one of the oldest of the main islands, Kauai, indicate ages from 5.6 to 3.8 million years. Most of the visible land in the Islands other than Hawaii dates from the Pliocene, between one and five million years ago. The island of Hawaii has lava flows mostly less than a million years old and is thus an island of the Pleistocene, or ice ages. If such a large island can be formed within a million years, we can imagine that some of the Leeward Islands, which have had plenty of time to erode into the sea, were once equally large.

On a single island we can see sequence in volcanoes if they are adjacent to each other. Lava flows from a new volcano overlap the base of a nearby older mountain. If differences in rainfall among the Islands can be taken into account, the degree of erosion is also an excellent indicator of age. From such lines of evidence, we can say that the major volcanoes became extinct in roughly the following sequence: (1) Niihau and Kauai; (2) Waianae Mountains, Oahu; (3) Koolau Mountains, Oahu; (4) western Molokai; (5) eastern Molokai; (6) West Maui (Puu Kukui) and Lanai; (7) Kohala Mountains, Hawaii; (8) Kahoolawe and East Maui (Haleakala); (9) Mauna Kea, Hawaii; (10) Hualalai, Hawaii. Flows from Hualalai have occurred within recorded history, so perhaps this mountain is just barely extinct. Mauna Loa and Kilauea are still quite active. The most recent flows on islands other than Hawaii are probably those on the southern slopes of East Maui (Ulupalakua) or within the crater of Haleakala, but we have no dates during human history for them.

Curriculum for Islands

The stages in island building begin with an eruption under the sea which finally reaches the ocean surface. These eruptions inevitably are explosive because of the steam generated. Undersea lavas form as "pillow lavas" (large, rounded chunks), pumice (foam-like glassy lava rich in gas bubbles), and ash. In the second stage of island formation, lava pours from the above-water crater, and from rifts on the sides of the cone. These lavas are mostly basalt, which is the most common type of lava in the Hawaiian Islands. There are no Hawaiian volcanoes still in this stage, although all Hawaiian volcanoes have gone through this stage.

The third stage of development features the collapse of the summit, forming a caldera. Calderas, which are depressions much wider than they are deep,

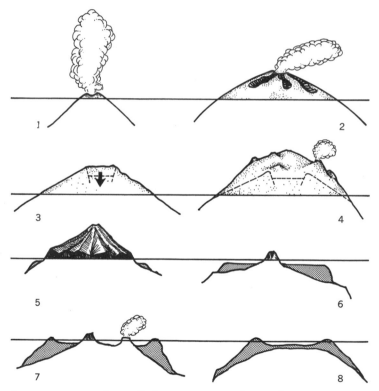

Stages in the origin, growth, and disappearance of a volcanic island include: (1) submarine explosive cone, (2) formation of a volcanic crater, (3) sinking of the summit area, forming a caldera, (4) addition of lavas over the caldera, formation of cinder cones, (5) erosion, formation of marine bluffs, beginning of fringing reefs, (6) disappearance of above-water land, conversion of fringing reef into barrier reef, (7) origin of lateral cone by submarine explosion, (8) barrier reef builds up, island submerges.

occur when the summit falters and sinks as liquid lava (magma) beneath the summit melts the core of the volcano. Volcanoes in the caldera stage continue to emit lava flows, both from the summit and from lateral rifts. Mauna Loa and Kilauea are good examples of volcanoes at this stage. The great activity of these volcanoes is evident from the fact that Mauna Loa produced four billion cubic yards of lava between 1850 and 1950.

The fourth stage is reached when lava flows fill and overflow the caldera, producing a rounded summit. Activity slows down and lava flows tend to be thick and composed of chunky fragments. Nonetheless, thousands of feet can be added to a mountain during this stage. The chemical composition of lavas tends to change. Lava fountains may burst out of rifts on the main dome, and form cinder cones which dot the surface of the volcano. The majority of volcano-building activity is now over, and the lateral cinder cones may be regarded as the "last gasps" in a mountain's eruption. Good examples of volcanoes in this stage are the Kohala Mountains (north end of the island of Hawaii), Mauna Kea, and Hualalai. Haleakala also qualifies as a representative of this stage, although its summit did not achieve a dome-like shape as did Mauna Kea and Hualalai; it retains instead a magnificent crater.

In the fifth stage, the volcanic cone is attacked by erosion. A sea bluff is formed as the surf eats away at the margins of the cone. Rainfall will be heavy on the high island, streams will cut deep valleys and leave sharp ridges, such as those so strikingly evident on Kauai and Oahu. A volcanic cone which does not exceed four thousand feet erodes into broader valleys with wider, rounded ridges; Kahoolawe is an example. All the major Hawaiian Islands could be said to have portions representing the fifth stage, but some have entered to next stage, described below.

A sixth stage can be said to occur when mountains are worn down further, becoming minor rocks which barely break the ocean's surface. Additionally, major shifts in the earth's crust may cause the island to sink. If this proceeds relatively slowly, a coral reef can build up on the fringes of the island. Often, these reefs can keep pace with the sinking of an island, so that reefs thousands of feet in thickness can accumulate. An example of an island in which a remnant lava pinnacle is combined with a broad fringing reef is French Frigate Shoal, in the Hawaiian Leeward chain.

The seventh stage involves a fitful and minor renewal of volcanism. On portions of an island above the sea, a few small cones or lava flows may be formed. These lavas, which in the Hawaiian chain were formed mostly during the Pleistocene, can be identified by their content of certain minerals (nepheline, for example). If eruption occurs underwater, ash is produced. The lateral cones of this stage are usually small, and may occur in various positions on an island unrelated to major rift systems. This stage can be said to be shown by Niihau, Kauai, both ranges of Oahu, western Molokai, and West Maui.

The final stage in degradation of a volcanic island is illustrated by the atolls of the Leeward chain. Above-water lava remnants have been eroded away or submerged, and only the coral reef remains.

Oahu: a Case Study

Most of these stages can be illustrated in a detailed way by viewing a single island. Because Oahu is one of the older high islands in the chain, a long history is displayed. The first step in the building of Oahu was the origin and emergence of a volcanic dome which is now represented by the Waianae

One of the Hawaiian Islands, Oahu, illustrates stages in the origin and changes of a volcanic island. The outlines of present-day Oahu are shown in each stage:

The Waianae volcano erupts.

The Waianae volcano enlarges, the Koolau volcano emerges.

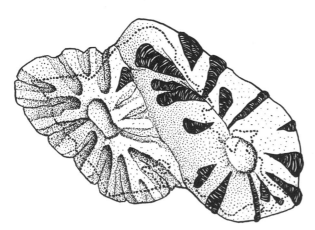

The Waianae volcano erodes while the Koolau volcano matures.

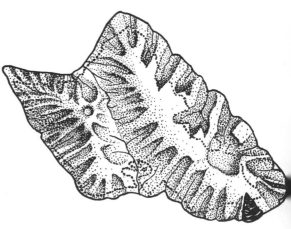

The Waianae volcano erodes into a mountain range, Mt. Kaala develops; the Koolau volcano begins to erode.

Mountains. A crater is shown in the drawing, with a rift zone foreshadowing the future orientation of the mountain range. From this rift northwest and southeast of the crater, lava flows are emerging. One or more lesser rifts are also formed at this time.

In the second stage shown, the Waianae volcano has enlarged greatly, with numerous flows. Collapse at the summit area creates a caldera approximately in the center of today's Waianae range. Meanwhile, the Koolau volcano has surfaced. Just as in the Waianae volcano, a northwest–southeast rift system forms, with minor rifts leading away from the center.

The third drawing illustrates the enlargement of the Waianae volcano caldera,

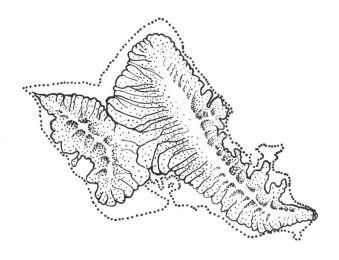

Erosion shapes both ranges to near their present state; the island submerges.

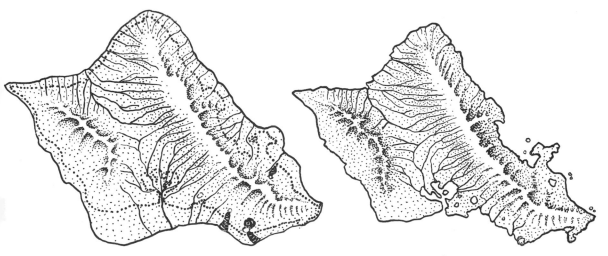

During the Pleistocene, the island re-emerges, the level of the ocean is lowered, lateral craters erupt in the southeast.

Eruption ceases, the sea rises.

and the beginnings of erosion. Valleys are intruding into the center of the volcano, and soon will break across the rim of the caldera. Lava flows are still occurring. Meanwhile, the Koolau volcano has developed a large caldera, centered over what today is Kuapa Pond, near Kaneohe. The northwest rift has become the center of more active elongation of the Koolau volcano. Unsymmetrical development of this sort is not unusual, and the Koolau volcano at this point is similar to the present appearance of Mauna Loa.

The fourth drawing depicts a Waianae volcano much altered in contours: the caldera is now obliterated by erosion, and by flows and other eruptions. A prominent cone, the present-day summit of the range, Mount Kaala, has erupted. At the same time, the Koolau volcano has been subject to erosion, which has affected the windward side most drastically. The greater rainfall has cut most deeply into the northern slopes.

The next stage shows Oahu "drowned": submergence has occurred. Studies have shown that today deep valleys on Oahu can be found thousands of feet beneath the sea. Such valleys cannot have been worn by ocean currents according to geologists. Therefore, we know that these valleys were formed when the island was at a higher level of emergence, and the island must now be submerged below its highest point.

The sixth drawing for Oahu brings us close to the present: the happenings during the Pleistocene, the past million years. During the ice ages, vast quantities of water were removed from the ocean and stored in the extensive icecaps which covered much of the earth at that time. The shoreline of Oahu must then have extended farther out. Eruptions occurred in the southeastern part of Oahu, producing small but familiar craters, such as Diamond Head. These craters will be described in greater detail later.

The final stage, Oahu today, indicates shorelines that have receded inward as the Pleistocene icecaps melted. The shallow basin between the Waianae and Koolau ranges has been partially invaded by seawater, forming Pearl Harbor. Other ponds and lagoons on the lower portions of the coastal plain are evident: Waikiki was once such a marshy lagoon, although now it has been drained.

Of the two volcanic domes which formed Oahu, more than half the land has been removed by erosion. This process still continues. If one views the coast of Oahu—or the other islands—after a heavy rain, one sees that rivers have delivered broad muddy deposits into the surrounding ocean. In the Koolau Mountains, the steep slopes are subject to frequent landslides, which have an even greater effect than erosion. We can expect that with such drastic erosion of the soft volcanic rocks and soils, Oahu will vanish in a few million years.

Lava Flows: the Island of Hawaii

A more magnificent display of lava flows, easily seen by road, probably does not exist than the series, varying in size, type, texture, and age, which we see on Hawaii. The number of flows since 1800 shows how very active volcanism is, especially on Mauna Loa and in the Kilauea region. Hualalai has

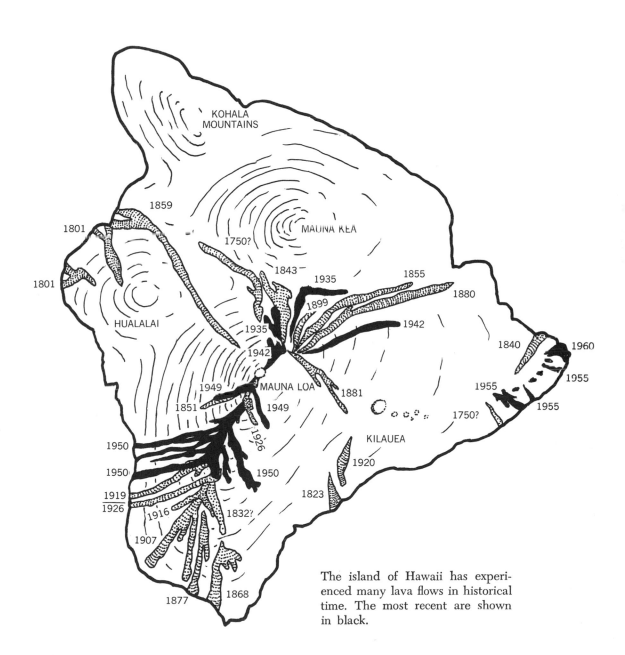

The island of Hawaii has experienced many lava flows in historical time. The most recent are shown in black.

reached dormancy: the most recent flows date from 1801. On Mauna Loa and in Kilauea, events continue with such great frequency that a dramatic display is offered about every five years, and minor eruptions can be seen almost every year. Volcanic changes on Mauna Loa can be correlated with those on Kilauea. At the Volcano Observatory in Kilauea (Hawaii Volcanoes National Park) a visitor can observe recording seismographs which simultaneously show tremors at various localities on Mauna Loa and Kilauea. Even when no visible eruption is in progress, minor tremors are frequently recorded. During the eruption of December 1959 at Kilauea, more than twenty-two hundred earthquakes were recorded. One can be certain that Kilauea and Mauna Loa will continue to erupt, but these events cannot be predicted accurately. Lava flows which have cooled are, however, more informative, and have the advantage of permitting a visit, whereas the fiery displays cannot be seen at close range. Most visitors will not see an eruption, but they will not be disappointed, because Kilauea is a perfect museum of volcanism, whether hot or cold.

An account of volcanic activity on Hawaii must, of necessity, draw on recent events as illustrations. These, of course, become outdated as subsequent eruptions occur. The eruptions described here should be considered only as types; similar ones have occurred earlier, and will in the future. Anyone interested in the early history of events on Mauna Loa and Kilauea will want to read the book by Brigham, *The Volcanoes of Kilauea and Mauna Loa on the Island of Hawaii*, which describes and illustrates events from 1789 to 1908. The Volcano Observatory has published illustrated bulletins which continue this history since 1913.

The greatest number of lava flows on Mauna Loa have emerged from the vicinity of the summit caldera, Mokuaweoweo. There we see a flat floor surrounded by a fault scarp. The floor is covered by recent flows. The 1933 activity

A volcanic eruption, like this one at the summit of Mauna Loa (Mokuaweoweo caldera) in 1933, is usually related to a rift. "Curtains of fire" can be seen (Hawaii Visitors Bureau).

On November 22, 1935, a flank eruption of Mauna Loa occurred. The snowy summit of the mountain is seen at upper left. One lava stream, producing the large steam cloud, disappears in a crater out of sight. In the foreground, a lava stream disappears into a steaming rift (Hawaii Visitors Bureau).

shown featured fire fountains—streams of hot lava forced out of narrow crevices. A fire fountain, while spectacular, produces only a relatively small volume of lava because the aperture through which it emerges is small. A massive flow may emerge with little or no fire-fountain activity.

From the summit caldera of Mauna Loa, a rift extends northeast in the direction of Hilo, while another rift system points toward the southern tip of the island. From these rifts, numerous flows have emerged. The photograph of the 1935 eruption illustrates this rift zone, and shows how lava emitted can set off fires.

Submarine eruptions. We are several milllion years too late to witness the eruption of any Hawaiian island from beneath the ocean surface, although these eruptions still occur in other parts of the Pacific. Late in 1967 such an eruption occurred in Tonga. Another in the Bonin Islands in 1946 is illustrated in *Island Life*. The photograph here of the 1960 flow entering the ocean at Kapoho on the island of Hawaii simulates in some respects a submarine eruption. Lavas from such a flow or from a submarine eruption, when they contact the ocean, form round balls. These so-called pillow lavas, spheres one to five feet in diameter, result from the rapid cooling of lava in water. A visitor can see pillow lavas at the base of Wailua Falls, where lava once spread over the

The 1960 flow at Kapoho entered the ocean (United States Department of Interior, National Park Service). When lavas enter water, they tend to form spherical masses, known as pillow lavas, which resemble this specimen at the Bishop Museum.

A flow of aa lava consists of rough blocks. It may occur in the form of a river, as in the 1950 South Kona flow at left, or spread over a nearly level area, as in the 1935 flow on the Humuula Saddle Road.

A pocket of forest surrounded by, but left intact by, an aa flow is called a kipuka. Aa flows, when they reach the sea, sometimes form embayments, natural quays. The lava blocks were rearranged by the Hawaiians to form fishponds.

Wailua River. Off the southeast coast of Hawaii, pillow lavas have been photographed at a depth of 14,400 feet.

Aa. The Hawaiian word for chunky lavas is aa, or a-a, and this word is now universally used by geologists for such lavas anywhere in the world. Aa consists of basalt, and forms sharp angular blocks and rough fragments. These fragments are vesicular—they contain trapped bubbles of gases. When active, an aa flow is relatively cool, below the temperature of liquid lava. Nevertheless, the front of an aa flow glows, and moves along like a river turning into ice. As it proceeds, "clinkers" of lava tumble forward. "Rivers" composed of these blocks can move considerable distances. Such a river can be seen in the 1950 flow where the highway crosses it in the South Kona District on the west coast of the island of Hawaii. Even where the terrain is relatively level, an aa flow can cover broad expanses. One can see nearly level aa flows near Pohakuloa, along the Humuula Saddle Road between Hilo and Kamuela. Aa flows are not exclusively different from liquid (pahoehoe) flows, and some flows are composed of both types. Blocks of aa may become wrapped together by liquid lava, and roll down a flow as "accretionary lava balls." Where hot lava blocks scrape against each other, they may form "plastic striated lava" or "grooved lava." Aa flows are the most common type now visible in the Hawaiian Islands, but many are covered with vegetation. In dry areas they remain rather bare for decades, even hundreds of years.

Inevitably, some aa flow will penetrate into forested areas. If the lava is relatively cool, the vegetation will not be set on fire. Just as a river shifts and forms islands in its midst, the lava rivers leave isolated pockets of vegetation, known as kipukas. Numerous kipukas may be seen on the Saddle Road between Hilo and Kamuela, and also in the Puna District between Pahoa and Kalapana.

Where an aa flow reaches the sea, it may add to the coastline. Lava blocks form natural quays and bays. The ancient Hawaiians often used these to form fishponds. By adding blocks to protrusions of lava into the sea to form break-waters, they formed circular enclosures in the tidal zone, which is usually shallow and paved with corals. These enclosures permitted fish to enter as the tide rose, and nets across the entry prevented the escape of fish, thus providing a convenient storage until the fish were needed. Fishponds of this sort, made of aa blocks, can be seen along the south shore of Molokai, in the north Kona District of Hawaii, and near Hilo.

Pahoehoe. The word pahoehoe, like aa, is a Hawaiian word now universal among geologists for lava emitted in the liquid state. The forms taken by pahoehoe depend on the conditions under which it emerges and upon its chemistry. If rapid escape of gas cools the pahoehoe, it may change into aa.

A pahoehoe flow, crossing a road in the Kilauea area, moves forward as a series of ropy flows (United States Department of Interior, National Park Service).

Hotter pahoehoe flows as highly liquid narrow ripples, often described as "ropy," whereas somewhat cooler pahoehoe turns into crass, bulky folds. Pahoehoe usually contains gas bubbles, but these are ordinarily smaller and less numerous than those of aa. If flow action continues after a pahoehoe crust has cooled, the crust may be raised and tumbled into a jumble of sheets and fragments. Many examples of upraised pahoehoe can be seen in Kilauea.

Because of the liquid nature of pahoehoe, it is capable of many curious formations as it invades an area. On the island of Hawaii, many of the areas penetrated by a pahoehoe flow are forested. If pahoehoe surrounds such trees, then subsides or flows away, there is a spectacular result. Tree trunks surrounded by pahoehoe cool the lava, and thus are coated by hardened pahoehoe; if the liquid pahoehoe then subsides, the lava casing on the tree trunks remains. So-called "lava trees" result, and can be identified as standing lava cylinders from which the contained tree trunk usually has rotted away, if it was not completely burned during the flow. Good places to see lava trees include Lava Trees State Park in the Puna District, and at certain localities in Kilauea.

Lava which invades a forest but does not recede forms tree molds. Again,

A pahoehoe flow at night in Halemaumau, Kilauea: as it expands, cracks open in the cooled surface, revealing the glowing lava beneath (photo by Camera Hawaii).

The typical appearance of pahoehoe lava is shown by this specimen along the Humuula Saddle Road.

Highly liquid pahoehoe forms a crust of fine ripples, as seen here near the summit of Hualalai.

Broad curved forms of pahoehoe can be seen along the Hilina Pali Road in Hawaii Volcanoes National Park.

Pahoehoe crusts may be raised into sheets if the flow cools but pressure continues.

"Lava trees" are formed when a pahoehoe flow engulfs trees, cools around them, then subsides, leaving tubular casts around the tree trunks, which ultimately rot away.

When lava surrounds and kills a tree trunk, the wood eventually rots away, leaving a tree mold: Kilauea-iki, 1959 eruption.

Pahoehoe lava penetrating into wood which was turned to charcoal produced this unusual cast. This specimen is displayed in the court of the Bishop Museum, Honolulu.

A natural bridge formed by a lava flow can be seen on the side of Koko Crater, southeastern Oahu; deposits of ash beneath the span have eroded away.

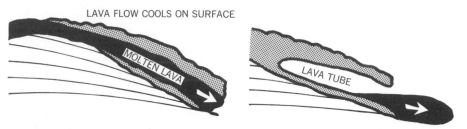

A lava tube forms when a pahoehoe flow cools on its surface, but pressure continues and the liquid center runs out.

Thurston Lava Tube, near Kilauea, is an example of a rather large lava tube (photo by Camera Hawaii).

trees are killed by pahoehoe, and ultimately rot away, leaving a hole the diameter of the original trunk. Very hot liquid pahoehoe can invade wood as it turns to charcoal. In particularly nice specimens the lava forms delicate impressions of the minute cracks in the charcoal.

If a pahoehoe flow covers softer deposits, such as ash beds, other interesting results can occur. On Koko Crater, Oahu, pahoehoe flows overlie beds of tuff (layers of ash and other volcanic debris). The tuff has eroded away, leaving lava exposed in one place in the form of a natural bridge.

A small lava tube can b[...] the surface of this roa[...] Kaumalapau, Lanai.

[...]Hualalai is a lava tube, the roof of which was thin and fell in.

This historic photograph, taken February 13, 1919, shows a vent, or lava cavern, resembling a blast furnace. This occurred at the margin of the lava lake which at that time rose out of Halemaumau and covered the floor of Kilauea (photograph by T. A. Jaggar, courtesy of Hawaii Volcano Observatory). Driblets of molten lava in a lava cavern can form stalactites and stalagmites. A stalactite from a Kilauea lava cavern is shown here.

A deep lava flow has been cut into by the Wailuku River near Hilo, at a locality called Boiling Pots. This lava flow cooled slowly, producing upright basalt columns as fractures developed in the cooling stone. These columns have been exposed by the river's eroding effects.

The liquid properties of pahoehoe permit it to form lava tubes. These tubes are sometimes so large that they were used as refuge caverns by the Hawaiians during wars and battles. A pahoehoe flow cools more rapidly at its surface than in its center. If pressure builds within the flow, the center may be released, leaving the outside as a hollow cylinder. Some of these lava tubes are quite large, for example the Thurston Lava Tube in Hawaii Volcanoes National Park (Kilauea). Others are very small, and may be seen on road cuts where a thickness of pahoehoe flows has been exposed. Near the summit of Hualalai, there is a collapsed lava tube. This tube probably had a rather thin ceiling, which ultimately fell in, leaving what today is a large trench. Another effect of pahoehoe is that it can flow over cliffs and fault scarps, coating them with a natural veneer of thin lava.

Near the source of a pahoehoe flow, the vent may contract into a cavern which appears like a blast furnace, and in fact acts rather like one, as hot escaping gases rush over liquid lava. Heat in such a cavern may melt lava on the roof, thus providing driblets resembling those in a limestone cavern. Lava stalactites and stalagmites have been found in such caverns.

A massive pahoehoe flow may, when it cools, contract into columns. Such angular basalt columns have been found in various parts of the world, and are given names such as "Devil's Postpile" or "Devil's Tower." One excellent example can be seen within the city limits of Hilo. The Wailuku River has cut into a flow, producing a series of waterfalls and splash pools. The river has worn away some of these columns, but has, in the process, exposed them.

Intrusive Lava: Dikes

When a volcanic cone erupts, the external results are only a part of what happens. As liquid magma rises beneath the cone, it swells, disrupting old lava beds, forming cracks into which the magma flows. Through some of these cracks, liquid lava will issue. Other veins of hot lava do not spill out at the surface. The intruded magma in these cracks eventually cools. During intrusion and cooling, it was under great pressure. Under such pressure, gas bubbles cannot expand, and the magma cools as a fine-grained rock usually pale gray in color. These intruded plates of magma are called dikes, and are easily distinguished when portions of a volcano erode away. Dikes are exposed as vertical or somewhat diagonal strips, very narrow or up to several feet wide, contrasting in their color and pattern with the beds of lava they traverse. Volcanic dikes tend to occur with greatest abundance near the center, or plug, of a volcano, and to radiate away from this center. If dikes are mapped, their direction gives a rough idea of where the center of an old volcano was. Of course rift zones, as well as the center of the cone, can be active in eruption. Consequently, rift zones are underlain by many dikes which tend to parallel the rift.

The columnar form of fine-grained basalt at the Boiling Pots in the Wailuku River at Hilo, mentioned above, resembles the basalt of dikes. In dikes, the cracks do not form polygonal upright columns, but they separate fragments which run at right angles to the dike. From the surface of a dike, one can pick up pieces which are prismatic or diamond-shaped. The size of a dike is merely an indication of the cracks into which the lava pressed. If extremely fine cracks occurred, magma can be forced into them, forming "dikelets."

Liquid lava (magma) forced into cracks in a volcanic cone forms volcanic dikes.

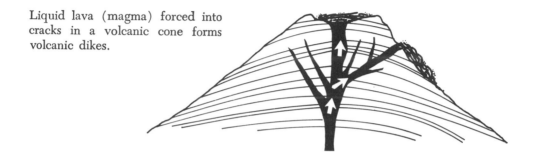

On the north side of Haleakala Crater is a swarm of dikes. They are evidently more resistant to weathering and erosion than the lava flows in which they occur, and they stand as walls and columns. One of the Haleakala dikes, shown here, is massive, about three feet thick.

A road cut at the base of Nuuanu pali has revealed a number of small dikes.

If cracks into which magma intrudes are very small, "dikelets" result (Gardner Pinnacles).

Erosion in Kalalau Valley, Kauai, has exposed dikes which can be seen as dark lines running diagonally down the ridges.

Dikes have a somewhat crystalline structure, break into prismatic or diamond-shaped fragments. These specimens were collected along Waikane Trail, Oahu.

Cones and Craters

None of the Hawaiian volcanoes are young enough to illustrate the form of a cone just emerged from the sea. However, some of the present-day Hawaiian volcanoes give us indications. Puuwaawaa, near Kamuela, Hawaii, is a lateral crater at the base of Hualalai. In its form, however, it mimics that of an independent young volcano. Puuwaawaa was rich in pumice and obsidian.

Haleakala is not a youthful volcano; its age is moderate, and the summit, although altered by erosion and cinder cones, is not a true caldera. There is not a series of downthrusts. Some of the eruptions within Haleakala Crater have produced lava flows, which have flowed down out of the crater through the two gaps in the crater wall: Koolau Gap, on the northwest end of the crater, Kaupo Gap on the southeast. Koolau Gap, on the windward side of the mountain, is covered by trees because high rainfall has permitted plant colonization on the new lavas. Kaupo Gap is much drier, and exhibits lavas almost as bare as when they were formed. When one walks the floor of Haleakala crater, one sees these and other flows, but more conspicuously, a collection of multicolored cinder cones, some gray, some orange, some reddish. These cinder cones occur nearly

Puuwaawaa is a volcanic cone, south of Kamuela, Hawaii, which is related to nearby Mt. Hualalai. Although a lateral cone, it shows a shape typical of an independent youthful cone.

Mauna Kea (13,784 feet) is an old caldera that has been covered by heaps of cinders from the numerous cinder cones that cover the summit. Mauna Loa is seen in the distance.

An areial view of Haleakala Crater reveals that it contains lava flows and small cinder cones which run in a line up to the summit and down over the crest (Camera Hawaii).

A view down the Koolau Gap of Haleakala Crater shows that lava flows have filled this valley with a broad, flat floor. Cinder cones within Haleakala, shown in the drawing, tend to occur in a line; the lava flows have drained out of the crater through the Koolau Gap to the north (above) and Kaupo Gap to the south (below).

in a line, running from within the crater up over the summit and down the southwest ridge. The cinder-cone activity in Haleakala seems extensive, but it has been much more pronounced on Mauna Kea. The rounded dome-like summit of Mauna Kea represents continual eruption of cinder cones, so that the upper portions of the mountain are largely cinders from innumerable cinder cones new and old.

Downthrusts and Calderas

There is no better place to see caldera activity than at Kilauea. However, the process of downthrusts is first illustrated here by an almost diagrammatic example one can see in Honolulu. Between Tripler Hospital and the Honolulu Airport, layers which compose the Salt Lake Crater show a marked displacement. A road cut has exposed the displacement of layers.

Kilauea exhibits downthrusts on every scale, from gigantic to minimal. Magma lies not far below the surface of Kilauea. As it wells up and melts beneath the surface, portions of the surface tend to crack. Magma swells and subsides, and as it sinks the crust falters and sinks. Calderas are usually circular or oval, and tend to follow areas of major weakness, or faults. Some of these faults are clearly displayed at Kilauea, as on the southwest rim of Kilauea not far from Halemaumau. Along these faults a series of small calderas have formed, the Chain of

A road cut on the south side of Salt Lake Crater, Oahu, has revealed a downthrust, like that of the diagrammatic drawing at right. Downthrusts are a conspicuous part of Hawaiian volcanic history.

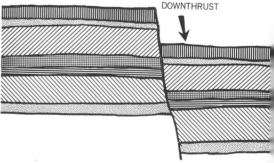

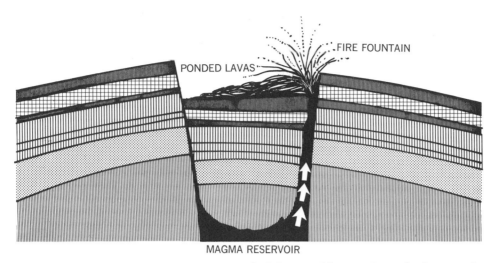

When the summit of a volcano falters and sinks, a caldera is formed. An eruption typically accompanies this process, filling the caldera with lava.

On the southwest rim of Kilauea, a fault which can be traced for several miles is evident.

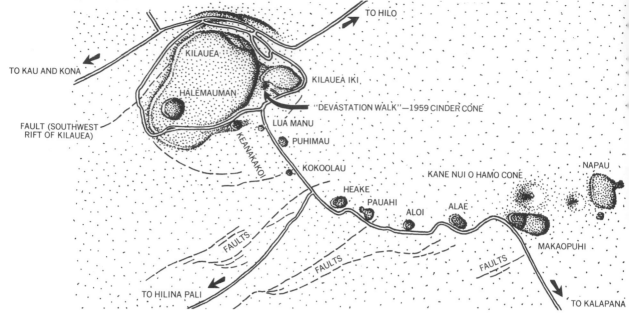

Kilauea is only one of numerous calderas in Hawaii Volcanoes National Park. The road which connects these calderas is known as Chain of Craters Road.

Aloi Crater, during its eruption of 1962. The eruption is also evident in a rift which leads away from Aloi (photo by Hawaii Volcanoes National Park). United States Department of Interior, National Park Service.

The Aloi eruption featured a fire fountain. Where a lava outlet is very narrow, the pressure of an eruption sends lavas high into the air (photo by Hawaii Volcanoes National Park). United States Department of Interior, National Park Service.

Craters. The Kilauea–Kalapana Road passes along the edge of these calderas. The range in size of the Kilauea calderas is from four miles across (Kilauea) to only fifty feet wide ("The Devil's Throat"). In December 1962 an eruption at Aloe Crater produced a small fire fountain on the floor of the crater. A lake of lava fifty feet deep was formed. The point at which the Aloi fire fountain formed was on the main rift which connects the calderas in the Chain of Craters. As the eruption continued, portions of the rift outside of Aloi opened, emitted lava, and with the pressure thus released, the Aloi eruption ceased. A similar occurrence in 1965 affected Aloi, but was more spectacular at Makaopuhi ("The Eel's Eye") and Napau. Napau Crater was, in fact, filled with lava. Active eruptions in 1969–70 featured flows into some of the sinks along Chain of Craters Road.

Kilauea proper is likely to have eruptions on a grander and more complex scale. The margin of Kilauea is not a single, circular cliff, but a series of scarps. This indicates that Kilauea has been subjected to a series of sinkings. The most recent and active of these is Halemaumau, the "fire pit," which has been the scene of the most numerous and spectacular eruptions. Halemaumau's history can be expressed in "ups and downs." High levels were represented, for example, in 1919–21. During these years, pahoehoe lavas overflowed Halemaumau, form-

The 1962 eruption of Aloi produced a lava lake fifty feet thick.

Kilauea, the largest of the calderas in Hawaii Volcanoes National Park, is four miles across. Within Kilauea is a secondary sink, the fire pit Halemaumau, from which steam can be seen emerging here.

In 1921 the lava lake in Kilauea undermined portions of the scarp, which broke away and floated on the lake like islands (a glass plate photo by T. A. Jagger, courtesy of Hawaii Volcano Observatory).

This photograph, from January 19, 1919, shows Kilauea when Halemaumau overflowed and a lava lake spread over the floor of Kilauea (photo by T. A. Jaggar,
courtesy of Hawaii Volcano Observatory).

A "low" in the rise and fall of Halemaumau is shown by this photograph, taken
after the 1959 Kilauea activity. Halemaumau has collapsed much lower than this,
as in 1928, for example (Hawaii Visitors Bureau).

The fire fountain in Kilauea-iki produced a cinder cone (left of the opening between Kilauea-iki and Kilauea), as well as lava flows on the floor of Kilauea-iki.

In November 1959, Kilauea-iki, a crater adjacent to Kilauea, erupted in the form of a fire fountain. (Hawaii Visitors Bureau.)

ing a broad lake on the floor of Kilauea. Pieces of the Kilauea scarp were undermined, and broke loose to flow like islands on this lake.

Halemaumau ultimately foundered again, and the 1967 photograph shows a "typical" condition. However, even lower levels have been reached from time to time, as after the 1959 eruption. Even though the eruption of Halemaumau may result in such a depression, the net result is the extrusion of much lava, and the volume of the island is increased a little.

The activity which underlies Kilauea is not limited to Halemaumau or the calderas southeast of Kilauea. In 1959 there was a spectacular eruption at Kilauea-iki, the caldera nearest to Kilauea caldera. Fire foundations and pahoehoe flows occurred. The fire fountains sprayed quantities of pumice and cinders into the air, forming a cinder cone. Pumice rained over many parts of Kilauea, smaller bits carried farther. The light weight of pumice permits it to be blown for miles away from the site of an eruption: a visitor can today find many bits of Kilauea-iki pumice along the Hilina Pali Road, twelve miles or more from Kilauea-iki.

The Kilauea-iki cinder cone killed ohia lehua trees, producing this interesting area known as Devastation Walk.

In 1960, eruptions related to Kilauea took place thirty miles away on the coast at Kapoho. This cinder cone buried the town of Kapoho, debris of which can still be seen.

In 1955, a cinder cone in the Puna District produced a small but spectacular display (United States Department of Interior, National Park Service).

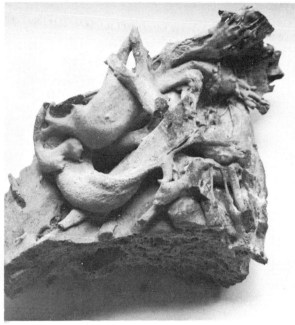

A unique photograph by T. A. Jaggar shows a small vent at Kilauea in which gas and liquid lava combine to form variously shaped bits of spatter (courtesy of Hawaii Volcano Observatory).

Spatter from the "Little Beggar" vent, Kilauea.

The Kilauea-iki eruption was not an isolated event but was part of activities that occurred as far as thirty miles away, at Kapoho, the easternmost tip of the island. At the village of Kapoho, a cinder cone much like that at Kilauea-iki formed, destroying the town. Likewise, 1955 eruptions in the Puna District (between Kapoho and Kilauea) produced both aa flows and cinder cones, and were related to Kilauea activity.

Cinder cones produce a variety of products, varying from bits of light, foamy pumice to heavy, dribbly spatter. The latter is illustrated in a remarkable photograph taken during the Kilauea eruptions of 1919–21. The vent shown is "spinning" lava spatter. The simultaneous escape of gas and emission of liquid lava result in the creation of irregular and strikingly sculptured lava fragments. These can be seen at various places around Kilauea, and in the crater of Haleakala.

Lumps of frothy, molten lava may collect on a vent, and by strong jets of gas be blown out of the cinder cone. Examples of such spatter may be of various shapes and colors. Iron in the lava may be oxidized into reddish colors if gases oxidize the surface while the spatter is still hot. Volcanic bombs are formed when large spatter lumps are fused to rounded shapes, then suddenly

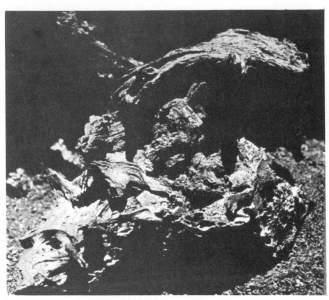

Spatter from a cone within the crater of Haleakala has produced elaborate forms.

Large, "bomb-like" lumps of spatter in the cone Nohonohae, near Kamuela, Hawaii.

Spatter and cinders in a cone near the summit of Hualalai.

Spatter of a pumice-like texture (specimen in Bishop Museum).

Spatter fused into rounded forms and flung out of cone explosively are known as "volcanic bombs" (specimen from Kilauea).

Volcanic glass spun out by a jet of gas is known as "pele's hair" (United States Department of Interior, National Park Service).

Volcanic glass from an eruption near Kilauea was molded into vases like these while still liquid. These artifacts may be seen in the Bishop Museum.

blown out of a cone under the pressure of escaping gas. Volcanic bombs are usually elongate or teardrop shaped, and have a surface with twisted or grooved markings.

If lava cools rapidly, it becomes volcanic glass. Volcanic glass takes various shapes, depending on whether or not gas sculptures the volcanic glass. Strong jets can blow glass into strands which look like fiberglass, called "Pele's hair" in honor of Pele, the Hawaiian fire goddess. Pele's hair can be carried great distances by wind currents, and one can easily find wads of it in crevices between rocks in the Kau District west of Kilauea.

Pele's tears is a name for rounded lumps of volcanic glass, but these are extremely rare in the Hawaiian Islands. Tourists should be warned that when they buy jewelry set with "Pele's tears" they are almost certainly buying inexpensive pieces of mainland obsidian which have been tumble-polished into smooth oval forms resembling those of Pele's tears.

If large amounts of gas are included in volcanic glass, pumice is produced. Volcanic glass which has been shaped not by gas but by humans can be seen in the form of small vases in the Bishop Museum. Intrepid Hawaiians used poles and sticks to shape these vases while volcanic glass was still liquid.

Explosive Eruptions: Steam, Ash, and Tuff

Water, as rainfall or as seawater, is abundantly present in the Hawaiian landscape. Rainwater continually seeps into cracks at Kilauea. Where it penetrates into hot areas near active sources of volcanism, steam may be formed. In many areas of Hawaii Volcanoes National Park, there is a constant seepage

Ground water seeping into hot areas produces steam in the crater Makaopuhi, which has two levels owing to successive events of sinking. On a cloudy day, more steam appears to be present because steam condenses more abundantly under these conditions. Water from a recent rainfall probably is also a factor.

If hot lavas come into contact with large amounts of water, a volcanic explosion occurs, releasing large clouds of ash. This explosion at Halemaumau was photographed by T. A. Jaggar on May 22, 1924 (courtesy Hawaii Volcano Observatory). Large blocks of lava ejected by this explosion can still be seen at Kilauea.

of rainwater into hot areas, because Kilauea lies in a zone of heavy rainfall. Steaming bluffs and cracks occur in various places throughout this area. This steam is often thin and inconspicuous, dissipating on a hot, sunny day, but if centers of condensation are available, it condenses into thick clouds. When low foggy stormclouds drift over Kilauea, steaming banks seem to billow forth as the clouds provide condensation centers for the steam. Automobile exhaust can also cause such condensation.

If a very hot thermal area is flooded with water, an extremely violent explosion may take place. Such an explosion was photographed by T. A. Jagger at the Volcano Observatory on May 22, 1924. Violent explosions of this sort unleash vast quantities of volcanic ash, which is magma reduced to extremely fine particles by sudden contact with water. The quantity of ash produced, as opposed to aa or pahoehoe, is an indicator of water present in an eruption site. Volcanic explosions which involve water are called hydromagmatic, and may result in the expulsion of even large lava blocks from the eruption site. Blocks of this sort can be seen in various places near Kilauea. The erosion of ash beds often reveals blocks or "bombs" embedded in ash. Fragments of various sizes accompany production of ash, and so ash is usually deposited as a mixture of dust and particles ranging from sand-like to gravel-like. Such a mixture is known as tuff.

Honolulu Geology

Southeastern Oahu offers a remarkable display of volcanic cones built up under the influence of water. The water in this case is mostly not from rainfall, but from the sea. These cones and other recent volcanic features stretch from western Honolulu to the eastern end of Oahu, and can easily be seen by car or bus. Most conspicuous are the tuff cones, small lateral craters which erupted when the land was beneath the sea, or so close to it that seawater leaked into the eruption site. A classic example of how seawater is involved can be seen clearly in the case of Lehua, an island just north of Niihau. Lehua is about half a cone, a crescent. More was probably present, but has now eroded away. Because a hydromagmatic explosion is powerful and because ash is very light, an entire cone may not have been formed: the explosive force of the eruption may have carried away portions of a cone as they formed, leaving only the crescent. The margins of Lehua are now eroded into cliffs by waves, and numerous valleys and gulches have been cut into Lehua's soft ash beds as the islet rapidly erodes away. Lehua can be said to be part of Niihau in the same sense that Diamond Head is part of Oahu. Niihau is an old island, much of which has worn down to an underwater shelf. On this shelf, Lehua was formed as the last (probably) bit of activity on the Niihau volcano.

These same events can be seen inland from the coast on Oahu—but not far inland, in most cases. Most conspicuous of the tuff cones is Diamond Head.

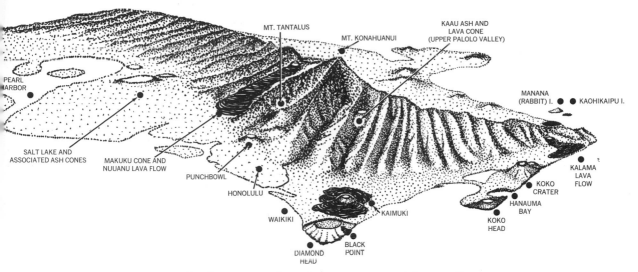

The eastern end of Oahu bears many lateral craters, some of them tuff craters, some of them lava cones. These are among the varied points of geological interest one can see in and around Honolulu.

About 150,000 years ago, only a coral reef existed where Diamond Head now stands. It was about a hundred feet above sea level. The opening of a rift in the reef permitted seawater to seep into the hot lava, setting off explosions which ejected limestone as well as huge clouds of ash. Nearby valleys were blanketed by falling ash. A succession of explosions added layer after layer of tuff to the Diamond Head cone, producing a layered appearance. The softness of the ash permitted rapid erosion to take place, and Diamond Head soon developed the gulleys we see today. However, like water added to cement, rainwater has the effect of solidifying ash to a semihard material known as palagonite. Limestone blown out during the eruption has probably aided in hardening of the tuff, just as lime does in concrete.

Inland from Diamond Head, another vent spewed out lava and spatter. It formed a dome across which one drives when one crosses the suburb of Kaimuki. Unlike Diamond Head, the Kaimuki vent did not erupt under the influence of seawater, so it emitted black lava rather than ash. Another lava flow occurred on the flank of Diamond Head itself, forming a strip of lava known as Black Point. Evidently this small flow, like that at Kaimuki, emerged just above the reach of seawater.

Other tuff cones in southeastern Oahu include Punchbowl, in the middle of Honolulu. This cone, inside of which is the National Cemetery of the Pacific, had a history much like that of Diamond Head, and is composed of much the same ash and small lava fragments consolidated into tuff. At the western edge

A submarine explosion of a small crater results in a tuff cone, composed of ash and small glassy fragments. This crater is Lehua, an islet off the northern shore of Niihau (Camera Hawaii).

Familiar Diamond Head (top) is a tuff cone which exploded when seawater penetrated into an area of hot lavas about 150,000 years ago (Hawaii Visitors Bureau).
Punchbowl Crater (bottom) is an ash and lava cone similar to Diamond Head,
although smaller. It is located in the center of Honolulu.

At the east end of Oahu is a ridge composed of a line of tuff cones; from left to right in the foreground are Koko Head Crater, Hanauma Bay (a crater invaded by the sea), Kahauloa Crater (a small depression), and Koko Crater. In the middle distance are Diamond Head, left, and the Koolau Mountains. In the far distance beyond Honolulu and Pearl Harbor are the Waianae Mountains (Camera Hawaii).

of Honolulu, near Pearl Harbor, is a trio of low, wide tuff cones. The largest of these is called Salt Lake. These cones, formed on a coral plain, were similar to Diamond Head, but they never attained the height of Diamond Head.

At the eastern end of Oahu is a series of picturesque tuff cones which lie in a line and form a sort of ridge, which can be called the Koko Head Ridge, because the series begins at Koko Head Crater. Koko Head Crater is mound-like. Next to it is Hanauma Bay, a crater broken through on the side facing the sea. Just north of Hanauma Bay is a small depression, Kahauloa Crater, followed by Koko Crater, a high cone which is actually conical, and which has sides deeply furrowed by erosion. Just behind Koko Crater is a small adjacent tuff cone. North of these and inland is Kalama cinder cone, situated upland from Koko Crater. Because of this location, its eruption produced cinders and the Kalama Lava Flow rather than ash.

Beds of tuff erode readily. Those shown at left are on Koko Head Crater; across Hamauma Bay is Koko Crater. Shown at right are two islets which, like an extension of the craters of Koko Head Ridge, continue the chain onto the windward side of easternmost Oahu: The farthest, a higher tuff cone, is Manana (Rabbit Island); the closer, a cinder cone, is Kaohikaipu.

On the windward side of the east end of Oahu are two islands, easily seen from the road, that are probably related to the Koko Head Ridge eruptions. The farther of these, Manana (Rabbit) Island is a tuff cone, formed like the tuff cones of Koko Head Ridge. The smaller and nearer of the two islets is Kaohikaipu, a cinder cone. It is opposite a lava flow on the Oahu coast. Probably this lava flow once extended out to sea (and may have been higher), and the cinder cone was evidently formed above sea level. If so, the portion of the flow connecting Oahu and Kaohikaipu has disappeared. Other tuff cones can be found on the windward side of Oahu; some inconspicuous mounds on the Kaneohe Peninsula are vestiges of tuff cones.

Inland from Diamond Head in upper Palolo Valley is an inconspicuous ash and lava cone, Kaau. A more prominent recent volcanic event in the Honolulu area, however, took place in Nuuanu Valley. At the head of the valley a small cone, Makuku, produced a large lava flow which filled Nuuanu Valley. The floor of the valley is consequently flat; one would otherwise expect it to be deep and narrow, like the other valleys of the Koolau Mountains. However, the floors of valleys other than Nuuanu are not sharply V-shaped, but somewhat rounded—a result of ash deposited during the eruption of Diamond Head and other tuff cones. Falls of ash have softened other features of the Oahu landscape as well; the tuff cones of Koko Head Ridge have probably blanketed each other with ash. Koko Head Crater is much more rounded than one would expect, for this reason.

All of these features of southeastern Oahu are probably results of events within the last 150,000 years. The most recent volcanic activity on Oahu occurred only five thousand years ago, according to carbon-14 dating. A fissure opened in the hills above Honolulu known as Round Top and Mount Tantalus. From this rift, fire fountains emerged, unleashing cinders which blanketed areas downslope from Tantalus and Round Top. These cinders even filled Punchbowl Crater. These cinders, and lava flows from Tantalus and Round Top, covered the area in Manoa Valley which is now the University of Hawaii campus. Along Round Top Road may be seen fine cinders, erroneously called "black sand," which represent debris from the fire fountains.

Lateral Craters on Other Islands

Islands other than Oahu and Niihau have experienced eruption of minor craters as a closing phase in their history. A small tuff islet which looks like Lehua, Kaula is such a lateral tuff cone which represents a termination of activity in the Kauai–Niihau volcano system. On Kauai itself, the southern coast near Koloa reservoir bears a series of small cinder cones. Between Lihue and the high central plateau of Kauai is a low, broad crater of relatively recent origin, Kilohana.

On Molokai, the last phase of eruption produced a peninsula on the north coast. This peninsula, which bears a small cone, has become famous as the site of the leper colony, Kalaupapa. On Maui, the cinder cones in Haleakala and on its southwest rift are not the only signs of relatively recent activity. At the coast south of Makena is a cone, Puu Olai, and a lava flow dating from around 1750. Off the shore of Maui at this point is Molokini, a crescent-like tuff cone which resembles Lehua and Kaula very closely.

Minerals

Volcanic islands are supposedly poor in minerals. However, a surprising number of minerals, including a few semiprecious gems, have been found in the Islands. Some of these are products of cooling of magma, some represent reactions between different components of magma, and some are reactions between magma and limestone.

When magma cools slowly, component minerals crystallize out—they become crystals in a lava matrix. One of the most common is olivine, a greenish crystal which can often be seen when one breaks a piece of basaltic lava. When tuff contributes to the formation of beach sand, the sand may have a

When lava cools slowly, minerals crystallize out. One of the most common is olivine, the olive-green crystals of which appear here as shiny spots in a piece of aa lava.

greenish color because of olivine grains which are included in the tuff. Olivine-rich sands can be seen at Hanauma Bay and Diamond Head, Oahu, and South Point, Hawaii. Pyroxenes, which may be colorless, opaque, or purplish (and thus can be called garnets), are similar to olivine crystals in shape. Augites can be found in certain cinder cones. Quartz crystals, sometimes doubly terminated, have been found. Agates, moonstones, sunstones, and jaspers occur in limited quantities. Most Hawaiian specimens are smaller, more poorly colored, and of considerably less value than samples of these minerals from mainland sources.

These diamond-shaped dark crystals are pyroxenes from Haleakala. Translucent purple pyroxenes are garnets.

Quartz crystals have been found in basalt cavities on Oahu.

Feathery aragonite crystals are a form of limestone, calcium carbonate. These were probably produced by the action of hot lava on limestone from coral reefs.

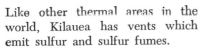

Like other thermal areas in the world, Kilauea has vents which emit sulfur and sulfur fumes.

When calcium from limestone reacts with sulfur from a volcano, gypsum (calcium sulfate) can be formed. Two types of gypsum crystals from the Islands are shown here.

Calcium, undoubtedly from limestone, has been involved in the formation of calcite and a more feathery mineral, aragonite. Calcite crystals can be found in the tuff of Diamond Head. In fact, these crystals, at first erroneously thought to be more precious than they are, are responsible for the name of Diamond Head.

Sulfur vents and sulfur banks are characteristic of active volcanic areas, and the Hawaiian Islands are no exception. In Hawaii Volcanoes National Park, just west of Kilauea caldera, such sulfur formations can be seen. Reactions between limestone and sulfur may be the source of the gypsum crystals which have been found in various Hawaiian localities.

Erosion

Many areas of the Hawaiian Islands receive heavy rainfall, and directly and indirectly rainfall has carved the dramatic valleys which rise from the lowlands on the older islands. An upland area in the Islands which is wet yet not deeply eroded can be suspected of being quite recent. The way in which age is related to degree of erosion can be seen on the island of Maui. Northern slopes of East Maui (Haleakala) and West Maui (Puu Kukui) have heavy rainfall at levels above three thousand feet, since both lie directly in the path of the trade winds. If we compare the relief of these two mountains, we can see that Puu Kukui is deeply worn into sharp ridges, narrow valleys. Valleys are apparent on the northern surface of Haleakala, but they are shallow. Haleakala Crater has been creased by erosion, but it has not been obliterated as has that of Puu Kukui.

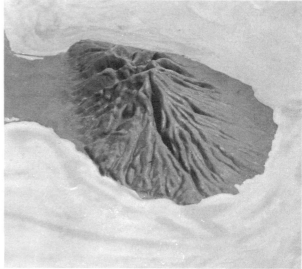

Slopes of East Maui (left) receive about the same rainfall as those of West Maui (right). The greater erosion of West Maui indicates it is an older mountain.

The eastern end of Molokai, seen from the south (left), is moderately eroded. Seen from the north (right) it is deeply eroded. The difference is due to the greater rainfall on the northern coast.

Differences in rainfall between windward and leeward slopes are conspicuous in the Hawaiian Islands—a difference clearly revealed in patterns of erosion. The south face of eastern Molokai has been eroded into a series of numerous valleys. Molokai is low enough so that rainfall from trade winds extends over the summit, and erosion on the leeward side is to be expected. However, rainfall is much heavier on the windward side, and the northern face of Molokai is not a series of small valleys, but drastically altered into a few broad amphitheater-shaped valleys. So steep are the walls of these northern valleys that it is very difficult to reach the northern coast of Molokai from the summit region.

As erosion of this sort proceeds, the ridges on a wet coastal face may be converted into steep, plunging cliffs, known to the Hawaiians as "pali." Because these ridges and cliffs are nearly vertical, they can support only scrubby growth, regardless of rainfall. Soil cannot be held on such steep surfaces, runoff of rain is rapid, and almost constant winds prevent the growth of normal trees. Good examples of pali can be seen on Oahu, where the eastern half of the Koolau Mountains has such a sudden dropoff, and on the northern face of Kauai, the "Na Pali Kona" Coast. That ridges should gradually erode from sloping to nearly vertical is not surprising; in only a few places, however, do these form such curtain-like vertical folds, and Oahu and Kauai are outstanding in this respect.

Lava beds which compose Hawaiian mountains are not uniform in density or thickness. When erosion acts on them, these differences are exposed, often exaggerated. A stream which eats into a steep slope will tend to erode softer layers first, but will eventually cut into harder layers later. Typically a stream forms a series of plunge pools, running more nearly vertically where

The northwestern coast of Kauai (Na Pali Kona Coast) demonstrates an advanced state of erosion. The large valley is Kalalau (Camera Hawaii).

Looking down into Kalalau Valley, one sees how narrow and sharp are the ridges produced by erosion of lava beds.

Ridges eroded until they are nearly vertical form the famous pali on the windward side of Oahu.

soft rock is eaten away, flowing more nearly horizontally over harder layers. Thus, a series of "hanging valleys" can be formed. Hanging valleys are a common sight in sharply eroded areas, especially on West Maui, Molokai, Oahu, and Kauai.

The influence of resistant versus nonresistant layers of lava is seen on a grand scale in the main mountain mass of Kauai. Kauai retains a summit plateau of about five thousand feet, an elevation greater than that of a younger island, Oahu (the summit of which reaches four thousand feet). Why has this summit plateau remained so high, not even worn into a narrow ridge like that of Oahu? The summit of Kauai was once a caldera like that of Kilauea, but much larger. Eruptions filled the caldera with lava flows. These "ponded lavas" were mostly dense pahoehoe, forming a thick mantle of hard lavas. Like the cap rock on a mesa, these ponded lavas have persisted, deterring erosion of soft layers beneath them. Of course erosion has eaten into these lavas; no volcanic rock can resist erosion indefinitely. The ponded lavas have certainly slowed this process greatly, especially when one considers the very high rainfall of the

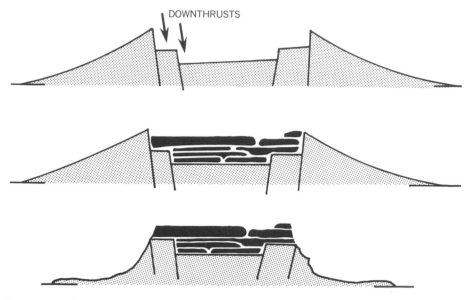

The main volcano on Kauai formed a huge caldera. This caldera filled with hard ponded lavas, and these lavas have acted as a cap rock, preserving a flat summit.

A segment of a ridge can be isolated by erosion on all sides: here is the famous Iao Needle, Maui.

If a portion of coast is eroded away so that it becomes an island, it is called a sea stack. Although Mokolii Island, off the coast of windward Oahu, looks like a crater, the lava beds which are the same as ones on nearby mainland areas show that it is a sea stack.

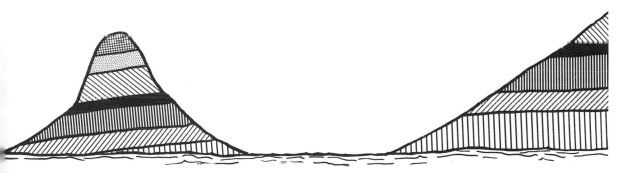

summit plateau of Kauai. The horizontal nature of the old caldera lavas probably account for the fact that the summit has broad bog areas.

As valleys eat into a mountain, small valleys adjacent to each other tend to fuse where they approach each other at their heads. As this happens, ridges are separated from the summit by saddles. Such saddles can be worn deeper and deeper, until peaks stand isolated from the summit area. This has happened in various places in the Islands. Most striking of these is the Iao Valley, where the well-named Iao Needle is the last remnant of a ridge.

Processes much like this can also occur at the shoreline. Wave action is a drastic form of erosion, and eats rapidly into a cliff. Some portions of the shore resist longer than others. As the shoreline is cut back, small islets, known as stacks, are left standing a short distance from the new shoreline. There are good examples of stacks off the coasts of West Maui and Lanai. Another example is Mokolii Island ("Chinaman's Hat Island"), located off the windward coast of Oahu near the town of Waikane. Mokolii looks like a small crater because of its conical shape. However, it proves to be composed of lava beds which can be correlated with those on the nearby coast.

Surf eats into cliffs, and sea caves may form, but usually overhanging layers fall, producing a higher cliff. Local conditions diminish or intensify the action of surf. Trade winds reinforce waves, driving them with greater power onto north- and northeast-facing shores. High marine bluffs will be expected on these coasts of the Hawaiian Islands. The northern coast of Molokai is exemplary, like one high cliff interrupted by valleys. The lower, drier western part of Molokai, where rainfall is too low to produce much erosion, is an uninterrupted marine cliff hundreds of feet high, virtually vertical along much of its length.

On cliffs facing trade winds, rains and waves can act together. Thus, the northern and northeastern parts of the Islands seem to have suffered more severe erosion. Kauai and Oahu show this, but perhaps Niihau shows it best: all the gradual slopes are on the leeward side, and the half of the island facing trade winds has disappeared.

Wave action quickly wears away the shoreline of a volcanic island, producing cliffs. As layers are undercut, they fall, forming a sheer drop. The best examples of such sea cliffs are on the northern coast of Molokai.

Black Sand, Blowholes

Most beach sand in the Islands is derived from pulverization of corals, and is bright white in color. This is to be expected because corals cover most offshore areas where contours are shallow enough to permit formation of beaches. If a new lava flow reaches the sea, however, lava may form the raw material for sand. Black sand can be found along coasts on the eastern part of the island of Hawaii. In addition to the famous black-sand beach at Kalapana,

Where a lava flow enters the sea, it provides raw material for a black-sand beach, such as this famous one at Kalapana. Offshore lavas soon become covered with corals, which provide fragments for white beaches, so coral beaches are much more common than lava beaches in the Islands.

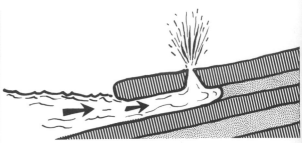

If surf undercuts a lava flow so that a tunnel upwards is formed or is present, a blowhole results. Inrush of waves creates an intermittent fountain. The blowhole shown is located on southeast Oahu.

others are forming in the Puna District where the 1950 and 1960 flows reached the sea. The tuff cones of Diamond Head and Koko Head Ridge discharge ash into the ocean, but the coarser components of the tuff remains as sand on beaches.

Waves erode caves into the shore of an island where softer rocks underlie harder ones. In such places, a hole may form in the resistant layer. If waves rush into such a cave, their force can be channeled through the hole, and jet upwards as a fountain. Intermittent fountains of this sort, known commonly as blowholes, occur in various places. One of the most famous is at Koko Crater, along the coast road, but another, at Poipu on Kauai's southern coast, is equally spectacular.

Erosion Plus Downthrusts

Where faulting occurs, it may affect the path of streams. This has happened strikingly in the case of Waimea Canyon, a noted tourist attraction on western Kauai. One would expect that streams would radiate symmetrically from the central dome of Kauai, and apparently they once did. Then a series of downthrusts occurred, creating a depression parallel to the west coast. Streams running toward the west coast were diverted into this depression, and joined to form a southward-running river. This depression became Waimea Canyon, a valley noted for its reddish lava beds which remind visitors of the Grand Canyon.

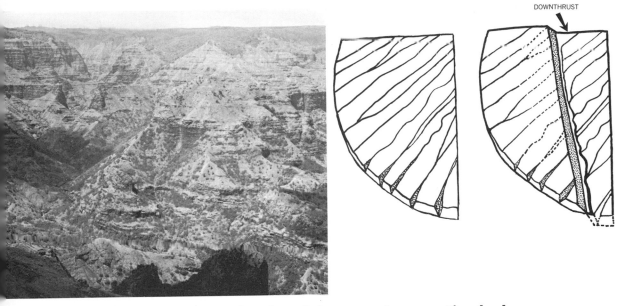

DOWNTHRUST

A downthrust on western Kauai has changed the course of streams. After the down-thrust, streams in this region emptied into a single river which carved picturesque Waimea Canyon.

Weathering

In addition to erosion, rainfall affects rocks by percolating into them, inducing chemical changes and softening them. Lavas in wet areas of the older islands become, in effect, rotten. On larger lava boulders this weathering works from outside inward, and tends to attack successive layers of a rock. The pattern becomes spheroidal, so that a boulder as it weathers looks like an onion with scales falling away.

As a lava boulder weathers, layers peel away, an appearance known as spheroidal weathering (Pihea, Kauai).

Lava boulders cemented together by limestone form conglomerate rocks.

Coral Effects

Corals, as they grow in shallow waters, tend to cement various debris together with their limestone. In some places, this debris consists of lava pebbles. Pebbles may be cemented together by limestone and eventually exposed on dry land by an uplift of the shoreline. These rocks, which can be called conglomerates, can be expected near uplifted coral reefs. The southwestern corner of Oahu, the Ewa Plain, is such a coral platform. Coral platforms of this sort indicate formerly submerged areas; in the Hawaiian Islands, all of these were submerged relatively recently.

An excellent place to see varied products of upraised shores is the isthmus of Maui. This isthmus is composed entirely of coral sand blown inland from the coast. The isthmus is about two hundred feet above sea level at most, but in effect it is much higher, for drillings show that sand dunes originally formed when the sea was sixty feet below its present level. These lower levels have become cemented firmly, forming a soft rock. Upper levels show progressively less consolidation, and surface layers are unstable except as plant growth on them prevents sand from blowing away. Along the road between Kahului and Wailuku on Maui the road cuts through some of these old sand dunes, and you can see how successive layers of sand, blown inland by the trade winds, have become added to Maui's land surface.

Coral sand blows inland, forming dunes which eventually solidify into rock. The shifting course of dunes is shown by the layering (near Wailuku, Maui).

The Pleistocene and Terrestrial Fossils

Pliocene fossils (one to five million years ago) do not tell us much about ancient Hawaiian climates—fossils of this age are few or none, and the climate might have been much like that at the present time. We do know that during the Pleistocene some cooling occurred, a change not surprising in view of the great ice sheets which covered high latitudes at that time. In the summit area of Mauna Kea, there are lava boulders which bear marks of glaciation. Glaciation probably did not last long there, and may not have influenced lowland climates very much. Lowlands were probably slightly cooler and wetter, and if the shorelines at that time were lower, on account of withdrawal of water from oceans and conversion of it into icecaps, then the forest belts would be expected to extend correspondingly lower.

Fossils are suggestive of this. The tuff cones of Oahu, which are of Pleistocene origin, have trapped plant fragments in their layers. Leaves claimed to be those of a wet forest tree, *Syzygium sandwicense,* have been found in Diamond Head tuffs. Seeds of *Pteralyxia,* a dry forest tree, have been reported from tuff beds of the Salt Lake Crater. Recently, borings for a tunnel in Salt Lake Crater exposed crushed portions of palm stems. These palm specimens, collected in 1966 by botanist Dr. George W. Gillett, are probably forty thousand years old. The palm was probably not a coconut palm, but a loulu palm (*Pritchardia*). Loulu palms now grow mostly in wet uplands, but a few still grow in dry forest, notably *P. remota* which lives virtually at sea level on dry Nihoa in the Leeward chain. Dry forest does not now extend down to Salt Lake Crater, but during the Pleistocene it probably did.

Recently discovered were these strands from a palm (probably the loulu palm, *Pritchardia*) which grew about forty thousand years ago beneath what is now Salt Lake Crater, Oahu.

Bogs preserve pollen grains which fall in them because the acidity of the water in bogs prevents the pollen grains from decaying. They are covered by layers of silt, and successive layers form, so that one could tell the history of the bog's vegetation if one could identify the pollen grains. This has, in fact, been done by the Swedish botanist Olof Selling. He concluded that conditions were somewhat cooler in the Hawaiian bogs during the ice ages.

Other fossils found in the Islands include a goose (*Geochen rhuax*), the bones of which were located in ash underlying lava beds in the Kau District of Hawaii. This goose is related to the Cape Barren Goose, which lives on the southern coast of Australia and is the only living representative of its group. The only other relative is a fossil goose from New Zealand. Pieces of vegetation were also found in this deposit. Other fossils which have been found include plant fragments under old mud flows on Oahu and silicified wood from the Humuula Saddle Road and South Point, Hawaii. All of these fossils are relatively recent, and not truly fossilized (subfossil).

Ground Water

The Hawaiian Islands have abundant rainfall in places, but their total area is small, so the total amount of fresh water available is limited. Volcanic soils and rocks are porous, so there is no use in damming streams: water would not form a large lake, it would simply leak downward beneath the surface. Watershed areas are porous, and so they do not yield much water into streams. For the same reason, streams do not discharge as much water into the sea as one might at first imagine—water sinks into the streambed. Most streams are small except after heavy rains and larger streams and permanent waterfalls are a rarity except where large areas high in rainfall are drained, as near Hilo, where Akaka Falls and Rainbow Falls are attractions.

The search for fresh water in the Hawaiian Islands led to well-drilling, and these wells revealed the existence of a curious phenomenon, a phenomenon discovered elsewhere and known under the cumbersome name of the Ghyben-Herzberg Principle. Fresh water has a slightly lower density than salt water. When fresh water sinks into the ground of an island, therefore, it does not tend to sink into the salt water beneath the island, it tends instead to float atop the salt water. If one were to cut a cross section of an island with abundant rainfall, one would see a lens of fresh water floating atop the salt water. If a well is drilled, one can obtain fresh water at any level above the salt water.

There is, of course, a steady leakage of fresh water into the ocean. Recently infrared aerial photographs showed fans of cool fresh water, invisible by ordinary means, spreading out into warmer sea water. The fresh water was not just from streams but had leaked through soils and rocks as well. Volcanic dikes form natural dams because they are not porous, and therefore tend to hold ground water at higher levels than one would expect.

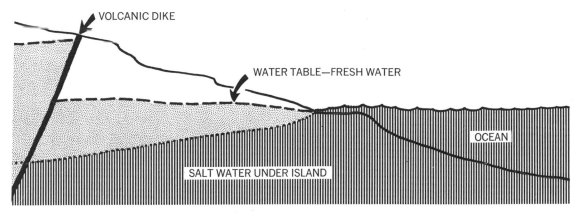

The Hawaiian Islands show well the peculiar accumulation of fresh water as a lens above salt water. Fresh water percolates easily into the porous volcanic soil and floats on top of salt water. A volcanic dike acts as an underground dam.

Interestingly, studies in the geology of the Hawaiian Islands were spurred very largely by the need for an understanding of occurrence of ground water. The publications of the Hawaii Division of Hydrography contain most of what has been learned about the geology of the Islands. Ground water in the Islands is now well understood, but studies in Hawaiian geology have certainly not abated, though today they tend more strongly toward geophysics.

Hawaiian volcanoes are excellent examples of volcanism because of the clarity with which phenomena are displayed, and so they become more important with the years, because volcanic phenomena relate to basic questions of the earth's early history.

Chapter 2 ❧❧ CLIMATE

THE Hawaiian Islands are justly famous for mild, uniform, subtropical weather but this is only one side of an extraordinary climatic story. Despite their small total area, the Islands have places which are desert dry and others which may be the wettest places on earth. Temperatures can go below freezing on high mountains, or can be above 90° F. at sea level. Humidity can stand at virtually zero in alpine areas, yet be 100 per cent nearly all of the time in wet mountain areas. In short, the Hawaiian Islands are a climatic showcase in which equable conditions co-exist with some of the most severe extremes in the world.

Temperatures

The Hawaiian chain lies roughly along 20° north latitude, so one would expect tropical to subtropical conditions. The twentieth parallel passes near such places as Mazatlán and Yucatán in Mexico, Jamaica, Cuba, Puerto Rico, and Calcutta, India. At this latitude day length never varies very much: the longest day in the Islands is thirteen hours and twenty minutes, the shortest is ten hours and fifty minutes. This relatively uniform amount of sunlight dictates that temperatures do not vary much throughout the year. Another factor which tempers the climate is the effect of the surrounding ocean. Like a vast insulation, the ocean moderates temperatures near the coast—and almost every place in the Hawaiian Islands is near a coast. Only on the islands of Maui and Hawaii do large mountain masses exert an effect which markedly counters the maritime influence.

In Honolulu the warmest month, August, has an average temperature of 78.5° F., but the coldest months, January and February, average 72.0° F. This uniformity of winter and summer temperatures is surprising. The highest temperature ever recorded in Honolulu is about 90° F., the lowest is 56° F. The hottest temperature ever recorded in the Islands is 100° F., at Pahala, near the southern tip of the island of Hawaii. This unusual record temperature occurred in freak conditions: it was produced by strong downslope winds, which increase in temperature as they descend because of "compressional heating." The coldest temperature officially recorded in the Hawaiian Islands is 18° F., which occurred near the summit (13,784 feet) of Mauna Kea on the island of Hawaii. Snow can generally be seen on the summits of Mauna Kea and Mauna Loa from January through March, although not much snow ever collects. Precipitation at these high altitudes is relatively low, for reasons mentioned later. Very likely, temperatures as low as 5° F. could be recorded on the mountains for, when cold air drains downward from the summits, it may accumulate in pockets below and drive temperatures lower than at the summit, where trade winds tend to remove cold air more rapidly. At the opposite extreme, temperatures above 100° F. could undoubtedly be measured on the surface of a dark-colored lowland lava flow. Where sunlight is absorbed by black lava near the seacoast, temperatures close to the surface of the lava probably go above 100° F.

Temperatures are highest near the coast in localities protected from the trade winds. Thus, warmer places in the Islands are such leeward localities as Mana, Kauai; Honolulu, Oahu; Lahaina, Maui; and Kawaihae, Hawaii. Even in these places the temperatures rarely exceed 90° F., and usually only during the hottest month (August). The summer months are also the months when trade winds blow most consistently, so the warm temperatures are much less

The summit area of Mauna Kea (13,784 feet) shows that high elevations even in tropical latitudes bear snow in winter. Snowfalls here are relatively light, however (United States Department of Interior, National Park Service).

unpleasant than the figures might suggest. Temperatures on the average decrease with altitude, and these figures from the island of Hawaii give an idea of how average temperatures are affected by altitude in the Islands:

Locality	Altitude	Mean January Temp.	Mean August Temp.
Hilo	40 feet	71° F.	76° F.
Olaa	280	70	75
Mountain View	1530	65	70
Kilauea	3971	58	64
Kulani Camp	5190	53	58
Mauna Loa Observatory	11,150	39	47

Wind and cloud cover modify the temperatures considerably, as does topography. Deep, shady canyons can be cool, while nearby ridges are warm and steamy. Within the city limits of Honolulu, there are both warm and cool sections. Extremes in temperatures tend to occur mostly on leeward coasts or leeward slopes of mountains, where the absence of trade winds permits heat or cold to accumulate.

Kona Storms

The familiar pattern of rainstorms is produced when a mass of warm, moist air meets cold, drier air. The cold front tends to slip underneath the warm air, which rises. As the warm air is cooled by the cold air, condensation and rainfall occur. This occurs in the Hawaiian Islands, of course, for weather fronts of this sort occur everywhere as major storm systems drift across the landscape. In the Islands, these major fronts occur chiefly in the winter months. If the Islands were flat, these storms would be the source of virtually all the rainfall. Indeed, the Leeward Hawaiian Islands, such as Midway, receive rainfall only from such rain squalls, which drop about twenty-five to thirty inches of rain per year. These squalls may be brief, as turbulent air cools a cloud bank, or a small wave of cooler air triggers precipitation.

The wetter winter months, from November to April, were known to the ancient Hawaiians as the hoo-ilo season. During hoo-ilo, hot tropical storms—from two to seven major ones—approach from the south and cover the entire surface of the Islands. The Hawaiians call these storms "kona storms" because they come from the south, "kona," when the trade winds, which blow from the north or northeast, slacken during the winter. Some of the kona storms are accompanied by high winds, even thunder or lightning. More typically, however, a kona storm approaches the Islands slowly, bringing a warm, humid, oppressive atmosphere.

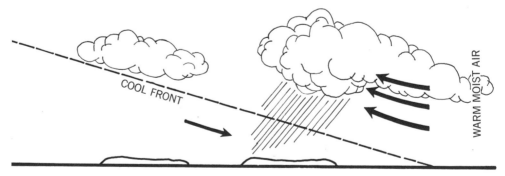

The major winter storms in the Hawaiian Islands, or "kona storms" follow the typical pattern of a cold front meeting warm, moist air. These storms can drop rain on lowland areas.

The kona storms provide a general rainfall. The lower elevations of the Islands and the southern coasts receive much or most of their rainfall from them. Recent photographs by the Tiros weather satellite have shown that these storms often originate off the Californian and Mexican coasts and move westward, sometimes nearly reaching hurricane intensity. Hurricanes from the western Pacific do not reach the Islands, and true hurricanes cannot be said to occur there. Air speeds of 60 to 100 m.p.h. have been reported, but an active kona storm usually carries winds below 30 m.p.h. If you fly to the Hawaiian Islands from California in the winter months, you may pass through a kona storm, which can rise to altitudes of 35,000 feet.

Trade Winds and Their Rainfall

The pattern of trade winds tends to follow the sun. During the summer months when the sun has moved north, the Hawaiian Islands lie midway in the belt of trades. This season was known to the ancient Hawaiians as the kau season. During a typical summer month such as August, trade winds come from north-northeast to east 90 per cent of the time, and half the time they exceed thirteen miles per hour. As these winds traverse vast stretches of the Pacific, they tend to pick up considerable moisture which can be condensed by a mountain system such as the Hawaiian mountains. In fact, the six major Hawaiian islands, instead of receiving the twenty-five inches of rain per year which would be expected in this part of the Pacific for flat islands, average forty-five inches per year over their entire surface—which means that some parts receive less, some more than forty-five inches of rain.

Islands tend to absorb heat which rises to certain levels, and this can create a so-called inversion layer, in which heat increases slightly with altitude up to five thousand to seven thousand feet, above which cold air lies. The warm air below the inversion layer tends to be held beneath the cool air. In the Hawaiian Islands, an inversion layer of this sort occurs 50 to 70 per cent of the time.

Thus, the constant trade winds, when they encounter a mountain slope, drive to the top of this inversion layer. If one looks at the higher Hawaiian mountains during the daytime of a summer month one sees an almost constant band of clouds. The trade winds rise to the top of the inversion layer, contact cool air and condense moisture as rainfall. If no other factors were present, levels between five thousand and seven thousand feet would be expected to be the wettest and this is, in fact, true. The two areas of highest rainfall are mountains with summits of 5170 feet (Waialeale, Kauai) and 5788 feet (Puu Kukui, Maui).

A rounded mountain summit near the inversion layer will condense rainfall on its windward side, and this precipitation will continue onto the leeward side of the summit until the clouds have lost all of their excess moisture.

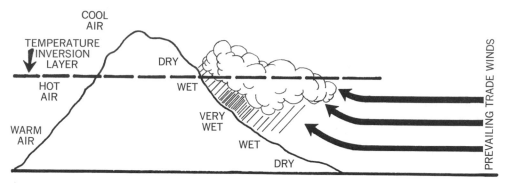

Trade winds are forced upward by mountain masses. When they penetrate cold air at the upper limit of a temperature inversion layer (air warmer than near ground level), they condense into rainfall on the windward side of an island.

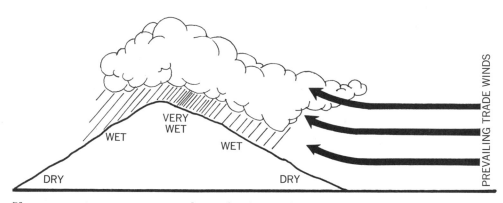

If a mountain summit is at about the level of the inversion layer, it receives a maximum amount of rainfall, which falls on the leeward side of the summit as well as on the windward side.

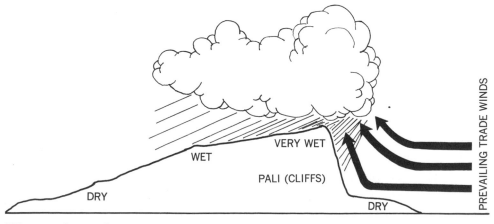

When trade winds are confronted by a steep cliff, like the pali on Oahu, they rush upward rapidly, and most rainfall occurs on the leeward side of the summit ridge.

When trade winds are stronger, the clouds will rise well above the inversion layer as thunderhead-like masses, and drop large amounts of rainfall on the wet belt of a mountain. But if a mountain is higher than seven thousand feet, there will be a marked lowering of rainfall above the six-thousand-foot level where maximal rainfall is reached. The highest summits, Mauna Kea and Mauna Loa on the island of Hawaii, probably receive less than twenty inches of precipitation annually.

The shape of a mountain range alters the normal patterns described above, however. A good example of this can be seen on Oahu, where the Koolau Mountains form a chain perpendicular to the prevailing direction of the trade winds. The windward side of this range consists of a sharp cliff, or pali. When the trade winds reach this sharp cliff, they are forced upward suddenly and swiftly. The updraft on this pali is so strong that visitors to Nuuanu pali, where the highway crosses over the cliff, find they cannot throw a coin over the side—it is blown back up. Near this point is a waterfall known as the upside-down waterfall, because the wind blows the water from it upward many days during the year. If one walks along the summit ridge of the Koolau Mountains and looks over the edge of the pali, one can have the unusual experience of feeling rain "fall" upward. So sudden is this updraft that condensation triggered by the rise is carried over the summit and most of it falls just on the leeward side of the summit. Rainfall levels exceed two hundred inches (or even in a few places three hundred inches) on the leeward side, while at the base of the pali, amounts are about fifty to seventy-five inches of rain per year. As rain showers build up over the Koolau Mountains, they may be carried by strong trade winds far over the summit areas, and in Honolulu there are often a few very light showers in the afternoon. Honolulu is famous for its rainbows, and the pattern of rainfall and cloud cover is the explanation. The clouds tend to dissipate on the leeward side—over Honolulu, for example. While Honolulu remains sunny, rains occur in valleys leading into the Koolau range. The Manoa Valley of Honolulu lies at the foot of the summit of Mt. Konahuanui, highest point in the Koolaus. In the Manoa Valley, showers often occur in the afternoon, and the afternoon sun, shining into the valley, makes rainbows an almost daily occurrence.

As mountain summits trigger rain showers from the trade winds, rainfall thins out on the leeward side, and so a rain shadow is created. A good example of this is seen on Oahu, where the two chains of mountains parallel each other. The Waianae Mountains are thus shadowed by the Koolaus, and receive very little rainfall in comparison. An exception to this is Mt. Kaala, highest point in the Waianae range. Mt. Kaala is 4025 feet high, whereas the highest point in the Koolaus (Konahuanui) is 3105 feet. Thus the upper reaches of Mt. Kaala are not cut off from the trade winds by the Koolau Mountains, although lower portions of the Waianae Mountains are. Still, Mt. Kaala does not receive as much rainfall as the summit ridge of the Koolaus. The explanation for this appears

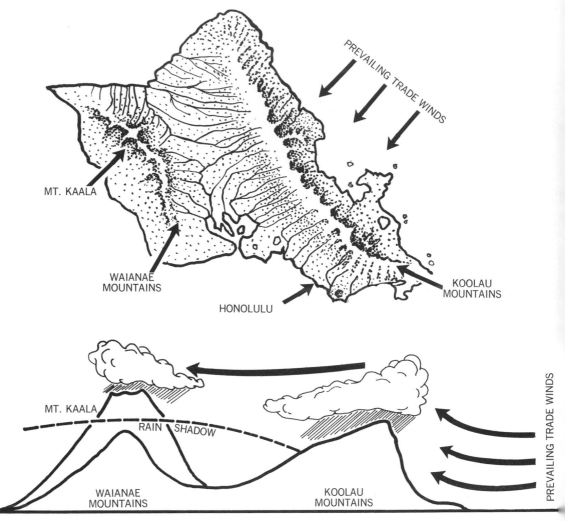

The Koolau Mountains, which run perpendicular to the direction of the trade winds, condense most of the moisture from this moist air. The Waianae Mountains are in a "rain shadow." Only Mt. Kaala in the Waianae Mountains is high enough to receive much moisture from the trade winds.

to be that even though they are lower, the Koolau range condenses part of the moisture, leaving less for Mt. Kaala. There are other interesting examples of rain shadows in the Hawaiian Islands. Niihau lies in the lee of Kauai; Kahoolawe and Lanai are sheltered by Maui. The driest place in the Hawaiian Islands is Kawaihae, on the island of Hawaii, which receives only about eight inches of rain per year. It is on the leeward side of the island, and is quite effectively cut off from trade winds by the highlands. If one looks at the location of Kawaihae from the aspect of typical storm tracks for the kona storms, one sees that

A sharp ridge condenses moisture from trade winds in such a way that much of the rain falls on the leeward side. On northwestern Kauai, a series of sharp ridges demonstrates this. The leeward side of Kalalau Valley is moist and forested. The windward side of nearby Awaawapuhi Valley is almost completely barren.

it also lies in the shadow of mountains. Mauna Loa and Hualalai, which lie south of Kawaihae Bay, can create rain shadows for the winter storms.

If a sharp ridge, or a series of sharp ridges, lies perpendicular to the trade winds, the rain shadow effect can be an unexpected one. Trade winds rise so sharply up such a ridge that most of the condensation caused by this rise falls beyond the edge of the ridge, on the lee side. There is a series of such ridges along the northwestern part of Kauai. The eastern side of Kalalau Valley is a steep slope which is obviously rather wet, covered with trees and shrubs. The western side of Kalalau Valley, although it faces trade winds, is covered only with grasses. The same is true of valleys farther east, such as Honopu and Awaawapuhi.

Just as knife-edge ridges can alter the rainfall pattern of the trade winds, so can deep valleys. Why is Mt. Waialeale, on the summit ridge of Kauai, the wettest place on the Hawaiian Islands—and perhaps even the wettest place on earth? If one looks at the topography which surrounds Waialeale, the answer becomes obvious. The trade winds, as we have seen, blow to the Hawaiian Islands from the east, northeast, or north-northeast. As they confront Mt. Waialeale from any of these directions, they are funneled into valleys which lead

The summit of Mt. Waialeale is a bog, some portions of which may receive as much as six hundred inches of rain annually. It is perhaps the wettest locality in the world because a series of channel-like valleys force trade winds to deposit most of their moisture at the summit. The relief map has been photographed from the northeast, showing a view of the valleys which received the incoming trade winds.

The summit ridge of Mt. Waialeale (left in photo), Kauai, can rarely be seen. This view, taken in December, was possible because neither trade winds nor kona storms were active at this moment. Wailua Falls in the foreground is one of the streams which drain the abundant rainfall received by Waialeale.

directly to the summit. The sharp updrafts at the narrow heads of these valleys send trade winds hurtling upwards so as to condense their moisture abruptly, and rain falls heavily at the edge of the summit ridge and just beyond it. On the south side of Waialeale are other valleys, such as Hanapepe Valley, which are undoubtedly effective in funneling clouds up to the summit from the south, as in the winter kona storms. Mt. Waialeale is rarely visible. It clears only when trade winds slacken to virtual calm, yet when no kona storm is approaching—conditions occurring occasionally during the fall and winter months. During trade-wind weather, Mt. Waialeale may be clear for a short period during the early morning hours.

As indicated, some sources state that Mt. Waialeale is the wettest place on earth. However, a locality in Burma, Cherapunji, which has a similar funnel of valleys nearby, may have a greater rainfall. The actual rainfall on Mt. Waialeale is difficult to determine. During the years between 1911 and 1958, readings were made once or twice a year. The rain gauge, which has a capacity of 900 inches, recorded an average of 466 inches per year, which has been corrected to 486 inches by the U. S. Weather Bureau in Honolulu. The driest year on Mt. Waialeale during this period of time yielded 218 inches, while during the wettest year 624 inches fell. However, there is reason to believe that the rainfall recorded in this gauge does not represent precipitation at its greatest. The rain gauge is located on the ridge very close to the edge of the pali, and, according to some observers, much of the rainfall blows up and over the rain gauge. The rain gauge is located on a bare area—as it should be. However, clouds which pass through trees condense much more of their moisture than they ordinarily would, because leaves and branches serve as centers for condensation. Thus a wooded area near the summit of Mt. Waialeale but a short distance back from the edge of the cliffs would probably yield much more moisture. Studies on various areas have shown that actual rainfall exceeds by 30 per cent the amount recorded by gauges under such conditions. If this is true, the average yearly rainfall on the wettest area in the Waialeale summit region would be expected to approach 600 inches per year.

The second wettest Hawaiian mountain is Puu Kukui in the western part of Maui. Figures for the summit bog of Puu Kukui show that the mean annual rainfall is 375 inches. The wettest year recorded was 1950, with 578 inches; the driest year was 1934, with 250 inches. Summer months are only slightly wetter (32 inches per month) than winter months (31 inches) on Puu Kukui summit. One can only imagine the weather of March 1942, when 107 inches of rain fell in a single month. Puu Kukui, like Mt. Waialeale, has a series of channel-like valleys which tend to funnel trade winds (as well as kona storms) toward the summit and hasten condensation over the summit.

"Kona-Coast Weather"

The Kona Coast, along the western side of the island of Hawaii, ought to be extremely dry. It lies on the leeward side of two large mountains, Mauna Loa (elevation 13,018 feet) and Hualalai (8251 feet). The saddle between the two mountains is five thousand feet high at its lowest, and thus the Kona Coast is quite effectively cut off from trade winds.

However, Mauna Loa and Hualalai are broad as well as high and thus present large expanses of land. During the day, these absorb large amounts of heat, which forms updrafts toward the summit. During the afternoon, air surrounding the mountains is rapidly drawn upward and the moisture it contains can be condensed rapidly. Air over the ocean west of the Kona Coast does contain moisture, so that if the updrafts can draw enough of this air to the top of the inversion layer, condensation will result. Along the Kona Coast, in towns like Kealakekua

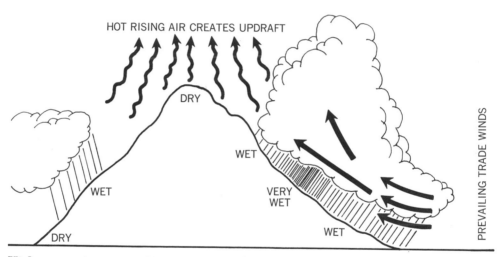

High mountain masses like Mauna Loa create strong upward air currents during the day, owing to heating. These mountains draw in moist marine air on the leeward coasts. At night, cool air descends from summit areas and drives clouds out to sea.

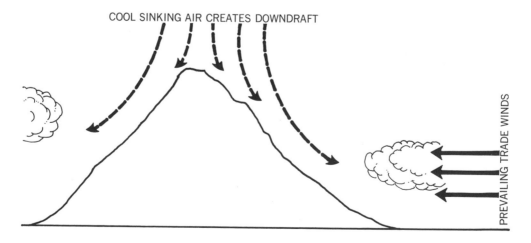

one can expect a light, gentle rain many afternoons during the year. In this way, annual rainfall of fifty to more than one hundred inches falls on the Kona Coast. Even if rain does not fall, a prominent cloud cover develops almost every afternoon. This helps to explain why the Kona Coast is so suited for coffee-growing. Coffee trees are cultivated elsewhere in the world in the shade of taller trees, for coffee plants cannot tolerate strong sunlight. On the Kona Coast, however, the cloud cover substitutes for shade trees, and coffee can be grown in the open.

During the night, the leeward-coast cloud cover is reversed: cold air descends from the high mountains, and drives the cloud cover out to sea. On the windward side of the island, it also tends to counter the trade winds, so that Mauna Loa can often be seen clearly from Kilauea during the early morning hours, but soon becomes cloudy as sun heats the mountain and updrafts pull in clouds.

The pattern of weather on the Kona Coast is duplicated to a lesser extent elsewhere. Clouds may often be seen in the afternoon on the leeward side of Haleakala, although they do not drop much rain.

The effect of thermal currents from land is not limited to the Kona Coast phenomenon. Heat which builds up on land masses tends to drive moist clouds from trade winds higher, making them penetrate the inversion layer. Consequently, rainfall from trade winds does not fall evenly during the day and night, but tends to occur in late afternoon, when heat currents from the land reinforce to the greatest extent the condensation patterns of the trade winds. If you hike along any of the trails which lead up to the summit ridge of the Koolau Mountains behind Honolulu, you will probably have a clear morning, but as you descend in the afternoon, so do the clouds, and you may walk in, or just in advance of, a gentle misty rain until you reach the lower elevations which remain dry.

The rainfall at Hilo (140 inches annually) is greater than one would expect at a sea level locality on the northeast side of a Hawaiian island. Not far inland from Hilo, the rainfall exceeds three hundred inches annually. The explanation for Hilo's rainfall may be related to heating of land. The large land mass behind Hilo may provide thermal heating which would cause moist marine air to contact the top of the inversion layer, and cause greater precipitation. Another possibility is that the thermal updrafts on the large mountains siphon in much larger quantities of marine air than would updrafts on smaller mountains; consequently, the action of trade winds is reinforced, bringing large volumes of moist air over the land.

One interesting phenomenon is the change of humidity during the day. At the Mauna Loa Observatory, the humidity is so low as to be unmeasurable during much of the day and night. It rises, however, during the afternoon, as thermal updrafts carry such moist air higher. At the same time, exactly the opposite changes in humidity occur downslope at Hilo: humidity decreases in the afternoon as the moist marine air above the coast is heated by the land.

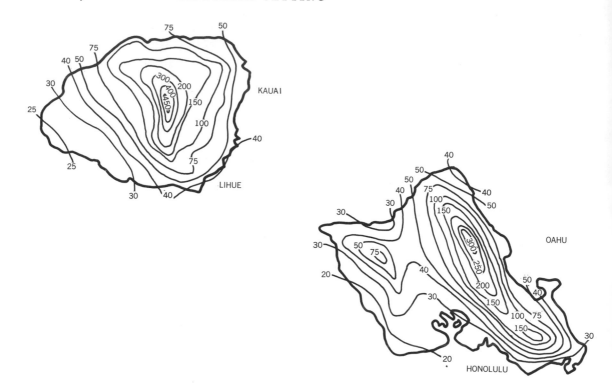

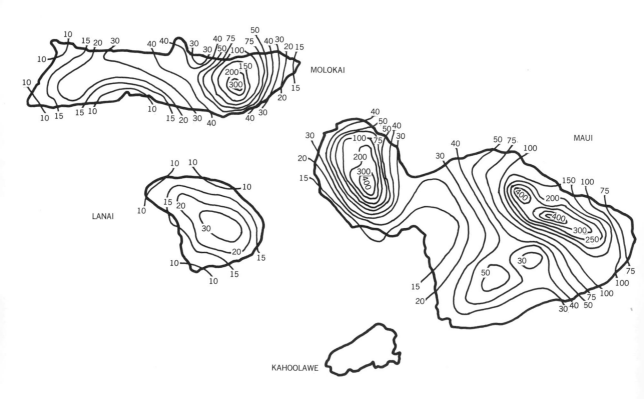

Rainfall maps of the Hawaiian Islands show a remarkable range in precipitation across short distances. These maps are highly simplified and many local conditions cannot be shown—and many are not yet known. No data are available for Niihau or Kahoolawe, which probably receive less than thirty inches of rain per year.

Microclimates

The Hawaiian landscape is exceptional in creating sharp changes from one locality to another. These are often so local that they cannot be shown easily on a map, and thus the rainfall maps shown here do not include them. In Haleakala Crater, on Maui, one can see several examples of this. The floor of the crater, about seven thousand feet in elevation, is dry because it is above the inversion layer and is sheltered from both trade winds and kona storms by the crater walls. A gap in the north side of the crater, the Koolau Gap, permits one to walk directly from the crater floor to the north side of Haleakala. In doing so, one goes from the desert-like dry cinder cones of Haleakala Crater down into the wet rain forest of Koolau Gap where annual rainfall probably exceeds one hundred inches of rain a year—a walk which takes perhaps an hour.

At the eastern end of the floor of Haleakala Crater is a place known as Paliku. Although most of the crater floor is nearly bare, there is a small grove of

Through the notch above Paliku, a locality in Haleakala Crater, clouds descend; their condensation permits a small grove of trees in this corner of Haleakala Crater, which is otherwise dry and bare.

trees there, apparently related to a notch in the crater wall above Paliku. One can watch clouds being drawn into the crater through this notch. They probably provide relatively little rainfall, but they do condense on the trees and shrubs and permit plant growth which could not survive only a few yards away where the clouds do not reach.

At the western end of Hawaii Volcanoes National Park, as one goes from Kilauea westward to the Kona District, one crosses an area known as the Kau Desert. This barren area is amazingly close to the forests of Kilauea, which are wet enough to sustain a lush growth of tree ferns. As the rainfall map indicates, there is a decrease of rainfall westward from Kilauea, although not so dramatic as to suggest a desert. Rainfall figures are lacking for the Kau Desert, but it probably is drier than the figures on the rainfall map suggest. However, soil conditions undoubtedly exaggerate the rainfall gradient. If the Kau Desert is very porous, it may have soils which are, in effect, drier than those of Kilauea, much drier than differences in rainfall would indicate. If the Kau Desert is sunnier than Kilauea, evaporation would exceed that at Kilauea greatly, and have the effect of magnifying greatly the difference in soil moisture between the two localities. Excessive evaporation and low humidity in Hawaiian lowlands undoubtedly does make such areas much drier for plant growth than rainfall figures suggest. In such a way differences in wetness between ridges and valleys may be very pronounced. Wet forest plants which cannot grow on a ridge can be found only a few feet down from the crest of the ridge.

Likewise, lava flows are probably less hospitable for plant growth, even in rainy areas, until they develop a vegetation cover which reduces evaporation and heat absorption by lava, and increases the possibilities of moisture condensation from clouds by foliage. Bare lava might be drenched during a rain, but baked to dryness a few hours later; development of a vegetation cover will temper these extremes.

Condensation of clouds by foliage permits what is, in effect, a wet forest to grow on the summit ridge of Lanai. This ridge receives about fifty inches of precipitation per year according to rain gauges. This is less than one would expect for a rain forest, and undoubtedly the condensation of moisture from clouds which cover the summit so much of the time permit this total to be perhaps doubled. The cloud cover decreases evaporation, rendering the moisture received more effective.

The porosity of Hawaiian land may lead one to underestimate rainfall in very wet localities. Bogs ought to form in many areas which receive more than two hundred inches of rain per year, but in fact this happens in only a fraction of these areas. For bogs to form, slopes must be almost level, and topography must hold water in pockets rather than permitting runoff. Likewise, many small streams lose water to underlying rocks rapidly, so that streams are much smaller, and waterfalls less conspicuous than one would expect. After a few hours of heavy showers, waterfalls are conspicuous, but they subside very quickly.

Peculiar strong wind currents sometimes occur in the Islands. Strong down-slope winds often occur in the Kula District, on the western slope of Haleakala, Maui. In the canyons of West Maui extremely strong gusts have been recorded. These, as well as other curious Hawaiian weather phenomena, need study, and would be interesting for amateurs to observe.

HAWAIIAN BIOLOGICAL PHENOMENA

Chapter 3 🙶🙷 *DISPERSAL TO THE HAWAIIAN ISLANDS*

OF ALL the high volcanic islands in the world, those of the Hawaiian chain are the most remote from any continent—or from other islands of appreciable size. They lie virtually alone in the North Pacific, separated from North America by about twenty-five hundred miles of ocean. Between the Hawaiian Islands and the Marianas Islands, none of which is very large, lie about thirty-five hundred miles of ocean without any land except the small atolls Wake and Marcus. Looking south from the Hawaiian Islands, only atolls dot the equatorial latitudes, and the high volcanic islands such as the Marquesas Islands, the closest high islands to Hawaii, lie two thousand miles away; Tahiti and the other Society Islands are even farther away. Even these islands are relatively small, and large islands, such as the Philippines, lie about five thousand miles away.

Geological evidence indicates that the Hawaiian chain has never been connected to a land mass. No now-vanished islands can reasonably be imagined between the Hawaiian chain and North America. The Leeward Hawaiian Islands and the reefs in the Leeward group once may have been high islands and probably were. They never, however, were a continuous land mass—only islands, and rather small ones. The Leeward chain was probably never even close to other island groups to the west. The most optimistic statement one can make about former land areas in the Pacific is that many of the atolls of the Pacific were once high islands, and that these may have served as steppingstones in the dispersal of animals and plants toward the Hawaiian Islands. Such former high islands, however, were not all in existence at the same time, and probably there were not many more, if any, high islands in the Pacific at any one time than there are now. At best, former high islands extended the dispersal possibilities of some groups somewhat. These groups still had to cross oceanic distances to arrive on the Hawaiian Islands, and so we are left with the task of explaining how this was accomplished.

The rainfall, soil, and temperature conditions of the Hawaiian Islands make them exceptionally inviting fields for occupation by many groups of animals and plants. The bottleneck of traversing vast oceanic distances to reach the Islands is a very narrow one, however, and only a small number of colonizations have succeeded over the five to ten million years during which these Islands have been available for occupancy. Many large and conspicuous groups are entirely absent, or were never able to reach the Islands in prehuman times. Among plants, conifers are notably absent in the Hawaiian flora, as well as many large-seeded forest trees of Indo-Malaysia. The native Hawaiian fauna contains no mammals (except a single bat), no reptiles, no amphibians.

The difficulties of a natural event of dispersal across twenty-five hundred miles of ocean or more may seem enormous. A few biologists, seeing these difficulties, and piqued by the disorderly qualities of dispersal (biologists like orderly processes), doubt that such dispersal ever occurred at all. Such biologists have to imagine numerous land bridges leading to the Hawaiian Islands from all corners of the Pacific, conveniently rising, then falling to transmit some immigrants to the Hawaiian Islands yet bar others. Perhaps because biologists are not geologists, they can imagine such fantastic bridges, but no such impunity applies to geologists. In fact, for either kind of scientist, a hypothesis involving natural dispersal over ocean proves to be by far the simplest and most believable one. This process does not need to take place frequently—in fact, if it did, Hawaiian plants and animals would be identical with those of mainland areas (whereas more than 95 per cent of them are, in fact, found nowhere else on earth). Long-distance dispersal may be "unlikely," but it is not impossible. And many "unlikely" events can take place when ten million years are available.

Botanists seem to have been more skeptical than zoologists about long-distance dispersal. This is rather amusing, because each time a plant reproduces, it *disperses,* for the new generation cannot grow exactly where the old one did. Long-distance dispersal is only the most spectacular form of the dispersal which occurs every time a seed is formed on any plant.

In fact, if we examine animals and plants in the native Hawaiian flora and fauna, we can see that each of them possessed some feature or features which gave them exceptional ability at long-distance dispersal. Some of these features have changed somewhat since the various groups arrived, but the mechanisms of transport can still be detected. To imagine the events which brought these arrivals to the Islands, we have only to look at them.

Drifting in Air

Transportation through the air is a means of travel possible for both plants and animals, but in the case of transport to the Hawaiian chain, they must be able to float exceptionally long distances. There are two ways in which this can be accomplished: the organism must be so small, or have a reproductive structure so small, that it is dust-like, as are spores, for example; or the organism must be able to fly, as do insects and birds. Over such long distances, even flying animals might be passively aided by air currents, however.

Plants which reproduce by means of spores include ferns, mosses, fungi, algae, and lichens, which are a combination of algae and fungi. The spores of these are mostly so small that a line of a thousand of them end to end would be an inch long. Any item this small can be carried almost indefinitely in air currents, especially if it reaches upper air levels. Plants with small spores can probably travel almost unlimited distances. This explains why particular kinds of fungi, fresh water algae, and mosses are rarely limited to any given area—or even continent.

Ferns generally have larger spores, ranging between twenty and fifty microns (2500 microns=1 inch). These still can travel in air, but not so readily. The ferns native to the Hawaiian Islands number about 168 species plus varieties, and these probably stemmed from about 135 original immigrants. Many (119) of the native ferns do not occur outside the Islands, which suggests that spores of their ancestors arrived only on a single occasion, and the population then changed so as to become different from the mainland one (or vice versa). The

The extremely minute size of fern spores makes them suited for dispersal by wind. Fern spores are shown in a mass to the right of the typewritten word, "spores" (with a few scattered over the letters). As a consequence of their good dispersibility, fern spores soon reach lava flows, as attested by these plants of *Nephrolepis exaltata* growing in a crack in lava of the 1950 flow, South Kona District, Hawaii.

number of kinds of ferns estimated to have originally arrived on the Islands (135) is remarkably large compared to the number of flowering-plant immigrants (about 255), for, in the world at large, the number of kinds of ferns is but a fraction of the kinds of flowering plants. Fern spores have obviously been more successful at reaching Hawaiian sites than have seeds of flowering plants. In most cases, these spores have arrived by flotation in air.

Flotation in air can account for the arrival of very small seeds only, preferably those which are winged or irregular in shape and would thus have more buoyancy. I have estimated that only 1.4 per cent of the 255 hypothetical flowering-plant immigrants to the Islands arrived in this way. Few seeds are small enough to travel in this fashion, and even the parachute-like seeds of a dandelion probably cannot travel the thousands of miles which separate the Hawaiian Islands from the source areas from which plant colonists have come. Orchids are among the few flowering plants which have seeds suitable for air flotation: orchid seeds are very small, exceptionally light. However, only three orchids are native to the Hawaiian Islands, a very small number for a wet tropical country. Perhaps orchid seeds do not travel exceptionally long distances well by air, or perhaps they are not resistant to freezing temperatures of the upper air. Perhaps they have such specialized pollination requirements that they cannot become established unless the right pollinating insect is present.

The ohia lehua tree, *Metrosideros polymorpha*, has seeds small enough so that one might guess that air flotation was possible. *Metrosideros* trees have reached virtually all the high islands of the Pacific, and thus can be said to be easily dispersible. *Metrosideros* seeds are very small as seeds go, but are appreciably larger than fern spores. We can clearly see the ability of ohia lehua seeds to travel on the wind where lava flows are concerned. New lava flows acquire a growth of young *Metrosideros* trees soon after the lava cools. Many plants which have wind-dispersed seeds may have reached the Hawaiian Islands in some way other than air flotation; such seeds can, nevertheless, travel by air *within* the Islands, and thus reach new lava flows. Plants such as the kupaoa *Dubautia* and the pawale *Rumex* are often seen as colonists on lava flows, and probably the seeds arrived there by air. *Dubautia* and *Rumex* seeds are probably poor at wind dispersal over thousands of miles, and may have reached the Islands via birds.

If passive flotation of seeds can account for arrival of seeds of only a few flowering plants, dispersal of small flying insects ought to be much better. It is. Entomologist Elwood C. Zimmerman has estimated that the approximately four thousand species of native Hawaiian insects evolved from between 233 and 254 original colonizations. Thus many more wind-borne insects than wind-borne seeds arrived in the Islands.

Those skeptical that insects could travel thousands of miles can become believers by reading the experimental work of the Bishop Museum entomologist, J. Linsey Gressitt, and his associates. To answer the question of whether insects

The ohia lehua tree (*Metrosideros polymorpha*) has very small seeds, as the comparison to typewritten letters shows. Seedlings appear very quickly on new lava flows; shown here is a shrubby specimen on the 1955 Puna District flow.

really are carried by air and thus reach remote areas, these scientists took collecting equipment into airplanes and onto ships. Scoops in the airplanes sampled air at high altitudes, and an appreciable number of insects were trapped. Likewise, nets on ships at sea far from any land mass picked up a broad collection of insects and spiders. When the entomologists analyzed which families and orders of insects and spiders were caught, they discovered virtually the same basic groups as are native in the Hawaiian fauna. The insects collected were apparently virtually all dead. This probably resulted from sudden impact when they were caught, although a large proportion of insects floating for long periods in the air might be expected to perish. It seems likely that the catches of insects would have been much poorer if insects merely floated passively. Probably insects are carried passively but stay afloat in part by wind updrafts.

The insects which have successfully colonized the Hawaiian Islands in pre-human times are those adapted to long-distance dispersal and subsequent colonization. Small body size is the most important key to this transport, and in fact most Hawaiian insects are notably small. Buoyancy in the air due to small body size may seem negligible where most animals are concerned, but with very small ones, small body size does, in fact, yield greater floatability on that count alone. There are some exceptions to smallness among Hawaiian insects, notably the crickets and grasshoppers. Can these travel such long distances as flying adults? Or did they arrive in some other way, such as in the form of unhatched eggs? Grasshoppers have resistant eggs, notably resistant to dryness and temperature extremes. Some large insects do migrate—dragonflies and butterflies, for example. The one large colorful Hawaiian butterfly, *Vanessa kamehamehae,* may stem from migratory butterflies. Likewise, the two large Hawaiian dragonflies may be explained in this fashion.

Birds are much too large to be carried passively, and only active flight can explain their presence on the Islands. Migratory birds, such as marine birds, shore birds, and waterfowl offer no great problems in this respect—and these groups are all rather well represented on the Hawaiian chain. The number of native Hawaiian land birds, however, is rather small. Only seven colonizations can account for all the land birds, in the strict sense, now native to the Hawaiian Islands. This seems a very modest number, but is perhaps understandable. Land birds do not stray very far from land ordinarily, so only a few exceptional instances of transport over such long distances would be expected.

The list of birds not native to the Hawaiian Islands but observed there on one or more occasions as stragglers include the following: pelagic cormorant, reef heron, white-faced glossy ibis, lesser snow goose, American white-fronted goose, emperor goose, black brant, cackling goose, mallard duck, green-winged teal, baldpate, gadwall duck, bufflehead, harlequin duck, red-breasted merganser, lesser scaup duck, canvasback, greater scaup duck, marsh hawk, American osprey, black-bellied plover, killdeer, Pacific godwit, Wilson's snipe, short-tailed sandpiper, pectoral sandpiper, red phalarope, northern phalarope, ring-billed gull, herring gull, California gull, Point Barrow gull, Bonaparte's gull, Pacific kittiwake, arctic tern, black-naped tern, marsh hawk, and belted kingfisher. This list consists almost entirely of migratory birds associated with water. We might note that some of these waterfowl, particularly the ducks, may have aided in dispersal of plants to the Islands, but regular bird visitors may be more important in this respect.

The few land birds which have succeeded in colonizing the Hawaiian Islands in prehuman time have probably done so by virtue of rare storms. A flock of land birds might be carried far out to sea during hurricane-like conditions, perhaps into strong upper air currents, and ultimately might arrive on the Hawaiian Islands.

All guesses concerning the role of air or wind in dispersal are valid only if suitable air currents do, in fact, reach the Hawaiian chain. In the preceding chapter we have seen that trade winds from the northeast form a steady stream toward the Islands during most of the year. During the winter months, the kona storms constitute large weather systems, some of which traverse long distances from the coast of Mexico or Central America. Storms that feed into these consistent Hawaiian weather patterns could contribute spores, insects, etc., to Hawaiian sites.

A significant source of strong wind currents which has not been generally appreciated yet with respect to dispersal is the northern hemisphere jet stream. The jet stream is a pathway of ultra-high-speed air which occurs as a continuous band at thirty thousand to forty thousand feet around the northern hemisphere. Typically, it accelerates over certain regions, decelerates over others, farther north at some seasons, farther south at others, in a predictable pattern which can, in fact, be mapped. In the map shown here, the January path of the jet stream leads from southeast Asia, where it begins to accelerate, to the Hawaiian Islands, where it decelerates markedly. The top speed, 122 miles per hour, could account for rapid transport: an object in the jet stream could be carried to the Hawaiian Islands in a little over two days, according to the speeds shown. The jet stream tends to sweep warm air upward on its equatorial side, cold high air downward on its northern side. Strong updrafts from storms could funnel plant and animal material upward to a point where the jet stream could catch it and hurtle it eastward. The vortex-like nature of the jet stream would tend to keep material air-borne. Deceleration of a jet stream could account for dropping of material. Another possibility is that rain clouds, rising high, as over the Hawaiian mountains, bring material down from high altitudes in rainfall.

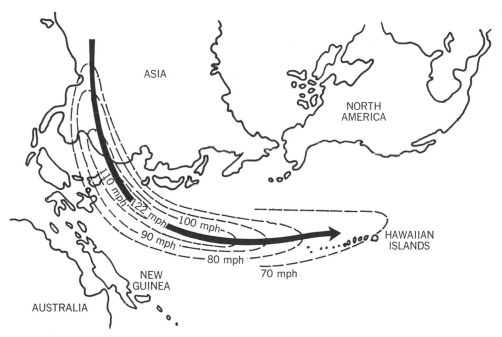

This map illustrates the typical January position of the Pacific portion of the northern hemisphere jet stream, a semipermanent ultra-high-speed wind between thirty thousand and forty thousand feet. Because this wind accelerates over Indo-Malaysia and decelerates over the Hawaiian Islands, it could help to account for dispersal in this direction.

The path of the jet stream from southeast Asia matches well the source areas which biologists have claimed must have contributed most heavily to the Hawaiian flora and fauna. Except for animals and plants brought by ocean currents—and these are relatively few in number—most have depended directly or indirectly on transport in air. The predominant west-to-east direction of air movement in the northern hemisphere, of which the jet stream is an exaggerated form, favors fulfillment of the Indo-Malaysia-to-Hawaii pattern. Of Hawaiian insects, 95 per cent are "Pacific" (as opposed to "American") in origins. "Pacific" implies Indo-Malaysia plus parts of the Pacific closer to Hawaii. Indo-Malaysian origin is stamped on a somewhat smaller, but still predominant proportion of Hawaiian land shells, ferns, and flowering plants. Some have commented that Indo-Malaysian affinity of Hawaiian organisms is based on the fact that a scattering of islands links Indo-Malaysia with the Hawaiian area, whereas there are no such steppingstone islands between Hawaii and North America. The Indo-Malaysian or "Pacific" character of the native Hawaiian flora and fauna might be due to the efficiency of transport from these areas. Another important factor, however, might be the fact that animals and plants best suited to the Hawaiian climate would mostly be those native to wet tropical areas which are most like those of the Islands—such as other Pacific islands. The coasts of North and South America are mostly drier, and subject to greater temperature extremes; organisms adapted to these conditions would be expected to be poorer candidates for success in the Hawaiian Islands. It is, then, perhaps surprising that as many as 20 per cent of Hawaiian flowering plants are, in fact, American in their relationships.

Attached to Birds

Seeds can become embedded in mud on feet or other parts of birds, and travel in this way. This is likely to happen if seeds are small, if the plants grow in wet, muddy places, and if the birds frequent these places and then migrate. Plants of marsh, bog, riverbank, or pond could be dispersed best in this way. In the Hawaiian flora, only a small number of plants have the appearance of having arrived via mud on birds' feet. Perhaps *Lobelia* and *Drosera* might have arrived in this fashion. Seeds small enough to be caught in mud on birds' feet might also be transported in several other ways, even possibly by wind dispersal. One cannot categorically state that seeds of the ohia lehua, *Metrosideros,* did not arrive in mud on feet of birds. Observations in various parts of the world suggest that this mode of transportation is genuinely effective. I have estimated that 12.8 per cent of the hypothetical original immigrants to the Hawaiian Islands might have arrived in this way.

Some plant and animal parts are viscid, and can become attached to bird feathers. Adaptations of this kind are sometimes subtle, and not easily seen. For example, *Plantago* (the weedy species of which are known to gardeners as plantains) has small black seeds that seem to have no special adaptation for dispersal. However, if *Plantago* seeds are soaked in water, they quickly develop a slimy covering which, when allowed to dry, can attach the seed to various surfaces, such as feathers or other parts of a bird. A mucilaginous covering on seeds can also be seen in Hawaiian species of *Euphorbia* (akoko) and *Lepidium*.

Slimy materials are probably also basic to long-distance transport of land snails. Land shells can withstand dryness by sealing themselves onto leaves, branches, even feathers, by means of this glue-like secretion. Land snails have, in fact, been seen attached to birds. The eggs of land snails can travel in a similar way.

Long-distance travel for land molluscs would be difficult for species with large shell size, unless travel is by eggs alone. Interestingly, many of the land shells native to the Hawaiian Islands are quite small, as the illustrations show.

 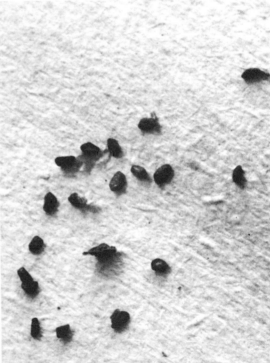

The Hawaiian species of *Plantago*, such as this plant of *P. pachyphylla* var. *hawaiiensis* (Kahuku, Kau District, Hawaii), owe their presence on the Hawaiian Islands to a peculiarity of *Plantago* seeds. These seeds, such as those of *P. major* shown at the same scale as the ohia seeds above, have a coat which becomes mucilaginous when wet. Just as they have adhered to their paper background here by this mechanism, they could adhere to birds.

Small size is one of the characteristics which favor natural dispersal of land shells over long distances. Shown here, compared with typewriter letters, are the native Hawaiian land shells *Auriculella auricula* (Nuuanu, Oahu), *Elasmias fusca* (Mauna-hui, Molokai), and *Tornatellinides procerula* (Kamuela, Hawaii).

Shells of this size could travel almost indefinitely while adhering to a bird. There are a number of native Hawaiian land shells of intermediate size, but at least some of these, perhaps all, could be supposed to have evolved from ancestors with smaller shell size.

Once a land snail has adhered to a surface, it seems highly resistant to further drying, and therefore could withstand the conditions of travel on a bird. In such a dormant condition they can also withstand very cold temperatures, as tests with a refrigerator readily show. Land snails are favored for establishment once they arrive: the simple plant foods they require are generally readily available.

Some Hawaiian plants have seeds coated with sticky substances, like rubber cement or pine pitch in texture. One such plant is *Boerhavia,* a common beach plant of the tropical Pacific. The small fruits of this plant are sticky at the angles, and adhere very readily to bird feathers. These fruits are borne a few inches above the ground, and are thus perfectly placed for coming into contact with feathers as a bird runs along the ground. A relative of *Boerhavia, Pisonia,* has fruits which are much longer, two inches or more in length. They are, appropriately, even stickier, and adhere very firmly to birds.

Boerhavia diffusa, a trailing beach plant native throughout the Pacific, has small fruits which are sticky. Their viscid surfaces attach them to bird feathers quite efficiently: several fruits may be seen beneath the eye of a juvenile sooty tern which has just run through some *Boerhavia* plants (East Island, French Frigate Shoal).

Viscidness of a different kind is involved in the dispersal of certain fleshy fruits. Some pulpy fruits attractive to birds have very small seeds. If the fruit has a slimy juice, these seeds might easily become smeared on feathers while the bird feeds. Many fruits in the native Hawaiian flora fall into this category. *Clermontia* and related lobeliads (*Cyanea, Rollandia*) have fruits which are bright orange, and break open at maturity to reveal many tiny brown seeds. When the fruit opens, drops of white latex exude from the split surfaces. This latex might also help to adhere the seeds to bird feathers. Other Hawaiian plants which have minute seeds in fleshy fruits include the ohelo (*Vaccinium*), *Cyrtandra*, and *Pipturus*. These fruits could, of course, be carried internally in bits as well as externally. The fruit type is versatile, and therefore an excellent candidate for long-distance dispersal.

Attachment of a fruit by a mechanical device is one of the most effective ways in which a seed or fruit can travel. Devices such as barbs, hooks, bristles, prongs, or even stiff hairs on fruits have evolved chiefly in relation to furry animals. Regardless of this mode of origin, these devices serve equally well to

Fruits of *Pisonia umbellifera* (left) are about two inches long, yet they adhere perfectly to birds: the ridges are very rough and sticky. Fruits of *Clermontia arborescens* (right) have minute seeds embedded in a pulp which might become smeared onto bird feathers. Fruits also contain sticky latex which might aid this adhesion (summit ridge, Lanai).

The shrub *Dubautia scabra* (kupaoa) has appeared on the new cinders of the 1959 Kilauea-iki eruption—"Devastation Walk." It probably reaches new lava quickly by air flotation of seeds, which have bristles which catch in the wind and are light. However, the dubautias may have arrived on the Islands by the tendencies of the bristles to catch in bird feathers.

attach fruits and seeds to feathers—all they require is contact with birds. I have estimated that 12.8 per cent of the Hawaiian flora's ancestors arrived in this way.

Some seeds are tipped by a circle of bristles, like the spokes of an umbrella. These seeds, like those of dandelions, can be said to have a parachute mechanism adapting them for wind dispersal. Some fruits have very fluffy bristles. These would be expected to be more efficient at long distance; however, the types with best-equipped seeds, such as thistles and dandelions, are absent on the Hawaiian Islands. Instead, types with nonfluffy bristles have arrived, as the kupaoa or naenae *Dubautia* demonstrates. Fluffy dandelion-like types are indeed efficient at wind dispersal, but they cannot cross extremely long distances in this way. The type with simple bristles is less efficient at flotation, but fits easily and compactly into feathers, and can thereby be carried greater distances.

Bidens, known to Hawaiians as kokoolau and to mainlanders as the weed Spanish needle or beggar tick, has fruits ("seeds") ideally suited for animal dispersal. They are often caught on clothing because they are needle-like and penetrate between fibers; the two or three prongs on the body of the fruit can

Each fruit of *Uncinia* has a recurved barb like a fishhook, which attaches the fruit to feather or skin. *Uncinia* has reached the Hawaiian Islands by this mechanism. Shown here are two non-Hawaiian species, *U. macrophylla* (Chile) and *U. brevicaulis* (Juan Fernández Islands). Fruits of *Bidens pilosa,* a mainland weed known as beggar tick, have sharp hairs and prongs ("awns") which are barbed. *Bidens* fruits probably caught in feathers of birds and reached the Hawaiian Islands by this mechanism.

also do this, mimicking the action of a fishing spear. These prongs are barbed, moreover, so once the fruit has lodged in a hairy surface, it is unlikely to fall off. Bristly hairs on the body of the fruit, like barbs on the prongs, double the likelihood of attachment.

Seeds with a miniature fishhook ought to be ideally suited to catching on feathers, and therefore reaching islands. And so they are, as is proved by the sedge *Uncinia,* which has reached other islands of the world in addition to the Hawaiian Islands. Although *Bidens* and *Uncinia* have special attachment mechanisms, seeds which are merely covered with bristles or hairs are nearly as good at long-distance transport. Seeds of grasses can travel in this way, for example.

Fruits Eaten by Birds

Surprisingly, the means of seed dispersal which seems the most difficult appears to have brought more flowering plants to the Hawaiian Islands than any other mechanism. My estimate is that about 39 per cent of the 255 plants ancestral to contemporary native Hawaiian flowering plants arrived via birds that ate seeds, carried them internally, and excreted them on arrival. Fruit-eating birds might also get fruits attached to them externally by chance, also. Fruits and seeds attractive to birds are exceptionally obvious in the Hawaiian flora. Because these are so typical of wet forests in Indo-Malaysia, they may have established preferentially in Hawaii despite the difficulties involved in dispersal. Fruit color is apparently not so important as fruit texture in attracting fruit-eating birds. The

The Hawaiian flora is rich in conspicuous fruits attractive to birds. The ohelo (*Vaccinium reticulatum*—Humuula Saddle Road, Hawaii) at left is related to mainland blueberries. The vine at right with greenish berries is a parasitic laurel, *Cassytha filiformis* (Puna District, Hawaii).

The sandalwood, or iliahi, has moderately large olive-like fruits eagerly sought by birds. Fruits of the Kauai sandalwood *Santalum pyrularium* (Kokee, Kauai), left, turn from red-purple to purple-black as they mature. *Exocarpus gaudichaudii* of the sandalwood family (right), bears white fleshy structures not part of the fruit, but which surround the seed and aid in attraction of birds (Hualalai, Hawaii).

Most of the Hawaiian pilos have orange fleshy fruits, as with *Coprosma stephanocarpa*, left (Waikolu, Molokai). A species typical of alpine regions, *Coprosma ernodeoides* at right (Kahuku, Hawaii), has shiny black berries. Both types of fruits are quite attractive to birds.

Although their fruits may not seem exceptionally conspicuous, the Hawaiian species of *Tetraplasandra* have berries of a sort often sought by birds. *Tetraplasandra meiandra* var. *hillebrandii* at left has deep purple fruits (summit ridge, Lanai). *Tetraplasandra hawaiiensis* at right has hairy gray fruits (Puu o Hoko, Molokai).

In the Hawaiian flora, fleshy fruits attractive to birds are exceptionally well represented. *Phyllostegia racemosa* (Kipuka along Humuula Saddle Road, Hawaii), left, and *Stenogyne purpurea* (Pihea, Kauai), right, show this well. Most members of the mint family have dry fruits, and the Hawaiian members of the family are unusual in having fleshy fruits exclusively.

Hawaiian flora contains an abundance of all colors, including white (*Cyrtandra*), blue (*Dianella*), black (*Coprosma ernodeoides*), and green (*Cassytha*), colors which would not be thought at first to be attractive to birds. The usual fruit colors are also present: yellow (*Nothocestrum,* the aiea), orange (*Astelia,* the painiu; *Coprosma,* the pilo), red (*Vaccinium,* the ohelo), and purple (*Santalum,* the iliahi or sandalwood).

Some plants, such as the sandalwood, would seem to have seeds too large for successful long-distance transport. Large seed size, however, may well have evolved after arrival, and the original colonists might well have had smaller seeds (see Chapter 8).

Plant families which mostly have dry fruits can be represented by fleshy fruits in the Hawaiian flora. This indicates that long-distance dispersal is relatively more successful for these fleshy types. Most members of the mint family have small dry seeds. The Hawaiian mints are unusual: *Phyllostegia* and *Stenogyne* have seeds covered with a succulent layer which is green, then turns purple. Many continental members of the lily and nightshade families have dry capsules which release seeds when capsules shake in the wind. Hawaiian representatives of these families all have fleshy fruits, as *Astelia* and *Nothocestrum* illustrate. But a fruit proper need not be fleshy to attract fruit-eating birds. The seeds and fruits of *Exocarpus* are not fleshy, but tissue below the fruit swells as a conspicuous white cup that is juicy and commands the attention of birds.

The problems and difficulties which biologists envision in dispersal of fleshy-fruited plants is not in the seeds or fruits, but in the birds required to carry

Most Hawaiian members of the lily family have fruits attractive to birds, as with the painiu *Astelia menziesìana* at left (Kilauea, Hawaii). The same is true in the nightshade family, as exemplified by the fleshy orange fruits of the aiea tree, *Nothocestrum breviflorum,* right (Puuwaawaa, Hawaii).

them. Skeptics say that fruit-eating birds do not migrate, whereas migratory birds do not eat fruit. They also claim that fruit-eating birds do not retain fruits long, but quickly excrete them. It is claimed that birds always fly on an empty stomach. These points are all well taken, and correspond to typically observed conditions. The exceptions, however, are all-important. Indeed, dispersal by fruit-eating birds is not frequent over long distances. It is quite rare and, if it were not, fleshy-fruited plants of the Hawaiian flora would be identical to those of other regions, as they are not. Marine birds, such as gulls, are not noted for eating vegetable matter, and probably usually do not do so. However, there are a number of reports that some marine birds do take fruits and seeds, some habitually. It is true that land birds typically undertake no long migrations, although two New Zealand cuckoos do migrate into Polynesia and the central Pacific each year. However, there are two categories of plant-eating birds whose migratory routes could account for introduction of plants to the Hawaiian Islands: waterfowl and shore birds. The list of occasional bird visitors to the Hawaiian Islands, given earlier, shows that many species of teals, ducks, and geese occasionally include the Hawaiian chain in their routes. Waterfowl may tend to eat marsh plants, but in fact include a wide range of articles in their diet.

Shore birds migrate throughout virtually all of the Pacific, are known to eat appreciable quantities of fruits and seeds, and are capable of retaining them for hundreds of hours. They retain relatively large fleshy fruits with hard seeds for especially long periods of time. Shore birds clearly seem to be a key to transport of fruits and seeds across long oceanic distances. Shown here are two such migratory shore birds: the Pacific golden plover, *Pluvialis dominica fulva*, left (photographed at Haleakala, Maui, by James W. Larson), and the bristle-thighed curlew, *Numenius tahitensis*, right (photographed on Midway Islands by Eugene Kridler).

Shore birds which regularly visit the Hawaiian Islands each year include the Pacific golden plover, the bristle-thighed curlew, the wandering tattler, the ruddy turnstone, and the sanderling. Each year, about the end of July, the golden plover migrates south from Siberia and Alaska. Individuals tend to travel from island to island in the Pacific by stages; the golden plover ranges far down into the Pacific, even to Indo-Malaysia, most of Polynesia, New Zealand, and Tasmania. The bristle-thighed curlew flies south from Siberia and Alaska to beyond the equator each year. The wandering tattler's migratory range includes most of the Pacific southward from Canada and Alaska. The ruddy turnstone and the sanderling have similar patterns.

Shore birds eat mostly molluscs and other small animals at the shoreline, but observations repeatedly indicated that they also eat a certain amount of fruits and seeds. Even if these are a minor item in their diet, they can be very effective in the dispersal of the seeds and fruits when millions of years and millions of individual birds are involved. Migratory birds surely do not *always* fly on empty stomachs, do not *always* preen off all seeds or adhering matter (which might contain seeds). Shore birds and waterfowl might have been effective in bringing the approximately one hundred fleshy-fruited immigrants which originally arrived in the Hawaiian Islands. Recent experiments by bird biologist

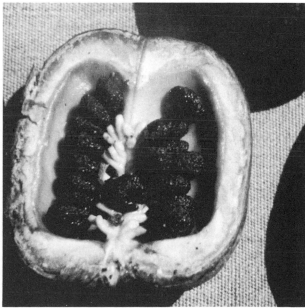

Pittosporum, the hoawa tree, has black seeds of a sort known to be attractive to birds; stickiness of seed surfaces may also aid in dispersal. Shown here is *Pittosporum hosmeri* (Honaunau, Hawaii).

Vernon W. Proctor have shown that shore birds and waterfowl retain some seeds eaten for hundreds of hours. Larger and harder seeds especially seem to be carried longer periods.

Black shiny seeds probably have been brought internally in birds, because they are quite attractive to birds even when their fruits are not fleshy. *Pelea, Zanthoxylum,* and *Pittosporum* are conspicuous Hawaiian plants that bear shiny black seeds in dry pods. Of these, *Pittosporum* has seeds which are sticky, perhaps sufficiently to adhere to feathers. Many birds pick up nonsticky black seeds and other shiny objects. Even marine birds appear very fond of such objects, and have been found both to carry them to their nests and on occasion to eat them.

Some plants are said to have "no obvious dispersal mechanism." Yet some of these plants have reached quite remote islands—so they must have a good dispersal mechanism. Some plants may merely be eaten frequently by waterfowl and have seeds resistant to digestion. Sedges fall into this category. Although not obviously attractive in color, sedges would be common items in the diet of water birds. Some plants may be dispersible merely on account of a relatively small seed size, which qualifies them for transport in any of several ways. The *Panicum* grasses have probably been aided by such small seed size. Minute hairs on seed-covering scale leaves surrounding seeds might have been sufficient for attachment to birds.

Shiny black seeds are attractive to birds, and may thus have secured transport to the Hawaiian Islands for *Zanthoxylum* (*Fagara*), the heae tree. Illustrated here is *Z. mauiense,* left (Puu Lehua, Hawaii), *Z. semiarticulatum,* above right (Waianae Mts., Oahu), and *Z. dipetalum,* below right (Kokee, Kauai).

The alani (*Pelea*) is yet another Hawaiian plant dispersed because its shiny black seeds are attractive to birds and eaten by them (but not digested). The species shown here is *P. clusiaefolia* from the Waianae Mountains, Oahu.

Some Hawaiian plants are said by some to have "no obvious dispersal mechanism." However, plants eaten by migrating waterfowl certainly do have such a mechanism. This probably accounts for arrival of sedges such as this one, *Cladium angustifolium* (Kahuku, Hawaii), in the islands. Minutely hairy scales surrounding very small fruits may have been sufficient to secure attachment to a bird for grasses such as this *Panicum koolauense* at right (Punaluu, Oahu).

Drifting in Seawater

Dispersal by flotation in seawater might be thought to be highly effective and to have brought many plants to the Hawaiian Islands. In fact, only 14.3 per cent of the original flowering-plant immigrants to the Hawaiian Islands are clearly adapted to oceanic drift, while another 8.5 per cent may have arrived by rare or freak flotation events. The best way to see plants adapted to flotation on ocean currents is to visit a seashore location. Plants which drift on ocean currents are beach plants—and rarely evolve into inland sites. An exception to this can be seen in the Hawaiian flora, however, where some of the coastal plants have, in fact, evolved inland into dry forest. Most of the coastal flora has seeds or fruits capable of floating—as shown by *Pandanus, Ipomoea,* and *Ery-thrina.* Some plants, such as *Portulaca,* have stems and leaves which float. In addition to floatability, seeds or plant portions must be able to resist seawater for weeks, and must arrive alive on beach sites and be able to grow there. Plants with these capabilities arrive on shores year after year, and so evolutionary changes, which require isolation of one population from another, tend not to occur.

Some plants typically grow well in beach situations and have seeds which can withstand exposure to seawater, yet they may have seeds and fruits poor at flotation or incapable of it. Such plants may take advantage of "rafting"—flotation of an entire plant, or entire mats of vegetation. Such a lucky arrival might

The coastal habitat of the hala tree (*Pandanus odoratissimus*) hints that it is a seawater-dispersed plant. In fact, the fruits do float readily (Puna District, Hawaii).

On tropical beaches of the Pacific, the pohuehue (*Ipomoea pes-cap-rae*) is a pink-flowered morning glory frequently encountered. It reaches these beaches by flotation of seeds in seawater (Lahaina, Maui).

Portions of a plant other than seeds can float in seawater and establish when they float ashore on a beach. This is true of stems of the ihi, *Portulaca oleracea*, a weed common in the northern hemisphere: it has reached shores far out in the Leeward Islands (Lisianski Island).

The wiliwili, or Hawaiian coral tree (*Erythrina sandwicensis*) grows near the shore, a habitat suggestive of arrival on ocean currents (northeastern Lanai). (*Erythrina* seeds can float in seawater, as shown here by seeds of *E. variegata*, a species from Asiatic shores.

The Hawaiian cotton (*Gossypium sandvicense*), known to the Hawaiian as mao or huluhulu, grows on Hawaiian coasts. Its seeds, although they withstand salt water, do not float; nevertheless, it may have arrived via a kind of rafting (northeastern Lanai). At right is *Calophyllum inophyllum*, a tree occasional on Hawaiian beaches; it was probably brought by Hawaiians, was barred from natural flotation by the contrary currents between the Hawaiian Islands and islands where it is native (cultivated in Honolulu).

never be repeated, so the new population would be isolated and might well develop into a new species. The Hawaiian cotton (*Gossypium sandvicense*) is a plant which seems to fit these specifications. A tree of the dry forest, the koa (*Acacia koa*) also may have had this history. Its closest relative is not in the Pacific at all, but is *Acacia heterophylla* of Mauritius. Both probably floated from Australia by some rare chance. The seeds of both could probably withstand seawater, even though they had no flotation mechanism. Perhaps branches or entire trees floated. The wiliwili (*Erythrina sandwicensis*) might be another example—the only relative in the Pacific is located on Tahiti, although one would expect a tree readily carried by seawater would become established on many Pacific islands.

Infrequent events of dispersal to the Hawaiian chain by oceanic drift may be explained in another way also. The seawater path to the Hawaiian chain is not as easy as it might seem. If we examine the currents of the Pacific, we see that across the equatorial zone, three currents run: the north and south equatorial currents flow westward, and between them the counter current runs eastward. If a seed from the southern hemisphere floated into the south equatorial current, it would likely by carried westward; if by luck it managed to enter the counter current, it would be swept far eastward again. Only by the rarest chance would it cross the three currents and arrive on a Hawaiian shore. There are many common South Pacific shore plants absent on Hawaiian beaches—evidently for this very reason. Some of these have been introduced to the Islands by man, and have gone wild readily, proving that the conditions were right for their growth; only their inability to disperse prevented their presence. Such plants include mangroves (*Rhizophora, Bruguiera*); *Calophyllum inophyllum* and *Terminalia catappa*, both known as kamani to the Hawaiians; and *Barringtonia* and *Hernandia*. We do not know for certain, but there seems a strong possibility that coconut palms did not occur on the Hawaiian Islands before the Polynesians brought them.

Establishment

A seed might arrive alive on Hawaiian shores after resisting drying, cold, or seawater, only to be deposited in a spot unsuited to its growth. A butterfly might evade mishaps while crossing thousands of miles of ocean, alight on Hawaii and lay eggs, yet its offspring might fail to survive because a required food plant—for example, a milkweed—is absent. Or a rhododendron seed might reach just the right forest habitat on the Hawaiian Islands, and grow to maturity, yet the climate might be just different enough from that of its original habitat so that the plant would be unable to flower and fruit. Or it might flower, but fail to set seeds because it requires cross-pollination and no other plant is available, or because a particular insect is needed to pollinate it, an insect not present in the Islands.

The requirements for success of an immigrant which arrives intact are so numerous that we might guess that establishment, not transport, is the narrower bottleneck. Successful colonists in the Islands seem to have the following qualities. They tend to be weedy, somewhat aggressive, capable of living in a pioneer habitat such as a beach, a bare lava flow, a landslide. Bogs could also be considered pioneer habitats, as could the branches of trees (for those plants which grow on trees rather than on the ground: epiphytes). In the case of animals, a versatile diet favors establishment. Plant-eating insects are more likely to establish on islands.

Barren lava flows, contrary to appearance, offer many opportunities for colonization. By observing the plants of new lava flows in the Hawaiian Islands, we can see re-creations, almost in the sense of a laboratory demonstration, of how original colonizations occurred.

Aa lava tends to favor plant growth because it contains many crevices which provide pockets of shade and which can retain water. The minerals of new lava certainly favor a wide variety of plants. The tall ohia lehua forest of the Kona District, Hawaii, is growing on lava which has very little soil, but rainfall conditions are good, and that overriding factor has permitted the forest.

The idea that vegetation of bare surfaces begins with a crust of lichens, that these develop pockets of soil which permit progressively larger plants to grow, and that a forest ultimately develops, is a theory clearly refuted by what happens on a Hawaiian lava flow. Lichens do appear on certain new lava flows, but most abundantly in wet, foggy regions. Even so, flowering plants appear at the same time, often even before lichens. And these flowering plants include trees.

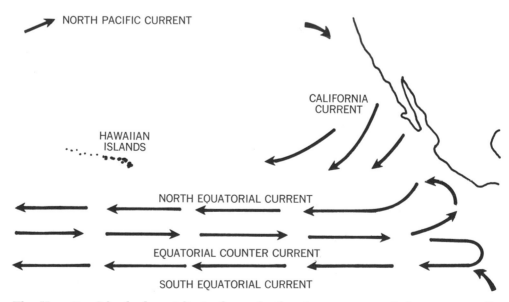

The Hawaiian Islands do not lie in the path of major currents, and they are cut off from the southern hemisphere by the westward and eastward sweeps of the equatorial currents.

Some ferns grow quite successfully on bare lava, as shown by *Sadleria cyatheoides* on the 1950 South Kona District flow. Where one plant starts, other seeds may be favored, as shown by this miniature colony of *Sadleria*, ohelo (*Vaccinium*), and a grass on pumice in Kilauea.

The common lichen on lava flows is *Stereocaulon vulcani*; it appears not prior to, but simultaneously with, or later than, flowering plants such as the kukainene *Coprosma ernodeoides*, left (Humuula Saddle Road, Hawaii).

The ohia lehua (*Metrosideros polymorpha*) can cope with eruptions, as shown by these trees which were half-buried in pumice from the 1959 Kilauea-iki eruption. They formed masses of roots high on limbs and rerooted themselves.

Ferns appear early on lava flows, a fact that upsets the idea of ferns as delicate plants of wet, shady regions. Ferns are actually often quite weedy—otherwise these ancient plants would never have survived to the present. *Sadleria cyatheoides,* a fern found only in the Hawaiian Islands, grows both on sunny new lava flows and in wet, mature forests. Good dispersibility of its spores aids the appearance of this fern on new lava.

Some plants, like the ohia lehua, are peculiarly suited for growth in pioneer situations. The ohia lehua forms aerial roots easily. If a grove of ohias is inundated by a thick blanket of pumice, ohias are not suffocated; the aerial roots on upper stems reroot the plant. This happened with ohias buried up to half their height or more by pumice in the 1959 Kilauea-iki eruption.

One plant often aids another to invade new lava. Where one plant takes root, it creates a small amount of shade and this may permit other plants to germinate under it. Or seeds may blow along a cinder field, lodging at the base of a fern and taking root. In this way, small colonies of plants may appear. The 1959 Kilauea-iki eruption killed some ohia lehua trees, but left them standing. At the bases of these trees, ferns and other plants have taken root because water seeps around the dead trunks and provides conditions just right for germination. Empty tree molds often contain seedlings—evidently the shade in these favors growth.

Some sites in the area devastated by the 1959 Kilauea-iki eruption invite seedlings more than others. Seedlings of *Buddleia asiatica*, a weed introduced by man to Hawaii, have sprung up at the bases of dead ohia trees.

Tree molds retain water, offer shady crevices, and provide good places for ferns to begin on new lava. At left, *Polypodium pellucidum*. At right, seedlings of *Buddleia asiatica* can be seen within a tree mold ("Devastation Walk," Kilauea-iki).

Lava flows stay bare for many years in areas of low rainfall, such as the 1801 flow in the North Kona District, left. The surface of pahoehoe lava is smooth, as shown by the Hilina Pali (Kilauea) flows at right. However, cracks in the flow provide suitable sites for plant growth, as this pukiawe (*Styphelia tameiameiae*) plant shows.

A pocket underneath a pahoehoe crust near Halemaumau has provided shelter for a seedling of the pawale (*Rumex giganteus*). Some plants characteristic of wet rain forest, such as the painiu *Astelia menziesiana*, can begin in such lava crevices (Hilina Pali, Hawaii).

If a lava flow occurs in a very dry locality, plants will be slow to appear. Lava flows known to have been formed before 1750 are still bare in some cases. Pahoehoe flows, with their smooth crusts, are less inviting for plant growth than are aa flows. However, pahoehoe crusts may collapse, and the shady recesses below the crust provide conditions ideal for germination of plants. Cracks eventually develop in pahoehoe flows, and these provide suitable sites. On the Hilina Pali near Kilauea, a light fall of pumice, evidently from the 1959 Kilauea-iki eruption, has filled some small crevices and depressions in pahoehoe. This has been all that was needed for plant growth, because these crevices can now retain water for days at a time, and so seedlings have appeared.

Wet forest plants can quickly invade lava—if the flow occurs in an area of wet forest. There always seem to be seeps or crevices that offer sufficient water for these plants. Once vegetation begins on a lava flow, the process tends to accelerate. Shady places are soon available for shade-requiring species. As a canopy of branches covers the flow, water no longer evaporates readily from the surface of the lava, and plants are increasingly favored.

Weeds introduced by man to the Hawaiian Islands can often be found on lava flows. Perhaps plant invaders of lava flows in prehuman times were also quite weedy. As the islands grew older and volcanoes became extinct, some plants of the Hawaiian flora appear to have become specialized for wet forest, and to have lost their original weediness. Thus, the ability a plant or animal now has to survive in pioneer conditions may or may not indicate similar qualities in its ancestors: they might once have grown successfully on new lava.

Chapter 4 PROBLEMS OF ISLAND EXISTENCE

PLANTS or animals that successfully reached the Hawaiian Islands were faced by three unique situations. They were cut off from all other individuals of their species, and remained cut off. They arrived, in most cases, only as a small number of individuals, ranging from a single individual to a small flock (perhaps in the form of eggs contained in a female). They had a finite, often small land area occupiable. The total land area in the Hawaiian chain is not very great, but only a small fraction of this is available to any particular plant or animal —a bog species, for example, is faced with only a few small bog areas.

The successful occupants of the Hawaiian Islands have developed ways of solving or coping with these problems, or they have become extinct and have been replaced by other immigrants. Perhaps the most severe implication of the three critical situations mentioned above is the problem of inbreeding.

Inbreeding results when a limited population of plants or animals has to mate within its own small circle, or even self-pollinate in the case of some plants. If a species continually inbreeds, fatal defects accumulate, eventually become common. The species is then decreased in numbers, so inbreeding becomes even more common, and the species is doomed. The antidote to this downward spiral is either the introduction of new genetic material from other individuals, or its manufacture by mutations.

Fortunately, the levels of genetic variability and outbreeding (breeding among

Hawaiian species are rarely uniform in the Hawaiian Islands, a fact shown by individuals, collected from a single area, of the land snail *Achatinella mustelina*.

If small differences within species were distinguished by naming them, we could, in some groups, have as many species as we have plants. A Kona Coast *Clermontia, C. caerulea*, may have extremely short sepals, or, as shown at right, longer ones. Plants like ones at right have unnecessarily been named no fewer than three times ("*C. rockiana*," "*C. loyana*," "*C. furcata*").

a large number of individuals) are high in most plants and animals. But when a colony begins on an island with only a few individuals, the variety of genetic material introduced is very limited, and, at least while the colony is a small one, inbreeding is going to occur. Species which can form new mutations and expand the number of their individuals can be "healthy" genetically.

If land area is limited, so are the number of individuals and the variety of genetic material. If we look at most Hawaiian animal and plant species, we find they are annoyingly variable; "annoyingly" to the biologist because they are difficult to name and cannot easily be classified. The Hawaiian agate shells, *Achatinella*, are notorious for this and in some Hawaiian plants and animals no two individuals are quite alike. Other species have little or no variability, are nearly uniform; these may be "declining" species.

If the number of individuals is limited by land area, some mechanisms for outbreeding must be found; one of these is hybridization. If there is no barrier

Hybridization occurs among the clermontias: *C. hawaiiensis*, upper left, has pear-shaped fruits and large, strikingly ribbed green flowers, has hybridized with *C. montisloa*, lower left, with smaller nonribbed purplish flowers and spherical fruits. The hybrid, lower right, has white flowers, tinged slightly purple, moderately ribbed, and spherical fruits (Kulani Road, Hawaii).

The moa, *Psilotum*, is a representative of a very ancient group of
land plants which coexisted with
the earliest ferns. Two species are
common in tropical regions: *P.
nudum* with upright habit, and *P.
complanatum,* which droops. This
appears to be the first place in
which hybrids (lower left) between
these two have been found (Waianae Mountains, Oahu).

(sterility) to crossing of closely related species, they can hybridize, and pool
their genetic material. If a group of species has evolved, and occasional hybrids
can take place between them, and all of the mutations in all of them can be
pooled, they can thus avoid the impoverishment of variety. This is what appears
to have happened in the ohia lehua (*Metrosideros*). Are there one species or
many in the Hawaiian Islands? One could say either with some justification.
One could even say that the Hawaiian ohia lehua is the same as a species found

There is no such thing as a typical ohia lehua (*Metrosideros polymorpha*). The one shown here has an appearance one might see in some places: a moderate-sized, rounded, tree, with smooth elliptical leaves and clusters of red flowers. Such an ohia tree would probably be found in a fairly wet rain forest (Kokee, Kauai).

in Tahiti and nearby islands, *Metrosideros collina,* although the name usually given to most Hawaiian ohias is *M. polymorpha,* a name which appropriately means "multiformed."

Perhaps at some remote time, an ohia like the Tahitian one arrived in the Hawaiian Islands. It evolved into a series of types suited to particular localities. A shrubby one ("*M. tremuloides*") with quaking leaves developed on wind-swept ridges. Types with greatly increased height have developed to suit wet forest; scrubbier forms have been produced in response to conditions on relatively dry ridges. Kinds of ohias with round hairy leaves (sometimes called *M. polymorpha* var. *incana*) tend to occupy lava flows. The hairiness of leaves may counteract the bright, dry conditions more effectively. A low tree with cup-like leaves, rusty-haired underneath, occupies exposed wet ridges; it is often called *M. rugosa*. In bogs, *Metrosideros* is exceptionally small: flowering individuals can be as little as six inches tall.

These various forms of *Metrosideros* have evolved by way of adaptation to various distinctive sites in the Islands. Where one ecological zone fades into another, such as the margin between a bog and a rain forest, intermediate individuals are found. Probably hybridization can provide these individuals "on demand," that is, intermediate types are formed by hybridization and

The "trembling" type of leaf is found in certain population of ohias from windy ridgetops on Oahu. These plants have leaves borne on slender petioles, and are called *Metrosideros tremuloides* by some (Punaluu, Oahu).

Metrosideros rugosa is a name applied to a curious ohia lehua which grows on high cloudy ridges of the Koolau Mountains, Oahu. It has small cup-shaped leaves covered beneath with dense reddish wool (Punaluu, Oahu).

Metrosideros polymorpha can be a very tall tree. Some individuals, as this one, for example, have yellow flowers rather than red ones. (Kulani Road, Hawaii.)

occupy intermediate areas. In this way, the Hawaiian ohias form a continual occupation of every sort of ecological opportunity from moderately dry forest to bog.

Possibly there has been a second, relatively recent introduction of *Metrosideros collina* or something like it from Polynesia. This would explain why there are some individuals in the Hawaiian Islands virtually identical with this species in other Polynesian islands, yet the distinctive types of *Metrosideros polymorpha* are also in Hawaiian localities. It would also explain much of the hybridization evident today; hybrids might represent mixing of the old and new immigrants.

Another possible explanation would be that *Metrosideros collina* immigrated to the Hawaiian Islands long ago, and while some races evolved into the distinctive *M. polymorpha* series, others stayed the same, and eventually hybridization among the original types and the newly evolved ones took place. This possibility is much like the one above. In any case, taxonomists shun the Hawaiian ohias because of the difficulty of naming particular specimens. If, however, we view *Metrosideros* as an evolutionary phenomenon, it becomes a

Ohias can be diminutive shrubs, consisting only of a few short twigs, when they grow in bogs. In the photo of tussocks from the Pepeopae Bog, Molokai, two plants, left and right, can be seen.

White, hairy young leaves characterize some trees of ohia lehua—especially those in drier localities (summit ridge, Waianae Mountains).

fascinating revelation rather than a difficult mess. Ohia lehua is the dominant tree of the Hawaiian forests, and it may hold this position precisely because it has such extraordinary variety—variety which keeps it "genetically healthy," leads to the development of new types, which in turn hybridize, retaining the variability. The ohia lehua is a model of a successful system under island conditions.

If the ohia lehua was introduced on more than one occasion to the Islands, it is not alone: the naupakas stem from at least three introductions, and, among insects, it is claimed that the wasp *Odynerus* and the dragonfly *Anax* were introduced more than once each.

Naturally, variability in a species often cannot easily be distinguished from hybridization. For this reason, a number of Hawaiian plants that represent various degrees of hybridization have been named as new species. Sometimes a hybrid population can become stabilized, so that it does seem to resemble a typical species. Analysis can show, however, that all of its features can be found in parental types. Botanist George W. Gillett recently analyzed Hawaiian naupakas, and showed that several populations named as new species can be shown to be hybrids from two basic species. Unfortunately, most botanists who have worked in the Hawaiian Islands have not searched for hybrids; rather, they prefer to find plants they can name as new species. Hybridization is very important among Hawaiian plants, however, and detecting hybrids in the Hawaiian flora will provide interesting work for the professional or amateur botanist of the future. Very likely some hybrids will be found among animals, too. This might help explain the tremendous diversity of the *Achatinella* snails, why one species can contain so much diversity, and why often a pair of species seems to merge into each other.

For animals, outbreeding is merely a matter of the mating of a male individual with a female individual within a reasonably large population. For plants, the situation is not so simple because most flowers contain both sexes, and many flowers can self-pollinate, a sure form of inbreeding. Some biologists have claimed that self-pollination would be an ideal condition for a plant immigrant. If only one individual begins a colony on an island, it could form seeds by self-pollinating, perhaps even without the help of a pollinating insect. But, as we have seen, because of the dangers of inbreeding, continual self-pollination is not a good system for most plants, and most Hawaiian plants have developed, or already had at the time of their arrival in the Islands, special mechanisms for outbreeding rather than inbreeding.

One way for a plant to avoid inbreeding is to adopt the animal system: to have male individuals and female individuals. This condition, known as dioecism in plants, is found in 27.5 per cent of Hawaiian plant species, 14.9 per cent of the genera. In most cases this has evolved in the Hawaiian Islands, although some immigrants probably arrived in the dioecious condition. Excellent examples of plants which bear either all male flowers or all female flowers are easy to find: *Broussaisia, Coprosma, Astelia,* and *Ilex,* for example. In some, the male flowers look very much like the female flowers until one examines them closely: *Pittosporum, Pelea,* and *Myrsine* are examples.

Some plants are "halfway to dioecism." Such a plant can have some male-flowered individuals, some female, some bisexual. Self-pollination of the bisexual plants is theoretically possible, but the male plants and female plants must

One of the most common shrubs of the rain forest is *Broussaisia arguta*, known to the Hawaiians as kanawau or puahanui. Individuals of this plant are either male (flowers shown) or female (fruits shown), thus assuring cross-pollination (summit ridge, Lanai).

At first glance, flowers of the hoawa (*Pittosporum*) appear to have both sexes, but close examinations reveal that flowers are male on some plants, female on others. In the closeups at right, female parts are at right, male parts at left in each flower. Organs of both sexes are present in both types of flowers, but in male flowers, the ovary is small and nonfunctional; in the female flowers, the stamens are small and vestigial. The species shown is *P. gayanum*, from the north edge of the Kokee plateau, Kauai.

Schiedea globosa is an herb found along the southeastern parts of Oahu. In any particular plants, the flowers are either all male (left), all female (right), or all bisexual (center).

crossbreed. This system has the advantage of retaining outbreeding, yet maximizing fertility. Hawaiian plants with this unusual system include *Schiedea, Charpentiera,* and *Styphelia.* Another possibility is that flowers which are all male and flowers which are all female can be formed on the same plant. This condition, found in a number of Hawaiian plants such as *Pipturus,* would at least theoretically reduce inbreeding. Special sexual conditions like the ones mentioned above characterize 44.6 per cent of Hawaiian flowering plant species, 35.3 per cent of the genera—much higher percentages than on any of the continents.

In bisexual flowers, self-pollination will not occur if stamens open before the stigma is receptive, or vice versa. This condition is found in 28.1 per cent of Hawaiian flowering plant species, 13.5 per cent of the genera. If we add this type to the special sexual conditions, we find that 72.9 per cent of Hawaiian flowering plant species, 49.5 per cent of the genera have one or more mechanisms for avoiding inbreeding. Thus almost three fourths have some obvious visible mechanism, and the remaining one fourth may well have another method. They may tend to hybridize, as with *Metrosideros* or many others. They may be wind-pollinated, as with grasses. Carrying of pollen about by wind tends to prevent inbreeding, because pollen can, and is likely to, reach distant individuals of the same species. Some other mechanisms may not easily be seen. However, even if a plant or animal has no obvious or invisible mechanism for avoiding inbreeding, it might have a high rate of production of new mutations. If it has no mechanism for avoiding inbreeding, it probably is doomed to a short career on an isolated island area.

Events of dispersal within the Hawaiian Islands tend to prevent inbreeding. If a colony of a species has lived in a single isolated valley for a long time, it might become inbred. Dispersal might deposit in this valley an individual of this species from another valley or island. If it breeds with the original colony, its descendants will become genetically "invigorated," as with hybrid corn. Isolation followed by contact within a species are ideal for "genetic healthiness" and also are believed to promote rapid evolution. The geographical plan of an archipelago may also aid evolutionary processes in other ways. If a group has exploited the possibilities on a single island, dispersal to a nearby island may lead to entirely new directions and developments. The time available for evolution of many groups within the Hawaiian Islands has been relatively short, yet the accomplishments in terms of species numbers alone has been amazing in such a small area. In the next nine chapters we see what, in visible ways, has been produced.

Chapter 5 ⟡ *ADAPTIVE RADIATION AND UNIQUE ADAPTATIONS*

"ADAPTIVE radiation" is one of those phrases often used by biologists and it has become encrusted by all sorts of subtle meanings or overtones not ordinarily, if ever, fully revealed. "Adaptive radiation" was invented to describe the process by which a group adapts to a broad variety of situations, rather than to a few special ones.

The implication is that a single small group (a family, or genus) is the unit considered. All of the major larger groups—say, ferns, or mammals—can be said to have radiated, so the term is intended to dramatize smaller groups with an unusual degree of diversification. This diversification is usually assumed to be relatively recent, and thus surprising (to be a "good" instance of adaptive radiation, the example must provide aspects which are at least somewhat astonishing, somehow unexpected). The term also implies that a broad range of ecological niches—especially extremes—are exploited by the group, and that these exploitations take place in a limited and easily defined geographical area—a continent, or an archipelago, or even a single island. The various adaptive types should mostly still be alive, not a scanty series of relict forms, so that the intermediate conditions, as well as the extremes, can be seen. The different products of adaptive radiation are usually regarded as *visibly* different (rather than different only in diet or in habitat).

Opportunities for adaptive radiation open when a particular area is poorer in certain kinds of occupants than normally is the case. This impoverishment of an island fauna or flora as compared to a mainland area is known as disharmony and is usually the result of a dispersal barrier. One notable example is illustrated by the marsupials of Australia: the placental mammals (except for a few rodents) did not get to Australia, so the marsupials radiated into

Insects have speciated remarkably in the Hawaiian Islands, but none so remarkably as the fruit flies, of which there are probably about five hundred species, perhaps more. Shown here is *Drosophila grimshawi* (Olinda, Maui). Other interesting insect groups which have speciated are represented here by the bugs *Nabis blackburni* (Nualolo, Kauai) and *Nysius fullawayi* (Laysan), center and right.

Dietary specialization among Hawaiian insects is illustrated by *Nesosydne argyroxiphii*, found only on the Haleakala silversword. *Dictyophorodelphax mirabilis*, right, lives only on *Euphorbia clusiaefolia*. Its gut is extended up into, then back down again, the peculiar snout-like horn. This structure, a unique one in this group, may be related to feeding or digestive habits (Kaumahone, Oahu).

many ways of life. The Hawaiian fauna and flora are extremely disharmonic —many groups which "should be there" are not. The fact that so many animals and plants introduced by man have prospered fantastically, gone wild and "taken over" shows that the Islands would have supported many groups not originally there, and that poor dispersibility is indeed the bottleneck.

Most of the successful immigrants to the Hawaiian Islands in prehuman time can be said to have been confronted with much greater opportunity than they had in their source areas. The degree to which they have exploited these new opportunities is limited by the genetic or evolutionary "momentum" they have—the ability to innovate new structures, new tolerances. Another limit, of course, is the time from the moment of colonization to the present: some groups have existed on the Hawaiian Islands longer than others.

One probably would not have been able to predict which groups could undergo the greatest degree of adaptive radiation in the Hawaiian Islands. The number of species which have developed may be only one criterion, but it does provide a clue. In this case, the native Hawaiian fruit flies (Drosophilidae) clearly have been the most enterprising group in the Islands. Actually, the Hawaiian fruit flies show some aspects of adaptive radiation well, others less or none at all. About two hundred and fifty species of *Drosophila* have been described for the Hawaiian Islands, and the number seems likely to rise to four hundred or five hundred as this group becomes better known. This speciation has occurred entirely within the Islands and does not represent species which range to other parts of the world. Another Hawaiian genus of fruit flies, *Scaptomyza,* has one hundred and fourteen species. About seventy species of *Scaptomyza* are known for all other parts of the world combined.

To some extent, these Hawaiian fruit flies have occupied niches which other insects would occupy on mainland areas—a good criterion of adaptive radiation. In food sources, the Hawaiian drosophilids are unusual. Most of the world's fruit flies seek sweet or vinegary slime, such as sap flows on plants, or rotting fruit. The Hawaiian fruit flies instead live in and on decaying leaves of araliads (*Cheirodendron, Tetraplasandra*). Some live on fresh or decaying stems, flowers, or fruits of lobelioids (*Clermontia, Cyanea*). These foods represent a shift from typical fruit fly foods, but they do not represent adaptive radiation, because if the flies had radiated with respect to diet, they would feed on a wide variety of different plant materials, perhaps on animal foods as well. *Titanochaeta,* a Hawaiian fruit fly genus of ten species, does demonstrate an unusual opportunity that was not missed: titanochaetas are parasites in spider egg cocoons.

Each of the Hawaiian fruit fly species appears to be distributed only over a small range, often a single valley. This, more than adaptive radiation, may explain the large number of species. Fruit fly ancestors reached numerous localities which could support them, and became pocketed there. However, recent discoveries have shown that sexual selection, a process which explains the colorful qualities of birds of paradise, has operated strongly in the Hawaiian drosophilids. Fruit flies elsewhere in the world mix feeding with mating, and can be seen pairing at food sources. Not so with the Hawaiian species: at a site other than a feeding site, a male will adopt and patrol a courtship area. A leaf, three or four inches of a fern-frond stalk, or a segment of a fern leaf may constitute the miniature courtship arena. Males advertise their presence in various ways, and lure females by attracting their attention, instead of pursuing and assaulting them. Interestingly, females of Hawaiian drosophilas have lost the ability to raise the abdomen so as to reject a male who intrudes upon her feeding with unwanted attention. Since male Hawaiian drosophilids do not bother females at feeding sites, the loss of this ability, which non-Hawaiian fruit flies have, is understandable.

For some Hawaiian fruit flies, experts can name the males easily, but the female of one species looks just like the female of another. The males may differ in mouthparts, forelegs, or distinctive patches of black, brown, or white on the wings. In one group of species, recognized as a separate genus (*Antopocerus*), males differ in antennae. A male will be successful in mating if he is more conspicuous, bigger, or more aggressive. Each species has special preferences for courtship territories, involving such factors as light, humidity, temperature, and spatial conditions. Males carry on rather curious courtship rituals: in one species, it may be elevation of the abdomen, in another, lowering it and smearing a liquid on the leaf it prowls. Courtship postures can be used to differentiate species.

Although living in a microcosmic world compared with the birds of paradise, the Hawaiian fruit flies have adopted the same curious "arena behavior" of those colorful birds. Other birds which have adopted arena behavior include bower birds, lyre birds, and the cock-of-the-rock; however, to find this syndrome in an insect group is astonishing. One may note in passing that Hawaiian fruit flies readily form hybrids in the laboratory, a parallel to the birds of paradise, which also form hybrids easily.

Hawaiian fruit flies are said to be well suited to avoidance of capture by birds, which are their chief predators. This ability seems to have been dramatically developed in the second largest group of Hawaiian insects, the flies of the family Dolichopodidae. Here protective colors are evident: species which inhabit the forest floor are dull, often brown. Species which prefer wet dripping banks are metallic-colored and glistening. Species which frequent streams are excellent water-skaters, those of ponds less good, and those from dry land quite inept in the water.

Nesosydne is an insect genus which has evolved color patterns according to plant background. In Haleakala, this insect may be found on silvery plants, the silversword *Argyroxiphium sandwicense* and the alpine geranium *Geranium tridens*. It is also found on the sooty looking branches and deep green leaves of *Coprosma ernodeoides*. *Nesosydne* individuals on the bright plants are pale, but are dingy on the dark-colored plants. A most remarkable distinction occurs between *Nesosydne rubescens* and *N. koae*. The former lives on the sickle-shaped phyllodes, the "leaves" (they are modified petioles) of an adult koa tree. The latter species lives on the fern-like true leaves, which can be found on seedlings of the koa. Adults of *Nesosydne rubescens* are greenish brown, whereas those of *N. koae* are pale green. These color differences match the color of phyllodes versus seedling leaves. *Nesosydne rubescens* lays eggs in the edges of phyllodes, whereas *N. koae* lays eggs in stems, a difference which includes different positions of the insect during ovipositing.

The proterhinid beetles are another group of insects which match their backgrounds: red species bore into reddish fern-front stalks, dark species occur on dark bark, pale ones on pale bark.

Plants influence diversification in insects not so much with respect to color in the Hawaiian Islands as with respect to food sources. An entire book, Otto Swezey's *Forest Entomology in Hawaii,* is devoted to listing host plants which are associated with particular insects. Often an insect species is associated with only a single plant, a specialization which might be cited as one event in a program of adaptive radiation. The role of plants in diversification of some insects is amazing. The longhorn beetles (*Plagithmysus*) are so specific that Hawaiian entomology expert Elwood C. Zimmerman says, "If we find borings in a species of tree unrecorded as having a species of the group, we conclude that the borings are probably those of a new species."

Both color pattern and food source may indicate diversification in insect groups: *Nesosydne blackburni* lives on *Clermontia parviflora*, on *Stenogyne*, and on *Pipturus*. *Pipturus* is grayish in color, and *N. blackburni* individuals on this plant are whitish, not grayish as they are on the other host plants. Could this be the beginning of a new species which is limited to *Pipturus?* *Pipturus* has probably "inspired" new species in various groups of insects, for pale-colored specimens of unrelated insect families live on *Pipturus*.

Very likely, the food source of the peculiar insect *Dictyophorodelphax mirabilis* may be related to the peculiar horn on the head of the insect, a horn which contains a long loop-like extension of the insect's digestive system. *Euphorbia,* the akoko, is an exceptional host plant for the group of insects to which *Dictyophorodelphax* belongs. Perhaps the peculiar structure of *D. mirabilis* permits digestion of the milky latex in *Euphorbia* leaves.

If an insect is partial to a particular host plant, it can be said to have a form of isolation: colonies of the host plant will be "islands," and consequently a population of the host plant on another island will be expected to have another species of the insect on it. In this way, entomologist Robert Usinger predicted that a new *Nysius* bug, known from mamani (*Sophora*) on Hawaii, would be found if the mamani plants of Haleakala, Maui, were examined. His prediction was fulfilled. Behind the radiation of many of the larger and more interesting insect groups, such as *Nabis* and *Nysius,* are diversification in preference for host plant. Diversification in diet and form would be expected to occur together in some insects, as they do in *Nysius*. Usinger claims that in the bug *Nysius* in the Hawaiian Islands, the range in features of the head, thorax, etc., is greater than it is in *Nysius* for the rest of the world.

Plant diversification is, of course, fostered by factors different from those in animals. Isolation, however, is just as basic to production of new species in

Cyrtandra is the group of plants which has formed the most species on the Hawaiian Islands. White, tubular flowers and white fruits, as seen above in *C. paludosa* var. *gayana*, (Kokee, Kauai), above are common to the entire genus, but other features show diversity. *Cyrtandra platyphylla*, below left, has hairy, round leaves (Kipuka along Saddle Road, Hawaii). *Cyrtandra lysiosepala*, flowers not at tips of branches but far down on the older stems (Puu Kukui, Maui).

plants as it is in animals. Is it what has permitted *Cyrtandra* to form so many species? A recent author has claimed that there are 129 species of *Cyrtandra* on the island of Oahu alone. Even if some of these species are grouped and fewer recognized, *Cyrtandra* is obviously producing a surprising degree of diversification. At first glance, there seems no obvious reason for this. True, *Cyrtandra* does have a range in growth form—one criterion of adaptive radiation. Some species are succulent herbs one or two feet high, others become large shrubs, perhaps twenty feet high, which could even be called trees. The latter occur in rain forests. Most cyrtandras tend to occupy wet shady gulches, and none could be said to grow in dry or even moderately wet forests, and none are truly bog species. Thus, not all the available ecological opportunities have been filled. Most of the species differ by features which have no obvious adaptive value: some flowers are shorter, some longer, some hairier, some smooth. Some cyrtandras have broad leaves, others have leaves quite narrow, and a wide gamut in leaf hairiness occurs. How can one explain why some species, such as *C. calpidicarpa* have long, string-bean-like fruits, whereas most have fruits of oval or spherical shape? How can one explain the various kinds of calyx form in flowers of *Cyrtandra*, forms which seem to have no advantage over one another for any known function? A few species do have curious adaptations which may be readily explainable. *Cyrtandra kaulantha* bears flowers only on shoots that trail along the ground; perhaps this places them in the range of crawling pollinating insects, such as beetles.

In *Cyrtandra*, we may be seeing a group which shows some adaptive radiation, but mainly speciation unrelated to marked shifts in ecological preferences. Random characteristics may have become isolated, and retained even if they have no particular value, and hybridization may have increased the apparent diversity we see. *Cyrtandra* certainly favors pockets which exemplify isolation: wet gulches on Oahu and other islands, kipukas on Hawaii. These many "islands within islands" may have permitted development of, and persistence of, many minor features which would be reduced to uniformity if *Cyrtandra* occupied long continuous strips of lowland and formed a continuous interbreeding series.

Having seen some examples of "partial" adaptive radiation, we can look at an example which more typically fulfills the expectations of this concept. The Hawaiian alanis, *Pelea*, are rather numerous (between fifty and one hundred species), and range widely in habitat and growth form. They occupy the majority of habitats available to them. No species grow in coastal areas or lower dry forest, but they do range from upper dry forest (the koa belt) to high, wet forests and bogs. In size, they run from diminutive shrubs to trees, although most could be called typical shrubs. Species which form trees, such as *P. barbigera*, generally have large leaves. The bog species, *P. orbicularis* and *P. waialealae*, have small leaves. One species, *P. rotundifolia*, has large leaves with round blades, borne directly on the stems (without petioles). This

Pelea barbigera, an alani from Kauai, has a primitive fruit with the four segments (carpels) well separated from each other. It is somewhat specialized in being a large shrub which can often turn into a narrow tree.

Pelea oahuensis can be a tree if it grows in a tall forest, but is more often a shrub. The fruit is specialized in that the four segments (carpels) are fused together.

Pelea clusiaefolia, an Oahu alani, probably resembles ancestral alanis in its shrubby habit. It has, however, a curious specialization typical of tropical trees: "cauliflory," the tendency for flowers and fruits to be borne on the surface of older stems (or on spur shoots on these older stems).

Pelea anisata, the mokihana from Kauai, is halfway between a shrub and a vine. It grows in deep, shady forests, and tends to lean, even to twine slightly, but does not form a "good" self-supporting shrub.

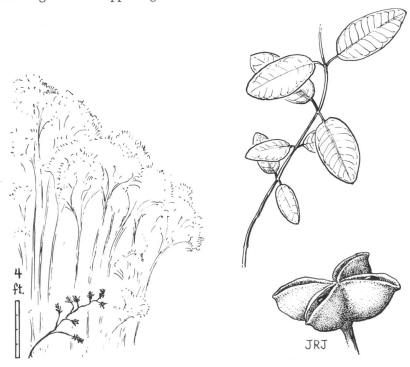

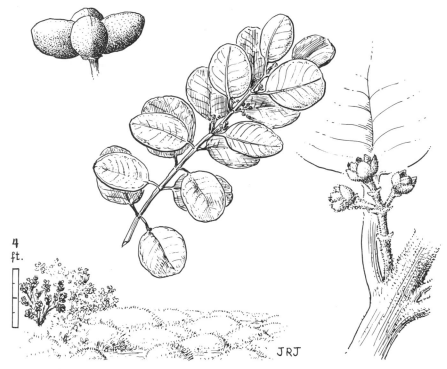

Pelea orbicularis is a small, stunted shrub which looks much like other alanis in features other than its size. It grows in bogs on Maui and Oahu.

Pelea waialealae grows in the Kauai bogs. It is a small, dense shrub with minute flowers and fruits. Among the alanis, it might be an early adaptation to the bog habitat.

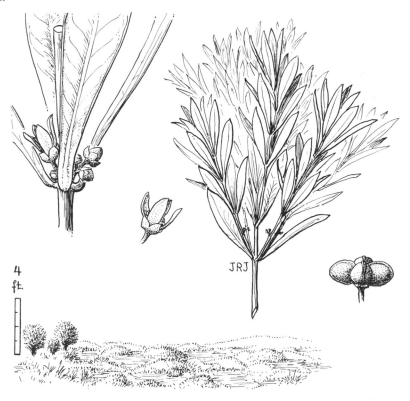

species has sprawling stems which emerge from scrubby ridge forest in the Koolau Mountains. A close approach to the vining habit has been made by *Pelea anisata,* known to the Hawaiians as mokihana. Some species of *Pelea* have acquired a curious habit common to many tropical trees, such as cacao or figs: cauliflory. Cauliflorous plants bear flowers on very short spur shoots along older main trunks; in this way large clusters of fruits can be formed on limbs. This may make displays of flowers more massive, thus aiding pollination and dispersal, or permit the production of large fruits on limbs stout enough to bear them without breaking.

Cases of adaptive radiation usually show older adaptations as well as recent ones. In the case of *Pelea,* we have an illustration: *Platydesma* is a close relative of *Pelea* which probably long ago adapted to wet forests. None of the platydesmas grows anywhere but in wet forests in the Hawaiian Islands. The growth forms show an intimate relation to wet forest. *Platydesma campanulata* is a small or medium-sized tree; it has elongate, shiny, leathery leaves, long stems, large flowers and fruits. Large-seeded plants are typical of wet forest

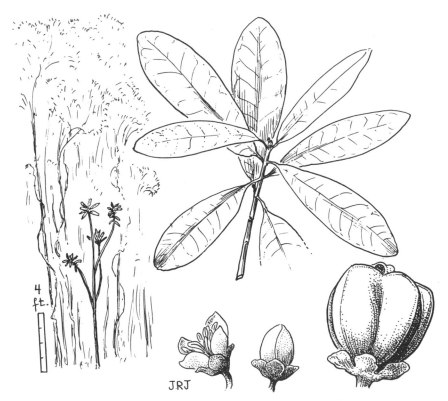

The species of *Platydesma* represent old adaptations by the ancestors of *Pelea* to the wet Hawaiian forest. *Platydesma campanulata* is a shrubby tree of very wet forest of Kauai, Maui, Oahu, and Hawaii, known to the Hawaiians as pilokea. Its leaves are three to ten inches long, and thus are longer than most *Pelea* leaves; its flowers and fruits are much larger than those of *Pelea.*

trees (Chapter 8). *Platydesma rostrata* has longer leaves, fewer branches, features which permit plants to grow in shadier forest conditions. The largest leaves are those of *Platydesma cornuta,* up to three feet long, in fact. The advantage of few branches and a rosette of huge long leaves is that the seedling will grow more directly up to better-illuminated levels of a forest and will utilize light better in shady situations. This type of growth mimics other plants of wet forest, such as tree ferns, palms, and the rosette tree lobelioids. *Platydesma cornuta* is cauliflorous. With its few, thick branches, flowering twigs must almost necessarily be smaller than those of the main shoot, and in this species division of labor between thick main shoots and tiny, flower-bearing spurs along those shoots is extreme.

If adaptive radiation means a multidimensional occupation of ecological opportunities, several groups in the Hawaiian biota are truly outstanding. These are worth discussing individually, and have been treated as separate chapters: the land shells (Chapter 10), the honeycreepers (Chapter 11), the lobelioids (Chapter 12), and the silverswords and their relatives (Chapter 13).

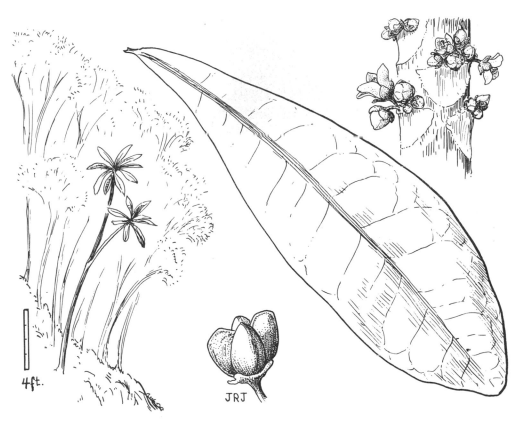

Platydesma cornuta from Oahu has gigantic leaves and is a typical, rain forest rosette tree. It is a perfect example of cauliflory, for clusters of small flowers are borne on the surface of older, thick stems.

Unique Adaptations

Many groups of animals and plants either cannot or do not, even in the Hawaiian Islands, succeed in occupying a wide range of opportunities. However, certain Hawaiian groups have shown rather startling innovations, innovations which might not be possible in continental environments, where such shifts would be forestalled by other groups, which tend to limit the opportunity of any particular group considered.

One curious group of adaptations is found in pollination relationships. Plants which have colonized on the Hawaiian Islands have been those with relatively simple pollination requirements. Self-pollinating ability is shown by many, and this often requires no insect. Wind pollination is ideal for an island plant, because no pollinating insect or bird is required. If a flower is insect-pollinated, a simple saucer-like form or a short-tubed form is best, for an insect of crude pollinating habits, perhaps merely foraging in flowers, may pollinate the flower, like flies visiting the puncture-vine flower. This principle works both ways. An insect must be capable of extracting nectar from a variety of flowers, must be able to cope with flowers shaped differently from those typical of its source plants, like the sphinx moth and the *Boerhavia* flowers.

The Hawaiian flora has some bright and conspicuous flowers, such as those of

When they colonize on islands, plants and animals can be forced into new pollination relationships. The nohu, or puncture vine *Tribulus cistoides* (Lisianski Island), may, on an atoll, be visited only by such poor pollinators as tiny flies, but may occasionally be pollinated by them. A butterfly or bee might be a more typical pollinator. A colony of sphinx moths on Grass Island of Pearl and Hermes Reef finds no long tubular flowers to which it is adapted. Consequently, it sucks nectar from the tiny flowers of *Boerhavia*.

the ohia or the lobelioids. Most of these are bird-pollinated plants. However, the Hawaiian flora is exceptionally rich in small white or greenish flowers. Why? Excepting the group of wind-pollinated flowers (which are typically small and greenish), these seem adapted to small insects instead of the typical spectrum of pollinating insects. The "good" pollinators, such as long-tongued bees, larger butterflies and moths, are absent or very scarce in the Hawaiian insect fauna. Insects with small body size predominate instead. It is with these that the Hawaiian flora must achieve pollination, and the smaller, inconspicuous flowers are suited to them.

A shift from insect pollination to pollination by birds has occurred a few times in the Hawaiian flora. We can see this by comparing a typical naupaka flower, such as that of *Scaevola chamissoniana*, with a derived type, *Scaevola glabra*. Increase in size, development of a brighter (yellow) color, attainment of a tubular form accompany this shift. Three flowers also illustrate adaptation to bird pollinators. Flowers of *Geranium* are simple and funnel-shaped. Most Hawaiian geraniums have white flowers pollinated by moths. *Geranium arboreum*, however, has evolved *curved* funnel-shaped flowers, bright crimson in color. I have seen these flowers visited by a honeycreeper, the apapane (*Himatione*), where this plant is native, high on Haleakala. The genus *Hibiscadelphus*, an exclusively Hawaiian genus, represents a derivative of *Hibiscus*. The flowers

Hawaiian plants have evolved to suit available pollinators. The fan-like white flowers of the naupaka, *Scaevola chamissoniana*, left, are split along one side and narrowly tubular. They are insect flowers. The long, tubular yellow flowers of *Scaevola glabra* are adapted to bird pollination; these have evolved from flowers somewhat like the white flowers of *S. chamissoniana* (Olaa, Hawaii; Wahiawa, Kauai).

Geranium arboreum has tubular, curved, bright red flowers, instead of ones that are white and radially symmetrical, as in other Hawaiian geraniums. This geranium has probably evolved this color and shape in response to pollination by honeycreepers (Haleakala, Maui).

Hibiscadelphus giffardianus is a nearly extinct species from the island of Hawaii. *Hibiscadelphus* is a kind of hibiscus, evolved on the Hawaiian Islands, in which flowers have become narrow curved tubes suited to nectar-feeding birds (Kilauea, Hawaii).

do not open out, but have a narrow tubular form, and are markedly curved—perfect mimics of lobelioid flowers and other bird flowers, and matching in size and curvature the bills of such honeycreepers as the iiwi, *Vestiaria*. The genus *Kokia*, also an exclusively Hawaiian genus, shows similar adaptations. Supposedly related to the cotton (*Gossypium*), *Kokia* has bright conical flowers, about the size of a hibiscus flower, which are curved to one side.

A sharp change in modes of food-getting has occurred in several Hawaiian

Achatinella does not eat leaves, but prefers the algae and fungi which grow *on* leaves. Nevertheless, it can be found preferentially on some trees, never on certain others. *Achatinella mustelina*, shown here, lives on *Pelea oahuensis* (left), *Dubautia plantaginea* (right), and *Myrsine lessertiana*, but not on the many other trees of the Waianae Mountains.

animals. One interesting instance is the damselfly *Megalagrion oahuense*. Damselflies have aquatic habits, and the nymph stage lives in water—except for *Megalagrion oahuense*, nymphs of which traverse the forest litter searching for their prey. As entomologist E. C. Zimmerman says, an entirely new group of terrestrial carnivorous insects originated from an aquatic one.

The "little agate" shells, *Achatinella*, have developed a rather simplified method of feeding. The radula (mouth parts) of *Achatinella* are not equipped, as are those of most snails, to cope with the rough textures of leaves. Instead, achatinellas are suited only to the soft fungi and algae which grow *on* leaves.

Shifts in habitat have occurred in some of the land snails, too. The family Tornatellinidae is basically a terrestrial family, but in the Hawaiian Islands it has developed a preference for living in trees. A similar change has occurred in the bug *Saldula*. In most parts of the world, this bug lives in rivers, but Hawaiian species of *Saldula* have taken to living in trees. The *Proterhinus* weevils are typically bark-boring or wood-boring beetles, but some of the Hawaiian ones have adapted to leaf mining. All of these shifts are more expected in the Islands, where each immigrant group has greater chance to reach into new ways of life, than on continents where new entrants are rarely successful.

A curious phenomenon which probably has several explanations—depending on the group concerned—is that of gigantism. Gigantism in plants is described in the next chapter.

Some insects clearly exhibit gigantism. The endemic Hawaiian dragonfly is a derivative of a wide-ranging dragonfly, *Anax junius,* which has also established in the Islands in more recent times. *Anax junius* is a lowland insect, but *A. strenuus* has penetrated into the rain forest. It is also bigger than *A. junius.* One can only guess that there might be a relationship between these changes, perhaps somewhat like changes in body shape and size of flightless insects which have adapted to wet forest (Chapter 7). Another interesting example of insect gigantism is the grasshopper *Banza nihoa.* This insect, which lives on relatively small Nihoa Island (Chapter 20), is by far the largest of the Hawaiian *Banza* grasshoppers. Is there a relationship? Some small islands have giant insects and lizards and there are several possible explanations. One is that predators may be absent in the environment of that particular island so that a small size, which may aid an insect under pressure from predators, is no longer of value. Another possibility is that food availability and food habits change. Larger articles of food, a wider range of diet, a greater total availability of food, all might tend to encourage greater body size. Gigantism can be a manifestation of an animal which takes over the role of, or substitutes for, a large animal. Gigantism of lizards on certain islands can be related to absence of mammals. Likewise, there is a possibility that gigantism of Hawaiian insects correlates with absence of any native reptiles or mammals.

There are a number of other special trends which deserve more extended consideration, and these are discussed in the four chapters which follow.

Exceptionally large body size is shown by some Hawaiian insects, such as the giant dragonfly, *Anax strenuus,* left. The largest grasshopper native to the Hawaiian Islands, *Banza nihoa,* right, is found only on a small island, Nihoa. Is there a correlation?

Chapter 6 🌿 *ARBORESCENCE*

"ARBORESCENCE" comes from the Latin, meaning "becoming a tree." The process of evolution from small nonwoody plants into large shrubs, even trees, is shown by group after group on the Hawaiian Islands. Probably no other area in the world (be it an island or non-island area) has fostered such remarkable changes in growth form as can be seen in the Hawaiian Islands. Why? There are some easy answers, such as "it is one phase of adaptive radiation" or "there's a niche available to trees, so trees evolve." The matter is more complicated than these or other quick answers would indicate. The best way to see why arborescence occurs in the Islands is to look at particular plants which have followed this curriculum in the Islands.

Euphorbia degeneri forms mats in lava crevices near the sea. It has small succulent round leaves, never becomes woody (Makapuu, Oahu).

Euphorbia, the akoko. An unusual series has developed in *Euphorbia,* known as koko or akoko to the Hawaiians. These are related to small garden weeds, sometimes known as *Chamaesyce,* which form prostrate mats. This mat-like tendency is evident in the coastal akokos, such as *Euphorbia degeneri.* In fact, at a very early stage in the development of a seedling of the *Chamaesyce-*type euphorbias, the central upright shoot dies, and only lateral shoots grow, forming the mat. *Euphorbia degeneri* is related to similar species of the Pacific, such as *E. atoto* and *E. taitensis* of Tahiti. The coastal akokos have small seeds which can float in seawater. Adaptation to a coastal site is revealed in leaves of *E. degeneri:* succulent leaves, rounded in shape, are to be expected in a dry coastal locality, where bright sunshine and dryness make these characteristics important ones.

Euphorbia celastroides, a lowland akoko, has probably arrived on the Hawaiian Islands in a way other than flotation in seawater. The seeds are covered with a film which, when wet, forms a sticky gel capable of adhering to various surfaces such as bird feathers. *Euphorbia celastroides* probably looks very much like the ancestors which arrived in these sites. It grows in dry, scrubby areas near the coast, areas where marine birds capable of bringing the seeds probably once nested. In the various localities where *E. celastroides* grows, it has formed varieties which seem to match the particular sites. *Euphorbia celastroides* var. *amplectans* on Lanai forms a low, wiry complexly branched mat-like shrub. The leaves are small and papery, grayish green because of a powdery covering of wax which helps protect them in this dry locality. The leaves can, however,

Halfway between a shrub and sprawling mat, the akoko *Euphorbia celastroides* var. *amplectans* grows in open dry forest areas (northeastern Lanai).

Euphorbia celastroides var. *lorifolia* is an akoko of open places of the koa forests. It is a shrub, although generally wider than high, with moderately large leaves (Waimea Canyon, Kauai).

In the dry Ulupalakua lava fields on Maui, *Euphorbia celastroides* var. *mauiensis* becomes a fountain-shaped shrub, even a small tree. Its leaves are small and papery —a fact correlated with the dry area.

Euphorbia multiformis var. *microphylla* is an akoko which forms shrubs, small to medium in size, on rather wet cliffs of the Koolau Mountains (Nuuanu pali, Oahu).

Euphorbia remyi has shiny, thick leaves. It grows as a sprawling, almost wiry shrub which forms tangles almost like a vine in the undergrowth of moderately moist koa–ohia forests (Kokee, Kauai).

dry up during rainless periods, and the plant can live by means of water stored in the rather succulent stems.

The variety *lorifolia* of *E. celastroides* represents an adaptation to somewhat moister inland conditions. The leaves are still gray-green and papery, but they are much longer—two to four inches. Greater leaf area is generally correlated with moister conditions. Although the branches of var. *lorifolia* tend to be spreading, the plant looks more shrub-like than mat-like.

The variety *mauiensis* of *E. celastroides* is much taller in stature. It forms what could be called a tree, branched from near the base, definitely woody. This shows how a tree-like type might have evolved from a low mat-like plant. Interestingly, in all the akokos the central shoot aborts, so that the tree-like ones are formed when one (or more) of the lateral shoots turns upward, forming a leader.

Adaptation to the rain forest is shown by *Euphorbia remyi*, a Kauai plant. Leaves of dry forest euphorbias withstand the dry months by losing their papery leaves. In the more uniformly wet upper forests, evergreen, leathery leaves characterize the akokos. Such leathery leaves are resistant to dry days, but are broad and can take advantage of shady conditions in the forest. *Euphorbia remyi* has a curious habit—its long, slender branches sprawl into trees and shrubs, reaching upward but not strong enough to be self-supporting. *Euphorbia remyi* can be found in the Wahiawa Bog on Kauai, where (as "var. *molesta*") it grows as a small, spindly plant. The leathery leaves are suited to this locality: it grows with roots perpetually in water, but the bog is sunny most of the time. On Oahu, *Euphorbia clusiaefolia* forms small sprawling shrubs which remind one of *E. remyi*, and confirm the relationship between sturdy, dark green leaves and the rain forest habitat.

The ultimate in arborescence and in adaptation to the wet forest is represented by *Euphorbia rockii*. This akoko grows only in very wet, cloudy rain forest along the high ridge of the Koolau Mountains. It is the tallest of the akokos, twenty to twenty-five feet tall, with a trunk up to five or six inches in diameter. The leaves are also the longest, six inches or more in length. The fruits of *E. rockii* are also exceptionally large, an inch in diameter. Coastal akokos have fruits only one sixteenth or one eighth of an inch across. The inland akokos not only have larger fruits and seeds, they lack the coat of mucilage on the seeds seen in *E. celastroides*. The reason for this is discussed in Chapter 8.

Lepidium. Sometimes the increase in woodiness is not very striking in the Hawaiian Islands until we consider the relatives of a particular plant. This is true in *Lepidium;* all lepidiums elsewhere in the world are less woody than the two native to the Islands, *L. serra* and *L. arbuscula*. Throughout the northern hemisphere *Lepidium* is familiar as a weed, usually a small annual, the pepperwort. The seeds, like those of *Euphorbia celastroides,* have a mucilage coating. The Hawaiian lepidiums, if not trees, can be called shrubs, two to four feet high. They can grow on dry ridges and cliff areas of Kauai and Oahu. *Lepidium*

Euphorbia remyi, left, can grow as stunted plants in Wahiawa Bog, Kauai. *Euphorbia clusiaefolia*, right, from Oahu, is a somewhat woody small plant from moderately wet forests. It has shiny thick leaves like those of *E. remyi* (Konahuanui, Oahu).

Large, leathery leaves and stature as a tree indicate that *Euphorbia rockii* is the ultimate rain forest adaptation of the akokos (Punaluu, Oahu).

belongs to the mustard family. There is a parallel on other islands of the world: members of this family have formed similar-looking shrubs on the Canary Islands and Madeira (*Cheiranthus, Crambe, Sinapodendron*).

Aweoweo, Kului, Papala. The three trees (or large shrubs) known by these Hawaiian names can be grouped together because they all have a peculiar method of developing a woody stem. Instead of forming a normal trunk with a solid woody core produced by a cambial layer, they form thin bands of wood alternating with rings of soft tissue, like rings of a beet. This comparison is an advisable one, because the beet belongs to the same family as the aweoweo (Chenopodiaceae).

Lepidium serra, a member of the mustard family, is a small straggling shrub (to four feet tall) on Kauai cliffs. Mainland lepidiums are small herbs, not shrubs.

The aweoweo, *Chenopodium oahuense,* can be a shrub or even a small tree. It is thus the largest *Chenopodium* in the world—and *Chenopodium* is a world-wide genus. The mainland weed familiar to gardeners as "lamb's quarters" never becomes woody (Pohakuloa, Hawaii).

Kului, *Nototrichum sandwicense,* grows in dry forest areas, as here at Kaupulehu, North Kona, Hawaii. It is a tree relative of cockscombs and amaranths.

The papala, *Charpentiera obovata,* belongs to the amaranth family. It is a tree which has evolved from herbs in the Hawaiian environment. Its closest relative is apparently a vining plant (*Chamissoa*) from Mexico.

The aweoweo, *Chenopodium oahuense,* is the woodiest species of *Chenopodium* in the world, and there are many species scattered over temperate zones of both hemispheres. Typically the aweoweo is a shrub, often low and prostrate, in coastal sites. In dry upland areas, as at Pohakuloa, Hawaii, it can develop a single trunk up to a foot in diameter, and can be called a true (if small) tree.

The same is true of the kului, *Nototrichum.* It is a member of a related family, Amaranthaceae, to which such familiar plants as the crested cockscomb belong. In dry areas of the Kona District, Hawaii, one can see shrubby or tree-like specimens of *Nototrichum,* easily recognizable because of their pale hairy leaves and their tassels of flowers. Kuluis are most closely related to an Australian amaranth genus, *Ptilotus* (*Trichinium*), which forms sprawling herbs without appreciably woody stems.

The papala, *Charpentiera,* grows in moderately wet forests, often on the floor of shady canyons or gulches. It is easily recognizable by its stringy tassels of inconspicuous flowers. Like *Nototrichum,* it is a member of the amaranth family. Papalas can be small trees, to twenty-five feet in height. A dried trunk is extremely light, for the bands of woody tissue are narrow, separated by much soft tissue. *Charpentiera* is, like the genus *Nototrichum,* found exclusively in the Hawaiian Islands. It is related to *Chamissoa,* a vining amaranth from Mexico.

Viola mauiensis (left) is similar to most violets in its form of growth; its long stems are adapted to growth in bogs (Pepeopae, Molokai). In wet rain forests of Molokai one can find *Viola robusta*, (right) which has unbranched stems up to a foot or so in height—an unusual manner of growth for a violet.

Violets. If the above groups of trees seem basically to have been derived from coastal or dry forest ancestors, and to have evolved inland, the reverse is possible, and may have occurred in the Hawaiian violets. Violets, common in temperate mountain areas, are typically associated with shade and moisture, or meadow-like areas. The bog violets of the Islands, *Viola kauaiensis* and *V. mauiensis*, resemble mainland violets. In their creeping habit and heart-shaped leaves, they offer little that is novel. However, their stems are conspicuously trailing and capable of rooting—abilities that suit them for growth among tussocks of Hawaiian bogs.

Viola robusta is different, however, for although its stems can grow horizontally and root, they are mostly upright, unbranched, up to two feet tall. They

Woodiest of all violets in the world is *Viola tracheliifolia*, which can be eight feet or more tall, definitely woody at its base. It grows in dry forest areas, tends to form long branches which reach upward through other shrubs (Kauai).

are woody enough to support themselves, but never become thicker than a pencil. This violet lives in very wet forests near the summit of Molokai.

Upper dry forest is the typical habitat for *Viola tracheliifolia*. This violet consists of one or more upright, sparsely branched stems which are sometimes taller than a man, and, at the base, up to an inch in diameter; clearly woody. This violet is not a "true tree," but it is definitely a marked increase in stature as violets go, the woodiest species of *Viola*. *Viola tracheliifolia* may have originated in upper dry forest from wetter areas, although there is an equal possibility that it originated in the moderately moist koa forests where it is now found.

Plantago. The plantain weed (not to be confused with the banana relatives

Two Hawaiian plantagos (plantain weeds) differ in growth form. *Plantago pachy-phylla* forms rosettes in wet forests. *Plantago princeps* at right, called ale by the Hawaiians, is strange in its long stems, which can be somewhat woody. It mimics the rosette trees of wet forest, although it is smaller (about three to four feet tall).

Scaevola gaudichaudii is a very rare yellow-flowered naupaka from low, scrubby forests. It is a low shrub which forms only a little wood (Lahainaluna, Maui).

called plantains) is familiar to north temperate gardeners. It is a rosette of leaves and is never woody. This is also true of most Hawaiian species of *Plantago*, such as *P. pachyphylla*. However, a peculiar Hawaiian species, *P. princeps*, is unique among plantain weeds. Its stems are long, up to three or four feet, and the elliptical leaves can reach two feet. Although photographs of this plant suggest it to be a shrub, a rosette plant on a stalk, the stems are in fact rather weak. Plants of *Plantago princeps* grow in shady wet forest, among other shrubs which appear to support the weak stems of *P. princeps*. There can be no doubt that the Hawaiian plantain weeds are basically wet forest plants. Indeed, most of them are bog species. *Plantago princeps* is not a marked representative of arborescence; it may represent a long-stemmed growth form evolved to rise to the height of surrounding low shrubs, rather than an entry into the shrub or tree habit.

Naupakas *Scaevola*, the naupaka, is an example of a plant which appears to have evolved in both directions in the Hawaiian Islands. mostly, the tendency has been toward the wet uplands, but in a few cases, adaptation to dry, even coastal sites must have occurred. In this discussion, I am excepting the white-fruited beach *Scaevola*, *S. taccada* (naupaka kai). This shrub, scattered over beaches throughout the Pacific, has had origins separate from those of the inland, purple-fruited naupakas.

Scaevola gaudichaudii (not to be confused with *S. gaudichaudiana*) is a rare Hawaiian foothill naupaka, and it probably resembles in stature and ecological preference the early inland Hawaiian naupakas. Other Pacific scaevolas, such as *S. floribunda* of Fiji, *S. beckii* of New Caledonia, or several Australian species, are found in dry locations near the coast *Scaevola gaudichaudii* is only

Scaevola chamissoniana, a naupaka common on the eastern Hawaiian Islands, tends to be a small but woody shrub (Koele, Lanai; Kehena, Hawaii).

A small to tall shrub, *Scaevola gaudichaudiana* is a common plant of upper dry or lower wet forests. Its flowers are white (Konahuanui, Oahu).

Named "*Scaevola procera*," naupakas of upper Kauai are hybrid in origin—probably combining features of S. *gaudichaudiana* and S. *mollis*.

A rounded shrub with purplish flowers and hairy leaves, *Scaevola mollis* is a naupaka of wet forests, especially on Oahu (Konahuanui, Oahu).

a small shrub. If one looks for a main "trunk," one finds none, for the plant, although somewhat woody, branches from the base, and does not live long enough for any of the branches to become very thick. The relatively small flowers are yellowish and borne singly, probably a specialized feature in *Scaevola*.

Scaevola chamissoniana and *S. gaudichaudiana* are two closely related naupakas which are easily seen in moderately wet to wet rain forest. They are shrubs, sometimes small, sometimes large. Specimens can branch from the base, but they can also form a single trunk, and some old specimens could be called small trees. The leaves of both of these naupakas are larger than those of *S. gaudichaudii*, and suggest adaptation to areas of more rainfall. The population of naupakas in upper Kauai (Kokee) has been called *Scaevola procera*, but it seems to be a hybrid population which has become stabilized, relatively uniform. *Scaevola gaudichaudiana* appears definitely involved, and *S. mollis* has contributed, probably, to a lesser extent. The "*S. procera*" plants can be trees, with trunks up to nine inches in diameter.

Scaevola mollis is related to the above group of species, but is easily distinguished by its purple flowers, hairy leaves, and contracted inflorescences. *Scaevola mollis* grows in wet forest areas where rainfall exceeds one hundred inches per year. However, *S. mollis* and *S. gaudichaudiana* do come into contact with each other, and hybrids are common, especially on Oahu.

Scaevola glabra grows only in very wet forest areas of Kauai (where it has

Scaevola glabra is a distinctive naupaka which represents an early adaptation to very wet forest areas on Oahu and Kauai. It has tubular yellow flowers (Wahiawa Bog, Kauai).

Scaevola kilaueae grows only near Kilauea, and is a low, sprawling plant with succulent yellow-green leaves.

Now nearly extinct is this coastal naupaka, *Scaevola coriacea*. It has succulent rounded leaves and scrubby stems (Maui).

been called "*S. kauaiensis*") and Oahu. It is clearly a *Scaevola*, derived from the purple-fruited species of Pacific islands, but it is probably an older immigrant than the remaining purple-fruited species, more "thoroughly" adapted to wet forest, and to bird pollination. The leaves are smooth and leathery, typical of those of rain forest trees. *Scaevola glabra* can be a shrub, but in favorable places it becomes a tree with a trunk up to a foot in diameter.

The purple-fruited Hawaiian naupakas have also adapted to drier areas. Kilauea is in an area of rather high rainfall, but the recent lava flows are, in effect, rather dry. On certain of these flows one can find *Scaevola kilaueae*. Its leaves are smaller than those of the rain forest species, and appreciably succulent. *Scaevola kilaueae*, like *S. gaudichaudii*, tends to branch from the base, and never forms a shrub which exceeds a sprawling habit.

The most extreme adaptation to dry situations is illustrated by *Scaevola coriacea*, a naupaka on the verge of extinction because its few localities are being pre-empted by farming or building. *Scaevola coriacea* can be regarded as a downgraded shrub, merely a series of stems trailing on the ground, none of which become much larger than a pencil in diameter. The leaves are round in outline, markedly succulent, and have a patchy covering of hairs. These features recall somewhat those of the coastal akoko, *Euphorbia degeneri*. *Scaevola coriacea* grows in sandy areas near the coast, and is clearly suited for this environment.

Others. Some of the best Hawaiian examples of progression toward treehood can be found among the lobelioids, and among a silversword relative, *Dubautia*. These groups are considered in Chapters 12 and 13, which can be considered extended annexes to the above stories.

Botanists have not really devoted themselves to explaining just how and why particular groups have taken the turn toward arborescence in the Hawaiian Islands and other islands. Different reasons may explain different cases, or operate to various extents depending on the group of plants concerned. So here are some of the reasons I would guess to underlie these trends:

(1) Forest trees tend to have large seeds—like walnuts, plums, avocados, and chestnuts. Although there are exceptions, trees tend to be adapted to stable forest areas, and to have seeds less capable of travel. Seeds of exceptionally good dispersibility, on the other hand, usually belong to nonwoody (herbaceous) plants adapted to growth in open or disturbed places. This means that an exceptionally high proportion of herbaceous plants and an exceptionally low proportion of trees were probably among the colonists that successfully established on the Hawaiian Islands. However, the ecology of the Hawaiian Islands—abundant rainfall, high humidity—is an ideal forest-tree ecology, probably much more so than ordinary areas. Processes of evolution will therefore tend to favor development of increased woodiness: trees from shrubs, shrubs from herbs, rosette trees and rosette shrubs from herbs. Rosette trees are trees with few branches (often only one stem), and large leaves clustered at the end of the branch or branches; rosette shrubs are smaller plants with this habit. Most rosette shrubs and rosette trees seem to be derived from herbs because they would represent continuations of the rosette (like that of lettuce) of an herb. The lobelioids and *Dubautia* are good examples of this.

(2) Because there are fewer immigrant stocks on the Hawaiian Islands, each of the ones which did arrive have more opportunity for adaptive radiation. Some products of this radiation in plant groups will tend to be woodier (this seems to apply to *Scaevola,* for example).

(3) Immigrants are mostly to coastal and dry forest, so there will tend to be evolutionary tendencies toward the wet forest. The greatest degree of woodiness can be said to characterize wet forest plants, so that ecological shift into wet forest almost inevitably involves increased woodiness. The fact that wet forest tends to be taller would also seem to favor increased stature of those groups which shift to wet forest.

(4) The Hawaiian Islands have a moderate climate. This is partly due to proximity to the equator, partly to favorable rainfall, but more significantly the maritime nature of the climate. Lacking extremes, plants which would go into dormancy or die each winter have on the Islands a continuous growing season. A plant which typically forms a leafy rosette, then flowers and dies, like a cabbage or lettuce, would continue to grow into a rosette tree, eventually flowering. Experimental work on some annual plants shows that, in fact, growing them in uniform conditions (no seasonal change) converts them into rosette

shrubs or rosette trees. In the Hawaiian flora, this tendency seems best illustrated by the two shrubby species of *Lepidium,* by *Plantago princeps,* by *Lobelia* and some of the other lobelioids and perhaps others. The native Hawaiian flora has no true annuals, only a few biennials (*Nama sandwicensis; Argemone glauca*). This indicates that the Hawaiian flora is a supremely perennial-plant flora; sooner or later any group of plants arrived in the Hawaiian flora will tend to respond to this tendency. The *Argemone* is probably a very recent, barely prehuman arrival in the Hawaiian flora. Quite conceivably, if it had arrived a million years ago, we would now expect a prickly poppy tree.

(5) Other explanations have been suggested, but these seem less likely to me. One of these (by A. R. Wallace) states that a plant will have a better chance of being pollinated and of setting seed if it can flower not once, but repeatedly. Wallace reasons that a plant which flowers a single time has less chance of establishing (failure of a suitable pollinating insect at that moment would doom the plant to die without setting seeds, for example). A perennial plant would flower repeatedly. Another suggestion (by Charles Darwin) suggests that in competition among individuals side by side, the taller will be advantaged. Competition among individuals of the same species was envisioned by Darwin; this seems relatively unlikely to me in the Hawaiian flora, although competition between two different species might more likely result in increased stature for one or both. However, both Wallace's and Darwin's ideas seem of lesser importance, or inoperative, in explaining arborescence in Hawaiian plants.

Chapter 7 🙰 FLIGHTLESSNESS IN INSECTS
AND BIRDS

ISLAND insects and birds are often and unexpectedly incapable of flying. An exceptionally high proportion of Hawaiian insects is flightless. The roster includes:

Orthoptera
  Locustidae: *Banza*
  Gryllidae: *Prognathogryllus, Paratrigonidium*

Hemiptera
  among Heteroptera: one species of *Metrarga* (Lygaeidae); the terrestrial Emesidae; *Acanthia;* many Nabidae.
  among Homoptera: many or most endemic Delphacidae.

Neuroptera: Hemerobiidae

Lepidoptera: *Hodegia apatela* (perhaps females only; males unknown).

Coleoptera
    Carabidae: of the endemic species, at least 184 (probably considerably more
        than that) are flightless, only twenty are fully winged.
    Staphylinidae: *Myllaena* (some species)
    Histeridae: some species of *Acritus*
    Nitulidae: wingless forms in four genera containing nine species.
    Ciidae: *Apterocis* (a derivative of *Cis*)
    Elateridae: *Dromaeolus, Dacnitus*
    Curculionidae: *Proterhinus, Heteramphus, Oodemas*
    Lucanidae: *Apterocyclus* (a relative of *Dorcus*)

Hymenoptera
    wingless species in much the same families as on continental areas, plus the
        flightless Diapriidae (*Platymischoides*) which were derived from flying
        types on the Hawaiian Islands

Diptera
    Dolichopodidae: Emperoptera (flightless relative of *Campsicnemus*)

Only two species of Hawaiian birds were flightless: the Hawaiian rail
(*Pennula sandwichensis*) and the Laysan rail (*Porzanula palmeri*). Other islands have been richer in flightless birds than the Hawaiian chain, probably
because they are in many cases less remote and much older than the Hawaiian
archipelago—New Zealand, for example. Both of the Hawaiian rails are now
extinct. *Pennula sandwichensis* had two subspecies: one (*millsi*) from Hawaii,
the other (*sandwichensis*) from Oahu and possibly other islands. Although
the Laysan teal is capable of flight, it shows much less tendency to fly than do
other teals and ducks. These birds are discussed and illustrated in Chapters
11 and 24.

The structural changes in insects which dictate flightlessness are interesting
and intricate, and are well shown in several groups. Because of their large
size, the *Banza* grasshoppers and the *Prognathogryllus* crickets offer the most
graphic examples. Here, reduction in wing covers and wings is easily visible.

The Hawaiian lacewings show a most interesting series in attainment of
flightlessness. This series, illustrated in detail in *Insects of Hawaii* and in my
book *Island Life,* shows the following progression:

(1) Less modified species, such as *Nesomicromus vagus* and *N. bellulus,*
have both front and rear wings. The wings are flat, have few hairs, and are
thin, with veins well spaced by the translucent panes.

(2) Irregular, indented wing shapes, as in *Nesomicromus drepanoides,* have
been developed.

The *Banza* grasshoppers of the Hawaiian Islands show obvious reductions in wing covers and wings. At left is near-normal *Banza nitida* (Hamakua, Hawaii); at right, the nearly wingless *Banza deplanata* (Lanai).

Winged and nonwinged crickets in the same group are represented by *Prognatho-gryllus alatus* (Oahu), left, and *Leptogryllus nigrolineatus* (Hamakua, Hawaii), right.

(3) Rear wings are reduced to minute vestiges (*Pseudopsectra*).

(4) Front wings become smaller. They develop heavier texture as veins are thickened and the panes between veins are thickened. *Nesothauma haleakalae* and *Pseudopsectra swezeyi* and *P. cookeorum* have only minute panes left, while *P. lobipennis* is intermediate.

(5) Rear wings have been completely lost in *Nesothauma*. Front wings, in addition to excessively heavy texture, may show odd contours (*Pseudopsectra swezeyi*) or be thickly covered with spines (*P. cookeorum*).

Among the beetles which have become flightless, flying ability is diminished in less conspicuous ways, because wings are concealed beneath the wing covers.

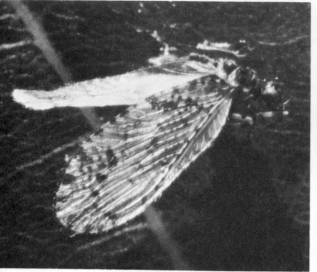

Minute lacewings of the family Hemerobiidae show clearly various features related to loss of flying ability. *Nesomicromus bellulus* (upper left; Puu Luau, E. Maui) retains nearly normal wing configuration: large, filmy front wings, papery rear wings (one of each is shown, but rear wing is folded). *Pseudopsectra lobipennis* (upper right; Haleakala) has vestigial rear wings and oddly cup-like front wings which are rather coarse in texture. *Nesothauma haleakalae* (lower left; Haleakala) represents an ultimate stage for this family in cancellation of flying ability: rear wings are altogether lacking; front wings are small, heavy in texture, with virtually no panes of thinner wing material between the crass veins.

However, wing covers themselves can reveal the flightless condition when they are fused together, a definitive cancellation of flying ability.

In the beetles we notice an exceptional number of species which have evolved flightlessness in the Hawaiian Islands. Beetles are, of course, a large group in the Islands, but so are Lepidoptera, which are all, with one small exception, capable of flight. Beetles appear to be much more "prone" to flightlessness. The parallel among bird groups is with rails. Flightlessness has evolved in rails on many island groups, whereas on only a few islands have other bird groups become flightless.

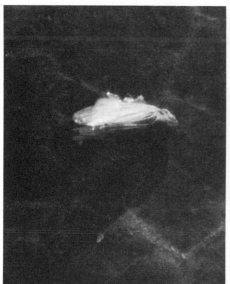

Both long-winged and short-winged individuals may be found in *Aloha ipomoeae*. A long-winged one is shown here. Representing a fascinating group of flightless beetles (weevils) here is *Proterhinus blackburni* (Waikolu, Molokai). A distinctive glistening flightless beetle, *Oodemas purpureum* (Kaala, Oahu) is shown at right.

The reasons for flightlessness of these insects and birds on the Hawaiian Islands appear to be as follows:

(1) The groups which have become flightless are typically those which feed on or near the ground, and which mostly consume plant material. These insects or birds typically would seldom use flight for activities related to obtaining food, plenty of which can be secured by crawling, walking, or hopping.

(2) Flight would be useful to these groups mostly for evading predators. On the Hawaiian Islands, many typical mainland predators are missing, so that flight as an evasive tactic decreases in value. Lizards, most kinds of

The large endemic flightless Hawaiian beetle at right, *Apterocyclus honoluluensis,* was derived from ancestors like the *Dorcus parallelopipedus* at left. The specimen of *Dorcus* was collected in Europe.

insectivorous birds, and many predaceous kinds of insects are absent on the Hawaiian Islands (or at least were in prehuman times).

(3) If flight is not of appreciable value in hunting food or escaping predators, it is a great luxury. The formation of wings and associated parts, and the expenditure of energy in flying are large items in the economy of an insect or bird. If the value, in terms of natural selection, decreases markedly one will expect that wings will be lost. Loss of flight would, in fact, be of positive value for a species which does not utilize it.

(4) The loss of flight in insect or bird groups might, to a certain extent, insure reproduction in, and remaining in, an area which offers the best (or perhaps only) suitable diet and climatic conditions. The young of an insect or bird species would stand a greater chance of survival if they did not wander far from the favorable sites in which they hatched. Many insect species are related to host plants with very localized distributions. Suitable pockets of wet forest are rather localized, and if Hawaiian insect groups typically evolve from drier to wetter forest, as may be true, flightlessness might be expected to accompany this process.

(5) There are many ground-feeding herbivores absent from the Hawaiian Islands—various groups of mammals, tortoises, etc. These groups are, of course, flightless. The opportunity for flightless birds and insects might seem to be enhanced by absence of such herbivores, and consequently the flightless insects

might be considered to "replace" the missing herbivores to a degree. There may be several advantages, as cited above, to flightlessness, and to dub nonflying insects as "hopeful monsters" or defective organisms seems an oversimplification. Flightlessness occurs in mainland situations, too, and is not considered a decadent tendency there. An ostrich, for example, is not a defective flying bird; it has lost flight as part of its adaptations as a grazing bird of plains areas.

(6) Under Hawaiian conditions, flightlessness is not likely to serve as a way of preventing excessive numbers of insects from being blown off the Islands. This may be true on windy subantarctic islands. The Hawaiian lacewings, which live in exposed alpine situations, might also be said to avoid wind pressure by flightlessness, but the vast majority of flightless Hawaiian insects are forest species, and the previous considerations would be more important to their cases.

If field studies on nonflying Hawaiian insects were undertaken, we could probably correlate their ecological habits with their lack of flight. It may be that some insects which have normal wings do not, in fact, fly, or do so rarely, but until such studies are done, we will not know the actual reasons in particular cases, and will only be able to guess.

Chapter 8 LOSS OF DISPERSIBILITY IN PLANTS

WHEN one knows the typical seeds and fruits in particular groups of plants, surprises come when one looks at these in the Hawaiian flora. Some of them are gigantic, some show unexpected alterations. In a number of cases, the largest seeds or fruits in a particular group of plants belong not to continental species, but to Hawaiian ones. Yet Hawaiian plants ought to have rather small fruits and seeds, if these functioned in long-distance dispersal. This paradox, unnoticed until recently, is easily explained and forms an interesting story. Although excellence at dispersal is required for arrival, many of these plants have lost dispersal mechanisms in subsequent evolution. How dispersal is lost— and why—is a matter which depends on the original mode of dispersal, so each case must be examined separately.

Plants which are transported by flotation in air would lose this ability if seeds or spores become markedly larger and, in fact, this has happened with spores of certain Hawaiian ferns. Ferns of the low forest show no changes, but ferns of intermediate forest and, especially, ferns of wet forest do. If we look at a single family (Blechnaceae), for example, *Doodia kunthiana* (dry forests)

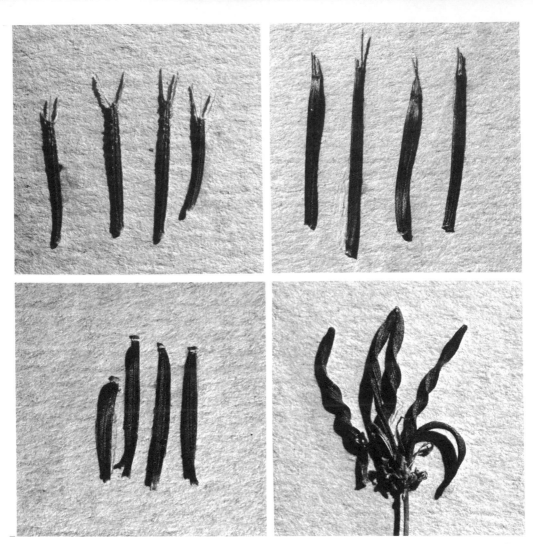

Compared with the "beggar tick" plant of the American mainland, *Bidens pilosa* (upper left), virtually all of the native Hawaiian species, known as kokoolaus, show loss of dispersal mechanism. *Bidens pilosa* has long, barbed prongs and thin, hairy fruits. *Bidens skottsbergii* (upper right) shows very little change—but note that the prong-like awns are shorter, and do not spread, and the fruits are longer and not hairy. *Bidens populifolia* (center left) shows absence of the prong-like awns, loss of hairs on the fruits. *Bidens sandvicense* (center right, fruits shown here are still attached to the plant) has larger fruits like those of *B. populifolia,* but twisted. In *B. waianaeensis* (lower left), the fruits take on odd contorted shapes. The largest kokoolau fruit are those of *B. macrocarpa* (lower right); they have functionless vestiges of awns, are broad, flat, and entirely smooth.

has spores 39.2 microns in diameter, while in *Sadleria cyatheoides* (intermediate forest) spores measure 49.6 microns, and in *Sadleria squarrosa* (wet forest) the spores average 62.0 microns. This pattern is repeated in many groups of Hawaiian ferns.

Plants which arrived by means of adhesion to bird feathers would lose their dispersal mechanism if they no longer could cling to feathers. A magnificent case is formed by the kokoolaus, *Bidens*. The ancestors of the Hawaiian species probably looked very much like a common American weed, *Bidens pilosa*, also known as beggar tick or Spanish needle. Fruits of this plant, adapted for traveling on animal fur, catch on bird feathers equally well (see Chapter 3). Change in these fruits in any of six ways will diminish their ability to catch on feathers or fur, and therefore to disperse:

(1) The prong-like structures (awns) at the tip of each fruit can become shorter.

(2) The awns, instead of spreading apart, can come closer together.

(3) The awns can lose their barbs.

(4) The awns can be lost entirely.

(5) The hairs on the body of the fruit can be lost in part or entirely.

(6) The shape of the seed changes from narrow and needle-like; strange shapes may be attained, and usually an increase in size is involved.

These changes are all evident in the kinds of *Bidens* illustrated. Interestingly, these changes form an almost perfect series when compared to the ecology of the plants. The kokoolaus which grow closest to the coast—as on sea bluffs where marine birds nest or once nested—generally have fruits most similar to those of *Bidens pilosa*, our "prototype." As we move inland, the degree of loss of the mechanism can almost be measured by how far from the coast a species of *Bidens* grows: those of the wet forest, such as *B. macrocarpa* or *B. waianaeensis*, show all six of the possible dispersal-mechanism deteriorations listed above.

The Hawaiian plants naenae (*Dubautia*), silversword (*Argyroxiphium*), and iliau (*Wilkesia*) stem from American tarweeds (Asteraceae and Madiinae). This Hawaiian colonization may have depended on bristles and hairs on the fruits, much as in the case of *Bidens*, but there is also a possibility that the tarweeds traveled by means of the sticky structures (bracts) which envelop the fruits in some of the tarweeds. In any event, the Hawaiian representatives of the tarweeds have the largest fruits of this group, and in the case of *Argyroxiphium* and *Wilkesia*, a fruit with very poor dispersal mechanism. These fruits fall from the head and are not enveloped by any sticky bract, but, more significantly, the fruits have only a few small scales at the tip, and no hairs; they are poor candidates for travel.

The Hawaiian euphorbias or akokos provide a clear example of a plant group which arrived by virtue of sticky seeds. *Euphorbia celastroides* still

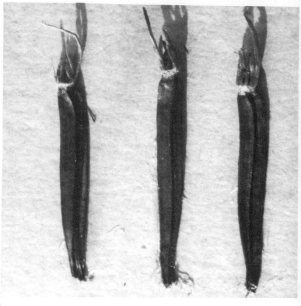

A tarweed from California, *Layia platyglossa*, has rather small fruits (compared to typewriter letters here) which are hairy and tipped with bristles. Shown at the same scale are fruits of the silversword, *Argyroxiphium sandwicense*, a relative of the California tarweeds. Its fruits are much bigger, with virtually no hairs and only a few scales at the tip.

The Hawaiian *Dracaena, D. aurea*, has exceptionally large fruits and seeds, as shown by comparison with the fruits and seeds of a *Dracaena* typical in these respects, (left). The gigantic fruits of the mahoe, *Alectryon macrococcus* (right), show a maximal size for this Pacific genus. From left to right in the photo of this plant are an entire fruit (peel below); an opened fruit showing the fleshy red structure (an aril); seed, side facing aril seen; seed, side facing peel seen (Waianae Mountains, Oahu).

has gelatinous sheaths on seeds but the inland species from rain forest—*E. clusiaefolia, E. remyi,* and *E. rockii,* for example—have lost their stickiness. In addition, they show a marked increase in fruit and seed size. Interestingly, these rain forest species are from the older islands, Kauai and Oahu.

Most Hawaiian plants probably arrived as seeds or fruits eaten by birds, so we would expect most examples of loss of dispersibility to fall in this category. In fact, they do. Here loss of dispersibility can be said to occur when seeds become larger than those readily eaten by birds.

The Hawaiian *Dracaena aurea,* or halapepe (often called *Pleomele aurea*), has notably large fruits and seeds. Seeds are about a quarter to a half inch in diameter, the fruits up to an inch across. These sizes are larger than we would expect to be carried by birds and, in fact, they are exceptionally large for a *Dracaena.* We do not know exactly where the ancestors of the Hawaiian *Dracaena* came from, or what they looked like, so we cannot precisely estimate how much change has occurred.

With the mahoe, *Alectryon,* we can more clearly estimate what seeds of ancestors of the Hawaiian plants were like. They probably were the size of those of *A. carinatus* or *A. excelsus*—about the size of a small pea. Other alectryons from the western Pacific have seeds this size also. The island alectryons, however, tend to show increase in seed size, the increase proportional to the remoteness of the island from the Indo-Malaysian "home base" of the alectryons. On each of these islands, small-seeded alectryons have given rise to larger-seeded types. On the Hawaiian Islands, the two species have evolved huge seeds, which probably could not migrate at all. *Alectryon* lives on older and moderately old land in the Hawaiian chain and has not·reached the newest island (Hawaii), perhaps because of its poor dispersal power.

Kauai and Oahu are the oldest of the major islands, and many of the gigantic-fruited or gigantic-seeded plants are limited to these two. This is shown clearly by *Tetraplasandra* and *Zanthoxylum* (*Fagara*). Hawaiian tetraplasandras are similar to a Philippine species, which has seeds like those of *T. oahuensis.* Two wet forest species of Kauai, *T. waialealae* and *T. waimeae,* have developed gigantic fruits. A smaller fruited species, *T. hawaiiensis,* is found on the four newest islands, Molokai, Maui, Lanai, and Hawaii. Likewise, the species of *Zanthoxylum* on the eastern Hawaiian Islands have relatively small seeds. The ancestors of the Hawaiian zanthoxylums may have been as small as those of the Japanese species. In any case, the gigantism of *Zanthoxylum* (*Fagara*) *oahuensis,* on Oahu, and *Z. (F.) dipetala,* on the two oldest large islands, Kauai and Oahu, is pronounced.

The modes of dispersal by which the hoawa, *Pittosporum,* and the loulu palm, *Pritchardia,* arrived are not certain, but both have experienced remarkable seed gigantism, and thereby loss of dispersibility. *Pittosporum* has sticky seeds, orange or black in color, which would be attractive to birds, and might have been eaten and carried internally, or carried externally stuck to

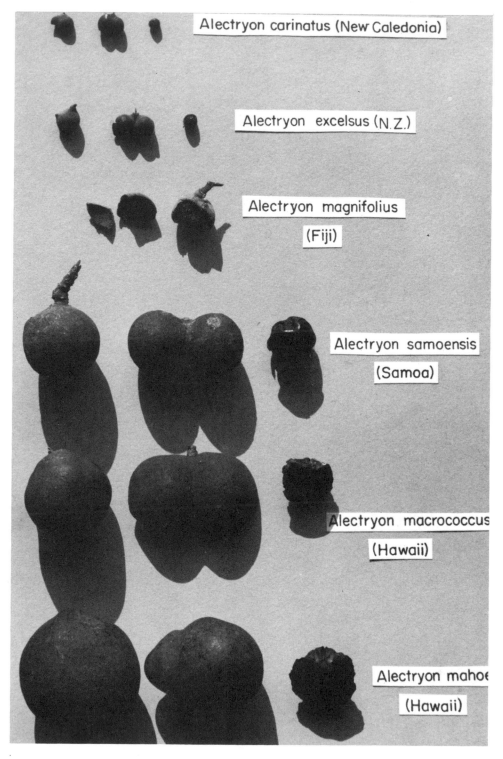

Alectryon carinatus (New Caledonia)

Alectryon excelsus (N.Z.)

Alectryon magnifolius (Fiji)

Alectryon samoensis (Samoa)

Alectryon macrococcus (Hawaii)

Alectryon mahoe (Hawaii)

Alectryons of the Pacific offer a graphic demonstration of how fruit and seed size has increased in eastern islands. For each species, a single and a double fruit are shown, with a seed to the right (seed with broken fruit shown for *A. magnifolius*). "Hawaii" in this and other illustrations means "Hawaiian Islands."

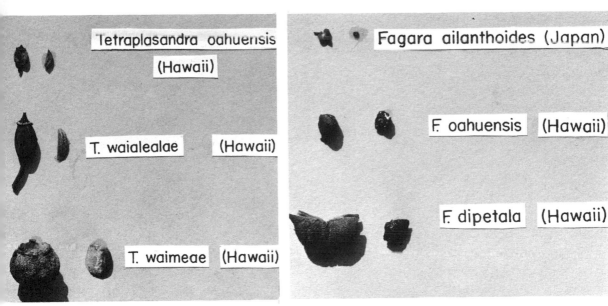

Most Hawaiian tetraplasandras have relatively small fruits and seeds, like those of *T. oahuensis*. On Kauai, however, two gigantic-fruited species can be found (fruit at bottom left one and a half to two inches in diameter when fresh).

Comparison of fruits and seeds of *Fagara* (perhaps better called *Zanthoxylum*) shows that fruits and seeds of a Japanese species are minute; even within the Hawaiian Islands, differences in seed size between moderately large and gigantic can be seen.

feathers. In either case, increased seed size diminishes likelihood of seed transport. Small *Pritchardia* fruits could easily be carried by birds—shore birds, for example. Flotation might have been possible, however, for loulus occur on low islands—Laysan, Nihoa, and, in the South Pacific, the Tuamotus. Dried fruits of *Pritchardia* will float, although their tolerance to seawater has not been determined. In any case, the wet forest loulus such as *P. lowreyana* have seeds much larger than those of the lowlands, the low islands, or those of Samoa and Fiji.

Loss of ability to float would clearly be a loss of dispersibility for a plant dispersed by floating in seawater. This can easily be shown by the wiliwili, *Erythrina sandwicensis*. The seeds do not float, although seeds of non-Hawaiian erythrinas can, as shown by seeds of *E. variegata*. Loss of floatability can also be shown for Hawaiian species of *Colubrina* (kauwila), *Canavalia* (awikiwiki), *Mezoneurum*, and others.

How can we explain these various manifestations of loss of dispersibility?

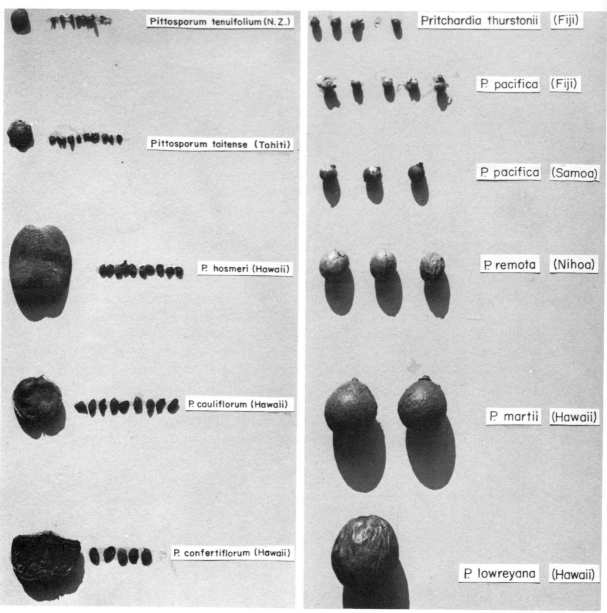

Pittosporum tenuifolium (N. Z.)

Pritchardia thurstonii (Fiji)

P. pacifica (Fiji)

Pittosporum taitense (Tahiti)

P. pacifica (Samoa)

P. hosmeri (Hawaii)

P. remota (Nihoa)

P. cauliflorum (Hawaii)

P. martii (Hawaii)

P. confertiflorum (Hawaii)

P. lowreyana (Hawaii)

Pittosporum shows increase in seed size in the Hawaiian Islands. Species from elsewhere in the Pacific are small-seeded. Fruits (indicated by dry half of capsule at left in each) are generally large in the Hawaiian Islands, but do not correlate exactly with seed size. the largest seed shown is about a half inch long.

The loulu palm, *Pritchardia*, shows increase in fruit size both outside of and within the Hawaiian Islands. The largest fruit shown is about two inches long.

Loss of dispersibility is shown by comparing floating seeds of an Asiatic coral tree, *Erythrina variegata* (floating), with seeds of the Hawaiian wiliwili, *Erythrina sandwicensis* (sunken).

The reasons are not identical with those for loss of flight in insects and birds, but similarities can be found:

(1) Dispersal in plants tends to be about as efficient as necessary to maintain a plant species in the area to which it is adapted. This means that if a plant becomes adapted to a condition limited in geographical extent, such as wet forest, poorer dispersal may permit most seeds or spores to land in favorable sites near the parent plants.

(2) Much immigration of plants to the Hawaiian Islands has taken place from coasts and dry forests of various continents or islands to coasts and dry forests of the Hawaiian Islands, because wet forest plants do not migrate so well. Therefore, if plants shift their ecological preferences in the Hawaiian Islands, the shift is likely to be toward wetter conditions. They will tend to assume the diminished dispersibility characteristic of wet forest plants, as, for example:

(3) The large-seeded habit is an adaptation to shady areas, because a forest seedling must have more stored energy to grow up into the brighter areas of forest undergrowth, where it can get enough sunlight to manufacture its own food and become self-supporting. In adapting to wet forest, groups with smaller seeds will tend to increase seed size and therefore volume of storage materials in the seed.

(4) If a plant shifts its ecological preferences, it will tend to lose contact with the agent responsible for its dispersal. For instance, if *Euphorbia* in the Hawaiian Islands evolves inland from coastal plains to rain forest, or *Bidens*

evolves from coastal bluffs toward rain forest, contact with the marine birds which probably brought these plants to the Islands originally will be lost. If the dispersal mechanism–dispersal agent link is broken, the dispersal mechanism may become of neutral value to the plant in its new location. It may even be a hindrance, for energy must be expended to form the dispersal device, as with the awns (prongs) on the *Bidens* fruits. Structures of neutral or negative value to a plant will, sooner or later, tend to be lost.

There have been some interesting changes in dispersal mechanism in the Hawaiian Islands, changes that have nothing to do with loss of dispersibility. One of these is the conversion of a simple dry capsule, from which seeds shake or are blown, into a "false berry" in *Alsinodendron*. In *Schiedea*, the closest relative and probable ancestor of *Alsinodendron*, the capsule matures, opens, and releases its seeds, while the calyx below the capsule wilts. In *Alsinodendron*, the calyx becomes fleshy and surrounds the capsule as it matures, changing to a purple color very likely attractive to birds; it looks like a typical berry, in fact. The difference between these two types of dispersal seems related to ecology. Dry capsule-type fruits are typical of dry areas, fleshy fruits are more common in wet forests. *Alsinodendron* is a sort of rain forest *Schiedea*.

Another interesting development in dispersal mechanisms is the origin of the "salt shaker" kind of seed dispersal in *Trematolobelia* (see Chapter 12).

Many discoveries about seed dispersal in the Hawaiian Islands can be made by the amateur. Little is known about which animals distribute which seeds, and how, or which plants have lost dispersal mechanisms, or how. As one

An odd change in seed dispersal mechanism is represented by *Alsinodendron*, a derivative of *Schiedea*. *Schiedea* has dry capsules and sepals which wither. In *Alsinodendron* the sepals grow around the capsule, become fleshy and purple, mimicking a berry and probably attracting fruit-eating birds (specimen from summit of Mt. Kaala, Oahu).

example, because of visible loss of dispersibility in Hawaiian plants, one suspects that there may be an invisible one: shorter seed viability. Do seeds in wet Hawaiian forest stay alive for shorter periods than their relatives in dry forest? Which seeds can withstand seawater and still germinate? These are only a few of the many questions which make the Hawaiian forests continually interesting.

Chapter 9   LOSS OF COMPETITIVENESS AND OTHER CHANGES

SOME of the changes discussed in the preceding five chapters seem to represent "dead ends" on evolutionary trees—specializations, overrefinements which can be tolerated on the Hawaiian Islands, but which might not survive well elsewhere. To a certain degree, this must be true.

Plant poisons are a good example. The Hawaiian flora is exceptionally poor in poisonous plants. A recent book called *Poisonous Plants of Hawaii* by Harry L. Arnold is, in fact, devoted almost exclusively to *introduced* plants, not native ones, because so few native plants are poisonous. Only one native plant (*Cocculus ferrandianus*, the huehue) is listed as definitely poisonous, and only the roots are supposed to be toxic. Hawaiians claim that the akia (*Wikstroemia*) is poisonous. According to Arnold's book, it is not, but this is probably not true; there are many akias in the Hawaiian Islands, and all have not been studied. Of those which have been, all but one have been found harmless, but one was found to be definitely poisonous. This akia probably is *Wikstroemia oahuensis* (*W. foetida*). In other parts of the tropics, *Wikstroemia* is famous as a poisonous plant, often used as a fish poison. The one poisonous akia in the Hawaiian Islands might be a recent (but prehuman) introduction, or a lowland relict which has changed little from ancestral types.

Poisonous substances in plants can be an evolutionary response to grazing animals—larger herbivores such as sheep, goats, pigs, cattle, etc. Before human occupation, no such herbivores—in fact, no mammals except one species of bat—were present in the Islands. The evolutionary pressure for plants to produce poisonous substances was therefore lacking, and these chemicals were gradually lost in the Hawaiian flora, for chemical substances, as well as structures, which no longer have importance for a particular group of plants, are likely to be lost sooner or later.

Allied to poisonous compounds are strongly scented oils. These appear, in

Rhus chinensis var. *semialata* is a sumac apparently native to the Hawaiian Islands. It is not, as far as known, poisonous, although many mainland sumacs are (Hilo, Hawaii).

Judging by its reputation elsewhere in the world, *Wikstroemia*, the akia of the Hawaiians, ought to be poisonous. Apparently only one of the approximately twenty-seven akias native to the Islands is poisonous. It seems to be the one shown at left, *W. oahuensis* (lower Punaluu, Oahu). At right is the nonpoisonous *W. bicornuta* (Lanai).

Raspberries ordinarily are thorny, but native Hawaiian species have lost thorns and prickles. Here is *Rubus hawaiiensis* var. *inermis* (Kehena, Kohala Mountains, Hawaii).

many instances, to deter herbivores. The lack of plants with strongly scented leaves in the Hawaiian flora is noteworthy. For example, members of the mint family are usually strongly fragrant. The Hawaiian members of the mint family (*Phyllostegia, Stenogyne, Haplostachys*) are odorless or nearly so. The Hawaiian pilos (*Coprosma*) have odorless leaves, but their relatives in New Zealand and elsewhere have foul-smelling leaves.

Another way in which plants typically deter herbivores is the presence of spines, prickles, thorns, and other textural devices. Most of the groups of plants represented in the Islands are not ones typically spiny or thorny on either mainland or islands. One group in which one would expect this is the raspberry, *Rubus,* but thorns have been lost in the native Hawaiian raspberries.

Ironically, there is one instance in which thorniness seems to have increased in the Hawaiian flora: *Cyanea* of the lobelioids (Chapter 12). Development of prickles on seedlings of certain species of *Cyanea* may be a mechanism for deterring insects or land snails—groups of animals which assume a preponderant role in plant eating in the Islands, since plant-eating mammals and reptiles are absent in the native fauna.

Endemism

After a group colonizes on the Islands, changes begin to accumulate. Changes may also accumulate in the mainland population "left behind," but perhaps not so rapidly as on the Islands. The two populations are then visibly unlike; we can say that the island population is now endemic. Endemism would begin at a low level of difference (subspecies), but the differences might eventually reach the level of species, even genus. Marked differences would result in the designation of an endemic family. There are no families of plants endemic to the Hawaiian Islands, but there are animal groups which have been considered to be endemic families: the honeycreepers (Drepanididae), and possibly also Achatinellidae and Amastridae, although these two land snail groups are now often regarded as subfamilies of Tornatellinidae and Cochlicopidae, respectively. The Hawaiian flora and fauna are extremely rich in endemic species, somewhat less so in genera:

Groups in the Native Flora and Fauna	Total Number of Species, Subspecies, Varieties	Percentage of These Which Are Endemic
Insects	3750	99+
Land molluscs	1064	99+
Birds	71	98.6
Flowering plants	1729	94.4
Ferns	168	64.9

	Total Number of Genera	Percentage of These Which Are Endemic
Insects	377	53.5
Land molluscs	37	51
Birds	40	37.5
Flowering plants	216	13
Ferns	37	8.1

These statistics do not tell much by themselves, although they are remarkable: the percentage of endemism at both the species and genus level is higher than for any other area in the world, a measure of isolation in time and space primarily, but also of the ecological richness which spurs change in immigrant stocks.

Loss of Competitiveness

Obviously with such a high percentage of endemism, there are few continental species in the Hawaiian flora and fauna except for man-introduced organisms. The result of this is that any species in the native flora and fauna is competing almost entirely against *Hawaiian* species. Hawaiian species tend to be less fierce competitors than mainland species. This pattern may derive from earlier times in the development of the Hawaiian flora and fauna, when fewer colonists were present, and when each new colonist was faced with less competition. Ability to compete, although a vague concept, seems governed by the prevailing level of "ferocity" in organisms contending for a given space. In the Hawaiian situation, competition is very low. Probably each new immigrant has begun its Hawaiian career in a weedy fashion, occupied suitable territory, then lost its "momentum" and competitiveness. Part of the reasons for this might be related to the genetic problems mentioned in Chapter 4.

This means that few Hawaiian plants or animals are "weedy" and most are much less competitive than their mainland equivalents. Some do retain their pioneering ability—especially those which colonize lava flows. Among the more aggressive plants are several ferns, such as *Dicranopteris* and *Sadleria*. Among more "aggressive" native flowering plants are the ohia (*Metrosideros*), koa (*Acacia koa*), naupaka (*Scaevola*), and mamaki (*Pipturus*).

Even the fertility of Hawaiian plants seems somewhat lowered, and this may be true of Hawaiian animals also. Although I have no exact information, the number of well-formed seeds and fruits seems very low in some Hawaiian species.

Each immigrant group has probably actively covered territory, speciated as populations respond to isolating factors (valleys, ridges, channels between islands, etc.). The larger genera, such as *Drosophila* and *Cyrtandra*, are in this stage. Then species may gradually have vanished. If older residents compete more poorly, if genetically they suffer from a degree of inbreeding, and if some species occupy very small areas, have a small number of individuals, and have highly specialized requirements, extinction is easy. Even before the destructive activities of man in the Islands, there were undoubtedly some "decadent" vanishing genera, such as *Carelia* among the shells, possibly *Drepanidis* among the birds, and *Delissea, Hesperomannia, Remya,* and *Isodendrion* among plants.

Some endemic Hawaiian genera do not have any close counterparts on mainland areas. In these cases, one may suspect that the mainland relatives have vanished, for if continental environments are more competitive, the Hawaiian Islands might preserve genera which are wiped out on mainland areas. The number of such relict genera is probably small, and the Hawaiian flora and fauna contains no "living fossils"; at best, the relicts would be "recent relicts."

Extinction and Conservation

If older or otherwise "decadent" plants and animals are exceptionally vulnerable in the Islands in prehuman times, human activity can have a catastrophic effect. Until recently, those in charge of conservation problems may have thought the Hawaiian situation was no different from others. Unfortunately, this is not true: conservation is far more difficult than on most mainland areas. The reasons given above are a clue to this. The high vulnerability

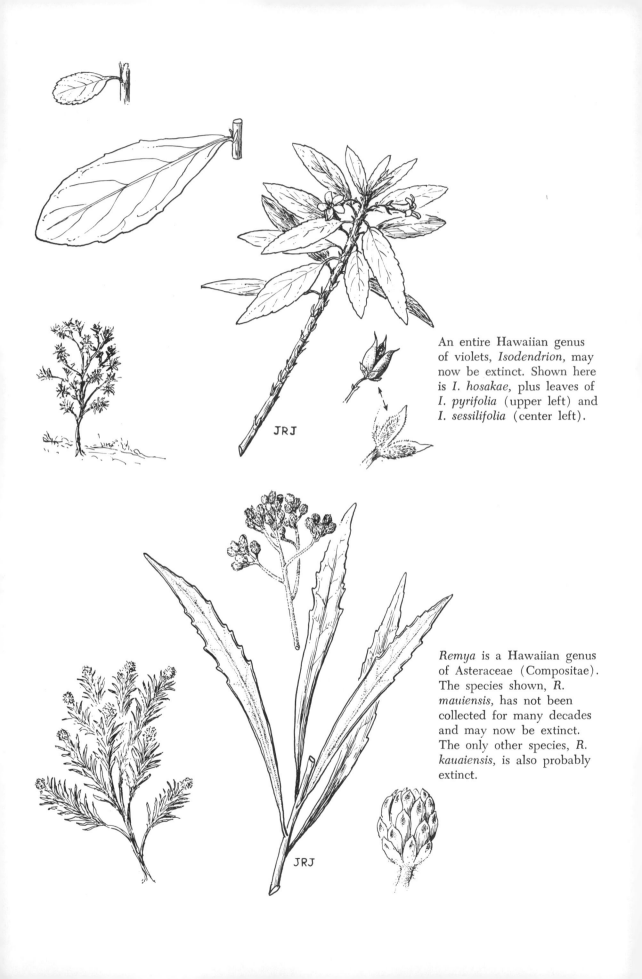

An entire Hawaiian genus of violets, *Isodendrion,* may now be extinct. Shown here is *I. hosakae,* plus leaves of *I. pyrifolia* (upper left) and *I. sessilifolia* (center left).

Remya is a Hawaiian genus of Asteraceae (Compositae). The species shown, *R. mauiensis,* has not been collected for many decades and may now be extinct. The only other species, *R. kauaiensis,* is also probably extinct.

JRJ

JRJ

of native Hawaiian species can virtually be measured by the rampant success introduced species have enjoyed.

Not only is it difficult to preserve native species, the pressure for their extinction is much greater. The limited land area of the Hawaiian Islands has been under exceptional pressure from agriculture, forestry, housing, and recreation. Lowland areas have been under greatest demand for land usage, and use of lowlands as cattle ranges early caused extinction of species—perhaps a number of species were exterminated without being seen by any biologist.

The destruction of Hawaiian flora and fauna has been indirect, as well as direct. Animals and plants introduced by man have gone wild. Pigs, goats, sheep, and other herbivores have been unleashed on a flora which has evolved under herbivore-free conditions. Therefore, the herbivores have been exceptionally destructive in the Islands. Moreover, the disturbance the herbivores create paves the way for weeds that otherwise might not enter. Thus, even in remote, "untouched" forest areas, weeds can be found. We have relatively little information on the recovery of damaged Hawaiian forests, perhaps because so few have been allowed to recover. However, I suspect that many of the Hawaiian forests cannot return to their original condition now because introduced weeds will not go away, and even if these weeds could be exterminated, the disturbance caused by weed extermination would, in fact, cause an even greater number of weeds to enter forest areas.

There has been a tendency, where Hawaiian conservation is concerned, not to preserve some areas because they have already been damaged. Thus, there always is an excuse for further destruction.

Conservationists may fault this account of Hawaiian problems because a full description of what has been lost is not given. A succinct statement should suffice: there have been more animal and plant species extinguished in the Hawaiian Islands than in the entirety of North America.

I do not wish to leave too negative an impression, however. The Hawaiian fauna and flora was the most interesting of any group of oceanic islands on earth, so that there was much more to lose than in other areas. Some plants and animals thought to be extinct, like the crested honeycreeper, *Palmeria*, have been rediscovered. Others in danger of extinction, like the Haleakala silversword, have been saved. There is much still intact, but there is a certain urgency in the need to study Hawaiian organisms now. Many of the interesting plants and animals available for study now may not survive indefinitely.

SPECIAL HAWAIIAN GROUPS

Chapter 10 ❧❧ *THE LAND SHELLS*

E. C. ZIMMERMAN, a noted student of Hawaiian animals, has said that "The endemic Hawaiian land-snail fauna is considered by some workers to be perhaps the most remarkable of all land-snail faunas." Although mammals were not able to immigrate to the Islands in prehuman times, land molluscs traveled rather easily, and thus have had exceptional opportunities—like having an area "all to themselves"—and fulfilled these opportunities. The land snails have been successful colonists because of their simple requirements. Their speciation has been remarkable, and seems mostly related to geographical isolation. Food sources are relatively uniform, so valley-to-valley and island-to-island isolation has operated more significantly. To be sure, Hawaiian land snails do show preferences for particular host trees, and avoid some tree species altogether. Because favored kinds of trees often grow in discontinuous patches, a further degree of isolation is possible.

The way in which a group of organisms develops diversity and is led to form species over a varied landscape is excellently shown by the Achatinellidae (or Achatinellinae, a subfamily of Tornatellinidae). The most primitive genus of the family is probably *Partulina,* which occurs on Maui, Molokai, Lanai, and Hawaii, in addition to a complex of species on Oahu. This pattern is an unusual one, for most important Hawaiian groups show their greatest representation, often most diversified species, on the older islands—particularly Kauai. *Partulina* has diversified in shell size, shape, and pattern. *Newcombia* represents an offshoot of *Partulina* with smaller, turret-like shells. *Newcombia* has about nine species and three subspecies on Molokai and Maui. *Perdicella* is another offshoot: eight species on Molokai and Maui. In small shell size, *Perdicella* may resemble the smaller-shelled ancestors from which the achatinellids very likely stem (See p. 181).

An early invasion of Oahu by *Partulina*-like ancestors has produced the tremendous diversity which is *Achatinella,* a genus nearly limited to Oahu (a few of the species of subgenus *Achatinellastrum* reach Maui and Molokai). How many species of *Achatinella* are there? The number shown represents

A grouping of shells of the family Achatinellidae (or Tornatellinidae subfamily Achatinellinae):

Newcombia plicata (Kalae, Molokai)

Newcombia sulcata (Pohakupili, Molokai)

Newcombia cinnamomea (Molokai)

Perdicella helena (Molokai)

Partulina marmorata (Makawao, E. Maui)

Partulina mighelsiana (Kalae, Molokai)

Partulina nattii (E. Maui)

Partulina proxima (Molokai)

Partulina splendida (W. Maui)

Partulina dwightii (Molokai)

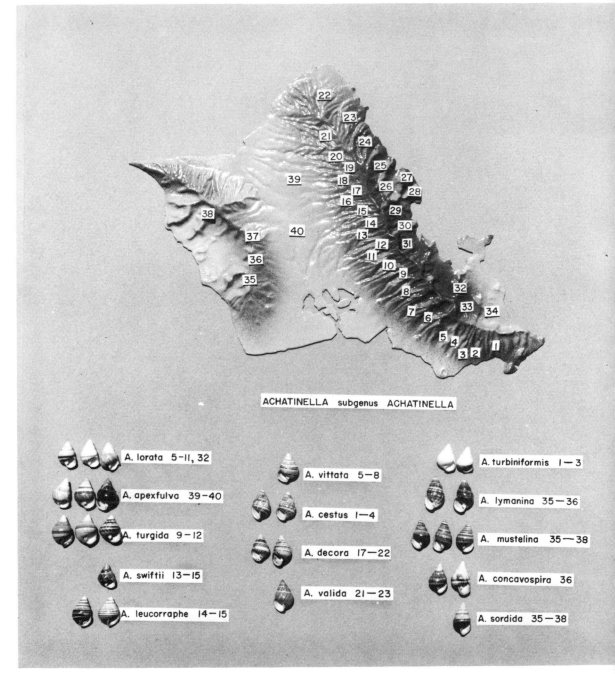

ACHATINELLA subgenus ACHATINELLA

A. lorata 5–11, 32

A. apexfulva 39–40

A. turgida 9–12

A. swiftii 13–15

A. leucorraphe 14–15

A. vittata 5–8

A. cestus 1–4

A. decora 17–22

A. valida 21–23

A. turbiniformis 1–3

A. lymanina 35–36

A. mustelina 35–38

A. concavospira 36

A. sordida 35–38

When a kind of land snail reaches an island and spreads out over a geographically varied area, in time it can produce many distinct species, as has *Achatinella* on Oahu. Ridges tend to isolate species from each other. Species recognized here are arbitrary—some authors would have many more, others fewer. Ranges would have to be changed if different species concepts were used, obviously. The valleys and other geographical features indicated by number are: 1=Niu; 2=Wailupe; 3= Waialae; 4=Palolo; 5=Manoa; 6=Nuuanu; 7=Kalihi; 8=Moanalua; 9=Halawa;

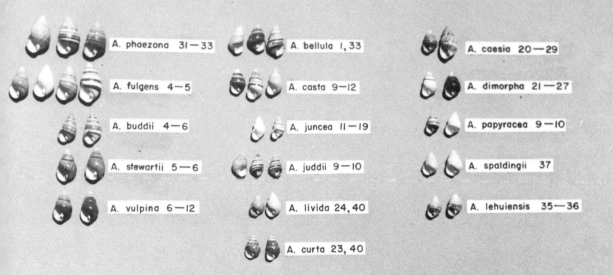

ACHATINELLA subgenus ACHATINELLASTRUM

A. phaezona 31—33

A. bellula 1, 33

A. caesia 20—29

A. fulgens 4—5

A. casta 9—12

A. dimorpha 21—27

A. buddii 4—6

A. juncea 11—19

A. papyracea 9—10

A. stewartii 5—6

A. juddii 9—10

A. spaldingii 37

A. vulpina 6—12

A. livida 24, 40

A. lehuiensis 35—36

A. curta 23, 40

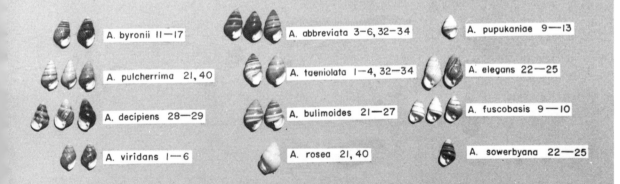

ACHATINELLA subgenus BULIMELLA

A. byronii 11—17

A. abbreviata 3—6, 32—34

A. pupukaniae 9—13

A. pulcherrima 21, 40

A. taeniolata 1—4, 32—34

A. elegans 22—25

A. decipiens 28—29

A. bulimoides 21—27

A. fuscobasis 9—10

A. viridans 1—6

A. rosea 21, 40

A. sowerbyana 22—25

10=Waimalu; 11=Waimano; 12=Manana; 13=Waiawa; 14=Kipapa; 15=Kau-
konahua; 16=Waikakalaua; 17=Wahiawa; 18=Poamoho; 19=Helemano; 20=
Opaeula; 21=Kawailoa; 22=Pupukea; 23=Laie; 24=Hauula; 25=Punaluu; 26=
Kahana; 27=Kaaawa; 28=Hakipu; 29=Waikane; 30=Waiahole; 31=Kahaluu;
32=Maunawili; 33=Konahuanui; 34=Waimanalo; 35=S. Waianae Mountains (Mauna
Kapu); 36=Palikea; 37=Kolekole; 38=Mt. Kaala; 39=Waialua; 40=lower Wahiawa.

only one judgment—and it is perhaps a compromise that might not be supported. In addition, many subspecies and varieties, not shown, have been recognized. One malacologist, Gulick, claimed that there were between two hundred and three hundred achatinellas. Those experienced in identifying achatinellas concede that only with a series of shells and a known locality can one name a collection of some species. Within each species, variability is usually considerable. While some species are easily identified, others seem to grade into one another. Some achatinellas are from dry forest, some from very wet forest. Species can overlap in a given habitat, but they usually are not found mixed together. *Achatinella* may have speciated more than other snail groups because of less competition from other groups. More importantly, the landscape of Oahu, which has more "texture" than do other islands, may have provided more pockets in which species could originate. The achatinellas tend very strongly to remain in one place, so that a valley to an *Achatinella* would have the same isolation value as one island in an archipelago to another kind of organism. Perkins has noted some good examples of lack of mobility in these snails:

"A white variety of *Achatinella redfieldi*, which I had occasion to pass by almost daily for many weeks, was always seen at rest just below the fork of a large branch of a lichen-covered ohia tree. Though there were many showers or wet days, it was never absent from the spot by day, though it may, of course, have moved at night and returned. This was a healthy animal, the shell not at all worn by age. A small dead lichen-covered tree, supporting individuals of *A. theodorei* in 1893, was still occupied by these or their descendants three years later, the adjoining bushes being unoccupied."

The two species of *Partulina* on Oahu evidently represent a relatively recent

The small size of the members of the family Tornatellinidae is shown by the typewritten letters beside them. Left, *Elasmias fusca* (Molokai). Right, *Tornatellinides procerula* (Kamuela, Hawaii).

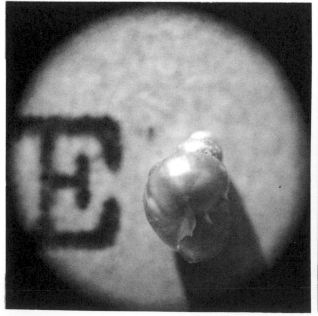 

invasion, subsequent to the successful occupation staged by *Achatinella*. The development of *Achatinella* on Oahu has probably forestalled speciation there by other shells with similar requirements.

If Achatinellidae are closely related to (and perhaps a subfamily of) Tornatellinidae, they may exhibit this in such features as tree-living habits, although the two groups differ markedly in size. Tornatellinids are widespread in the Hawaiian Islands, as well as in the Pacific, a fact related to their very small size. They have unusual distribution patterns in the Pacific, including many islands in their range, but only barely touching continents. They may be adapted to the disharmonic conditions of oceanic islands, but unable to compete with continental land snails or other continental animals. Or, Tornatellinidae may be adapted to maritime climates and do not survive well inland.

If Tornatellinidae are inconspicuous by virtue of small size, Achatinellidae are often inconspicuous by virtue of their patterns. Although some of the banded achatinellas look as though they could readily be sighted, only skilled observers will find them easily in the field. The achatinellas probably had no active predators in prehuman time, although the thrush *Phaeornis* might have eaten a few.

Predators must be considered a possibility in the evolution of a close pair of Hawaiian shell families, Amastridae and Cochlicopidae (sometimes considered two subfamilies, Amastrinae and Cochlicopinae, under an inclusive family, Cochlicopidae). The cochlicopids (narrowly defined) contain three genera: *Leptachatina* has 125 species and 13 varieties, native to all of the major islands, including fossil species on Niihau and Kahoolawe. One species of *Armsia* and three of *Pauahia* are native to Oahu. These are all rather small shells, and

These relatively small shells (about a third to a half inch in length) belong to the family Cochlicopidae (subfamily Cochlicopinae). From left to right, *Pauahia chrysalis* (Oahu); *Leptachatina pachystoma* (Kauai); *Leptachatina fusca* (Oahu); *Leptachatina gracilis* (Oahu).

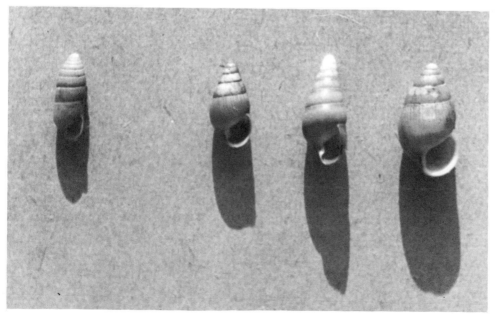

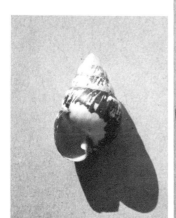

suggest that the ancestors of both Cochlicopidae and Amastridae—like those of Tornatellinidae and Achatinellidae—were small-shelled. Evasion of predators is suggested by the colors of amastrid shells, which vary from pale, like lichens, to brown of dead leaves, and near-black of bark—backgrounds on which these snails live. The amastrids further conceal themselves by emitting masses of a mucus-like substance, on which bits of forest debris collect. The shells are, in this condition, nearly invisible. *Pterodiscus*, which has an extraordinarily flattened shell, is dark brown with a rough surface and looks like a bit of bark.

Evolution in the amastrid shells has featured increase in size and diversification in shape. We can imagine that ancestors of the amastrids were rather small, perhaps like *Amastra cornea*, perhaps smaller. The genus *Amastra* is terrestrial in its habits, living in rotten logs, among bark fragments, on dead leaves or stones. The genus *Laminella* illustrates a shift to life above the ground; it is found on trees or other plants. *Laminella gravida*, for example, lives on the fronds of soft-leaved ferns.

The amastrid snails have diversified remarkably in the Hawaiian Islands, probably beginning with a small rounded conical shell such as *Amastra cornea*. The arrangement here demonstrates different shapes, and derivations from one given species to another should not be interpreted literally. Bottom, side, and top views given for *Planamastra* and *Pterodiscus*.

Carelia turricula (Waipio, Kauai)	*Carelia necra* (Hanamaulu, Kauai)	*Carelia bicolor* (Kauai)	*Carelia dolei* (Limahali, Kauai)	*Carelia paradoxa* (Moloaa, Kauai)	*Carelia sinclairii* (Niihau)
			Amastra turritella (Oahu)		
			Amastra hutchinsonii (E. Maui)		
Laminella gravida (Nuuanu, Oahu)	*Amastra rubens* (Waianae, Oahu)	*Amastra textilis* (Manoa, Oahu)	*Amastra cornea* (Waianae, Oahu)	*Amastra magna* (Lanai)	*Amastra knudseni* (Kauai)
			Amastra obesa (Maui)		
			Amastra sphaerica (Kauai)		
				Planamastra diginophora (Haleauau, Oahu)	*Pterodiscus wesleyi* (Waimano, Oahu)

The 158 species of *Amastra* show a variety of tendencies. Gigantism is clearly shown by some, such as *A. knudseni,* which is the size of a large common garden snail. Shorter, wider shapes characterize other species, such as *A. obesa* and *A. sphaerica.* The genera *Planamastra* (five species) and *Pterodiscus* (seven species) appear to be continuations of this trend. Some amastras show narrower, longer forms, such as *Amastra hutchinsoni* and *A. turritella.* This trend appears to be continued in, is certainly strongly represented by, the amastrid genus *Carelia,* a genus of about twenty species. *Carelia* exhibits

There are perhaps a hundred species of the family Endodontidae in the Hawaiian Islands. Here is *Endodonta jugosa* from Kauai.

Limnaeidae is a family of shells which live in wet places. Here is *Limnaea reticulata* from Kauai.

The widespread family Zonitidae is represented in the Hawaiian Islands by various genera, including this endemic genus, *Godwinia.* Shown is *Godwinia caperata* (top and side views).

Thin papery shells characterize the Hawaiian species of *Succinea*. These succineas are browsing on a leaf of *Clermontia drepanomorpha* (Kohala Mountains, Hawaii).

a number of characteristics typical for Hawaiian organisms. The shells show marked gigantism (up to three inches in length). It is evidently an older, "decadent" genus, and consequently it is not surprising that *Carelia* is known only from Kauai and Niihau. The Niihau species and some of the Kauai species are known only in the fossil state, and all species of *Carelia* are rare. In the amastrid snails, most of the extreme forms are on Kauai: *Amastra knudseni, Amastra sphaerica, Carelia.*

The two pairs of families considered above (Achatinellidae-Tornitellinidae and Amastridae-Cochlicopidae) contain the majority of Hawaiian land snails. The other families do not bulk large in numbers of species. These other families include Endodontidae, which has small flat spiral shells. The conically shaped Limnaeidae are perhaps not properly considered land snails, for they tend to inhabit fresh water. The Zonitidae are flat spiral shells, and include one endemic genus, *Godwinia*. The family Succineidae is represented by a cluster of ill-defined species, all of which have scoop-like almost papery shells. Succineas are especially abundant on the easternmost island, Hawaii. Two families not illustrated here, Helicarionidae (subfamily Microcystinae only) and Pupillidae, are represented by extremely small shells, which go unnoticed by inexperienced collectors.

The affinities of most Hawaiian land shells can be described as "Pacific" —related to species on islands in the western Pacific. Only a few groups, such as Pupillidae, Cochlicopidae, and Zonitidae, are called "holarctic" in relationships—that is, derived from groups widespread in the north temperate zone.

Chapter 11 ✦ *THE HONEYCREEPERS*
AND OTHER BIRDS

THE Hawaiian Islands have only a few groups of land birds. Other than honeycreepers, we find marsh birds, waterfowl, and representatives (and not many at that) of merely five families of land birds. The poverty of land bird groups is no doubt a result of the difficulty in successful transport and establishment across vast oceanic distances. Although many birds have been reported as stragglers or chance visitors to the Hawaiian Islands (see Chapter 3), none of these are true land birds. That land birds should be so poor at dispersal seems at first a paradox, because the ability to fly ought to make them superior at crossing ocean.

The honeycreepers, as seen in the Hawaiian Islands, show us the reason for this paradox; many other land birds could also show us the same thing in other areas. During occasional strong Hawaiian storms, honeycreeper individuals are blown to lowlands. They are unable to find their way back to forests and soon die, in fact, in the unaccustomed lowland environment.

The Hawaiian honeycreepers have exploited so many avenues and habitats that they can be called an outstanding example of adaptive radiation. This entrance into so many different niches was probably permitted partly by default: the small number of competitors among land birds. In fact, the honeycreepers may have been the earliest land-bird colonists in the Islands. If so, this would explain why the other land-bird immigrants have diversified so little, formed so few species. Some have colonized only a single island, like the crow.

The Hawaiian honeycreepers belong to a specialized group of birds, but there is no general agreement about which familes might be related. Possibilities include finches (Fringillidae), American wood warblers (Parulidae), tanagers (Thraupidae), and creepers (Certhiidae). Until we know what the relatives of the honeycreepers are, we cannot guess where they came from. A slight preponderance of opinion favors America as their site of origin, however.

The honeycreepers can be divided into two subfamilies (Psittacirostrinae and Drepanididae), and each of these has undergone its own adaptive radiation. Even within genera, the process of adaptive diversification is evident.

In Psittacirostrinae, the most primitive type is probably represented by the akepas (*Loxops coccinea*), the creepers (*L. maculata*), and the amakihis (*L. virens*). Although these all belong to the genus Loxops, they differ in diet and therefore bill shape. Most of the species of *Loxops* have small beaks for probing through debris or shallow flowers in search of insects. *Loxops sagittirostris,* the greater amakihi, has a longer, stouter bill capable of grappling with larger insects. *Loxops virens* appears to show greater intake of nectar compared with the other *Loxops* species. This seems a natural development, for birds visit nectar-rich flowers, such as those of the ohia (*Metrosideros*), in search of insects. *Loxops* appears basically an insectivorous group, but capable of mixed feeding. It may have been that latent capabilities for switching diets permitted *Loxops*-like ancestors in the honeycreepers to diversify.

Long, tapering curved bills, a tendency seen in *Loxops,* is prominently represented in the akialoa (*Hemignathus obscurus*), the Kauai akialoa (*H. procerus*), and the nukupuu (*H. lucidus*). Of these, the nukupuu has shorter bills with markedly unequal mandibles. These are correlated with the probability that the nukupuu consumed a greater proportion of insects and a smaller proportion of nectar than the akialoas. The shorter, stouter lower mandible serves both for crushing insects and for digging into wood and bark in search of them, while the two long mandibles of the akialoa beak suggests less crushing ability. However, the akialoa beak does permit entry into long, narrow crevices in search of insects. The akiapolaau (*H. wilsoni*) represents a sort of intensification of the nukupuu in its shorter, stouter lower mandible, which can be used like that of a woodpecker. All of the species of *Hemignathus* have tongues capable of rolling into a tube, and by this means nectar can be sucked.

Abandonment of nectar feeding in favor of eating insects is shown by *Pseudonestor xanthophrys. Pseudonestor* has a powerful beak of unequal mandibles and is capable of crushing stout, hard twigs. Some of the beetles and larvae of beetles eaten by *Pseudonestor* live only in live wood, so the correlation with strong mandibles and associated muscles is understandable.

A final series of adaptations in the subfamily Psittacirostrinae is shown by the six species of *Psittacirostra.* The ou (*P. psittacea*), which occurs on all the main islands, is close to *Pseudonestor* or *Hemignathus wilsoni* in its bill, but both mandibles are shorter and stouter. The ou eats fruits, seeds, leaves, and caterpillars, but apparently does not crush wood or large, heavy seeds. This seems in contrast with *Psittacirostra kona,* which has an appreciably more formidable bill for crushing large, tough seeds. Such differences in bills and diet within *Psittacirostra* suggest a secondary cycle of adaptive radiation, in which massiveness of bill correlates with size and toughness of seeds or insects eaten. *Psittacirostra cantans* has reached two of the Leeward Islands, Nihoa and Laysan. This is curious, for neither of these islands is forested, yet *Psittacirostra* on the main islands is definitely a forest bird. On Laysan, *P. cantans* eats various kinds of seeds, but, opportunistically, takes to eggs, roots, and insects. This may explain why *P. cantans* survived on Laysan when the island was nearly denuded by rabbits, while the Laysan honeyeater (*Himatione*

PSEUDONESTOR (*P. xanthophrys:* beetles and larvae, often extracted from stout twigs by crushing; no nectar)

PSITTACIROSTRA (*P. Kona:* large seeds, such as those of *Myoporum,* crushed in beak; no nectar)

HEMIGNATHUS subgenus Hemignathus (*H. lucidus hanapepe:* small beetles in bark, some nectar)

HEMIGNATHUS subgenus *Heterorhynchus* (*H. procerus;* nectar, chiefly that of lobeliads; insects of small size in deep crevices or debris)

LOXOPS subgenus *Viridonia* (*L. virens stejnegeri:* insects, trunks, limbs of trees; little or no nectar)

LOXOPS subgenus *Paroreomyza* (*L. Maculata bairdii:* insects in mosses, lichens, easily-reached bark crevices; little or no nectar)

SUBFAMILY PSITTACIROSTRIN

DREPANIDIS (*D. funerea:* nectar, chiefly from lobeliads)

VESTIARIA (*V. coccinea:* nectar from tubular or bell-shaped flowers; caterpillars)

CIRIDOPS (*C. anna:* fleshy fruits?)

PALMERIA (*P. dolei:* nectar from *Metrosideros* flowers; caterpillars)

SUBFAMILY DREPANIDINAE

HIMATIONE (*H. sanguinea sanguinea:* nectar from *Metrosideros* flowers, caterpillars)

The genera and the subgenera of the Hawaiian honeycreepers (Drepanididae) show the most dramatic example of adaptive radiation among birds of the Hawaiian Islands—or any other islands. Beak size and shape signify adaptation to a wide spectrum of diet articles.

SUMMARY OF HAWAIIAN HONEYCREEPERS

SCIENTIFIC NAME	FORMER SCIENTIFIC NAME	HAWAIIAN NAME	DISTRIBUTION	DIET
Loxops subgenus *Viridonia*				
L. virens	*Chlorodrepanis virens*	Amakihi		primarily small insects from ohia flowers; considerable nectar (ohia); a few berries
subsp. *virens*			Hawaii	
subsp. *wilsoni*	*Himatione wilsoni, H. kalaana, H. chloroides*	Amakihi	Lanai, Maui, Molokai	
subsp. *chloris*	*Himatione chloris*	Amakihi	Oahu	
subsp. *stejnegeri*	*Himatione stejnegeri*	Amakihi	Kauai	
L. parva	*Himatione parva*	Anianiau	Kauai	primarily insects, some nectar (ohia)
L. sagittirostris	*Viridonia sagittirostris*	Greater Amakihi	Hawaii	medium to large insects, **some nectar**
subgenus *Paroreomyza* *L. maculata*				insects from mosses, trunks, branches; rarely nectar
subsp. *maculata*	*Himatione maculata*	(creeper)	Oahu	
subsp. *mana*	*Himatione mana* *Oreomyza mana, O. perkinsi*		Hawaii	
subsp. *montana*	*Himatione montana, Oreomyza montana*	Alauwahio	Lanai	
subsp. *newtoni*	*Himatione newtoni*	Alauwahio	Maui	
subsp. *flammea*	*Loxops flammea*	Kakawahie	Molokai	
subsp. *bairdi*	*Oreomyza bairdi*	Akikekke	Kauai	

SUMMARY OF HAWAIIAN HONEYCREEPERS (CONT.)

SCIENTIFIC NAME	FORMER SCIENTIFIC NAME	HAWAIIAN NAME	DISTRIBUTION	DIET
subgenus *Loxops*				
L. *coccinea*	*Fringilla coccinea*	Akepa		insects, caterpillars in leaf bases, a little nectar (ohia)
subsp. *coccinea*		Akepa	Hawaii	
subsp. *ochracea*		Akepa	Maui	
subsp. *rufa*		Akepa	Oahu	
subsp. *caerulei-rostris*	*Chrysomitri-dops caeru-rostris*		Kauai	
Hemignathus				
subgenus *Hemignathus*				
H. *obscurus*		Akialoa		some nectar (esp. from lobelioid flowers), but
subsp. *obscurus*	*Certhia obscura*	Akialoa	Hawaii	
subsp. *lanaiensis*	*Hemignathus lanaiensis*	Akialoa	Lanai	primarily insects in crevices, debris, decaying wood, leaf bases (weevils, other beetles)
subsp. *ellisianus*	*Drepanis ellisianus*		Oahu	
H. *procerus*		Kauai Akialoa	Kauai	
subgenus *Hetero-rhynchus*	*Heterorhynchus* (as a genus)			
H. *lucidus*		Nukupuu		
subsp. *lucidus*		Nukupuu	Oahu	prob. similar to *H. lucidus* but less nectar
subsp. *affinis*	*H. affinis*	Nukupuu	Maui	
subsp. *hanapepe*	*H. hanapepe*	Nukupuu	Kauai	
H. *wilsoni*		Akiapolaau	Hawaii	insects secured as does a wood-pecker; no nectar

SUMMARY OF HAWAIIAN HONEYCREEPERS (CONT.)

SCIENTIFIC NAME	FORMER SCIENTIFIC NAME	HAWAIIAN NAME	DISTRIBUTION	DIET
Pseudonestor *P. xanthophrys*			Maui	larvae and adult beetles obtained from twigs it crushes
Psittacirostra *P. psittacea*	*Psittarostra* *Loxia psittacea* *Dysmodrepanis munroi*	Ou	6 main islands	fruits and flowers of ieie (*Freycinetia*), berries of lobelioids, leaves, caterpillars
P. cantans subsp. *cantans*	*Telespiza cantans*	(Laysan finch)	Laysan	insects, larvae, birds' eggs, dead birds, *Boerhavia* root, *Tribulus* grass and sedge seeds
subsp. *ultima*	*Telespiza ultima*		Nihoa	eggs, seeds, insects
P. bailleui	*Loxoides bailleui*	Palila	Hawaii	mamani (*Sophora*) seeds, naio (*Myoporum*) seeds, poha (*Physalis*) berries, caterpillars
P. palmeri	*Rhodacanthis palmeri*	Hopue	Hawaii	koa (*Acacia*) seeds, aalii (*Dodonaea*) seeds, caterpillars
P. flaviceps	*Rhodacanthis flaviceps*	(lesser koa finch)	Hawaii	prob. as in *P. palmeri*
P. kona	*Chloridops kona*		Hawaii	naio (*Myoporum*) seeds, leaves, caterpillars

SUMMARY OF HAWAIIAN HONEYCREEPERS (CONT.)

SCIENTIFIC NAME	FORMER SCIENTIFIC NAME	HAWAIIAN NAME	DISTRIBUTION	DIET

Himatione
   H. sanguinea
     subsp. *sanguinea*
	Certhia sanguinea	Apapane	6 main islands	nectar from ohia, caterpillars

subsp. *freethii*		(Laysan honey-eater)	Laysan	nectar, insects from atoll vegetation
Palmeria *P. dolei*	*Himatione dolei*	Akohekohe; (crested finch)	Maui, Molokai	nectar from ohia, caterpillars
Ciridops *C. anna*	*Fringilla anna*	Ula ai hawane	Hawaii	prob. fruit of loulu palms (*Pritchardia*)
Vestiaria *V. coccinea*	*Certhia coccinea*	Iiwi	6 main islands	nectar and insects in lobelioid and other flowers; caterpillars
Drepanidis *D. pacifica*	*Drepanis, Drepanorhamphus*	Mamo	Hawaii	nectar from lobelioids, etc.; a few insects
D. funerea		Hoa; (black mamo)	Molokai	

sanguinea freethii) did not survive. Laysan birds are shown in Chapter 24.

The other subfamily of the Hawaiian honeycreepers, Drepanidae, has coarser plumage, blackish juvenile feathers, and truly truncated primary feathers which give a whirring sound in flight. The most primitive representative of this subfamily is one which looks like *Loxops* but is red, the apapane *Himatione*. *Himatione*, like *Loxops*, consumes both insects and nectar, although more nectar than the various species of *Loxops* typically do. This also applies to *Palmeria*, the rare akohekohe. This crested bird is distinctive in its colorful feather patterns.

Ciridops, a reddish bird, represents an interesting entry into a fruit-eating habit if we can trust the Hawaiian name, ula-ai-hawane ("eater of palm-fruits"). The habits of this bird were not studied before it became extinct; however, the shape of the bill does suggest a fruit-eating bird to ornithologists.

The iiwi, *Vestiaria coccinea*, is a bright red bird which represents a tendency toward nectar feeding. Iiwis do not eat nectar exclusively, though. In fact, recent observations by entomologist Herman Spieth show that iiwis visit flowers of a lobelioid, *Clermontia arborescens*, to capture the native fruit flies (*Drosophila*) which live in these flowers. Iiwis are still relatively common in a number of forest areas of the Islands.

The mamo, *Drepanidis*, has disappeared. This black, sickle-billed bird represented an adaptation to feeding almost exclusively on nectar. Mamos were expert in negotiating the curved flowers of lobelioids, and probably other tubular flowers. In the process of feeding on nectar, they probably ingested a few insects, but only small ones.

The akepa (*Loxops coccinea rufa*) from Kauai has reddish plumage and a short beak. It may resemble the warbler-like birds believed to be ancestors of the Hawaiian honeycreepers, of which it is a member. The beak of the akepa is suited to search for insects in leaf bases and flowers (from *Aves Hawaiienses*, by Wilson and Evans).

The amakihi (*Loxops virens chloris*) is a greenish honeycreeper which eats small insects from relatively open, shallow flowers like those of the ohia; it also eats considerable nectar from those flowers, a fact perhaps suggested in the shape of the beak. The male is shown above, female below (from *Aves Hawaiienses,* by Wilson and Evans).

The nukupuu (*Hemignathus lucidus hanapepe*) has a bill suited to delicate searching through litter, crevices, and in flowers for insects. It may represent a stage transitional toward nectar feeding (from *Aves Hawaiienses*, by Wilson and Evans).

The akiapolaau (*Hemignathus wilsoni*) is a drab greenish Hawaiian honeycreeper
that used the stout lower half of its beak much as does the woodpecker, chipping
into wood in search of insects; the upper half of the bill was a probe, could enter
narrow crevices (from *Aves Hawaiienses,* by Wilson and Evans).

The Kauai akialoa (*Hemignathus procerus*) is a dull green honeycreeper with a long beak, both halves of the same length. A bill like this suggests adaptation to nectar feeding, a habit this bird is known to have in addition to eating of insects (from *Aves Hawaiienses,* by Wilson and Evans).

No Hawaiian name is known for *Pseudonestor xanthophrys*, a now-extinct yellowish green honeycreeper with a bill known to have been used in crushing stout twigs to obtain insects (from *Aves Hawaiienses*, by Wilson and Evans).

The ou, *Psittacirostra psittacea,* was a yellow-green honeycreeper fond of flowers, fruits, and caterpillars. The upper bill is appreciably longer than the lower (from *Aves Hawaiienses,* by Wilson and Evans).

The palila (*Psittacirostra bailleui*) was a parrot-billed honeycreeper in which the upper mandible of the beak was only slightly longer than the lower (from *Aves Hawaiienses*, by Wilson and Evans).

Psittacirostra kona is the end product in evolution of honeycreepers toward a large, short bill shape. The upper and lower beak mandibles are equal, and strong muscles attached to the bill of this extinct bird permitted crushing of tough seeds and leaves (from *Aves Hawaiienses,* by Wilson and Evans).

The apapane (*Himatione sanguinea sanguinea*) is a red honeycreeper that eats nectar of ohia blossoms (shown in this picture) as well as caterpillars. Apapanes can still be seen easily in some Hawaiian forests (from *Aves Hawaiienses,* by Wilson and Evans).

The akohekohe, or crested honeycreeper (*Palmeria dolei*), was thought to be extinct but has been rediscovered in remote forests of northeastern Maui. The plumage is mottled, usually dull brown (from *Aves Hawaiienses*, by Wilson and Evans).

Ula-ai-hawane is the Hawaiian name of this reddish honeycreeper (*Ciridops anna*). Now extinct, it is thought to have eaten small to medium-sized soft fruits, a diet unlike that of other honeycreepers (from *Aves Hawaiienses,* by Wilson and Evans).

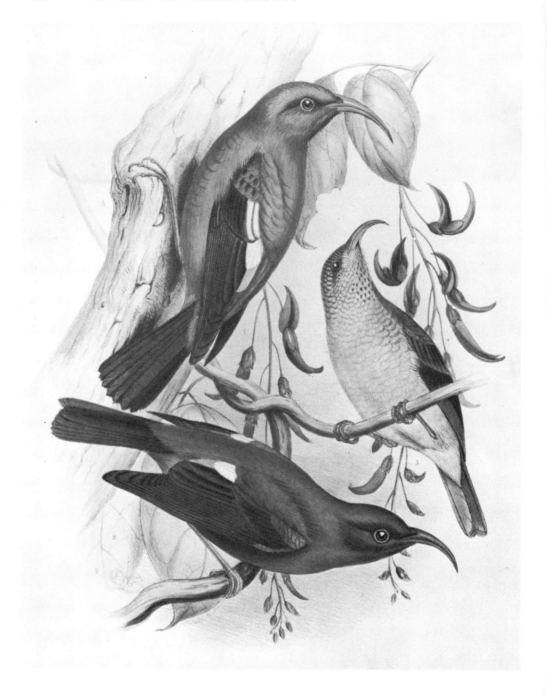

The iiwi, *Vestiaria coccinea*, is a bright red honeycreeper; its feathers were used in Hawaiian feather cloaks. Iiwis still survive in forest areas of the larger islands (from *Aves Hawaiienses*, by Wilson and Evans).

The mamo (*Drepanidis funerea*), a now-extinct honeycreeper, was the end product of evolution in this group from insect feeding to nectar eating. The mamo drank nectar from tubular flowers, and ate only a few insects. Its feathers were black (from *Aves Hawaiienses*, by Wilson and Evans).

Honeycreeper nests are shallow and cup-like. Apapane nests are made of grass or sedge leaves, while those of the iiwi incorporate other leaves as well. The honeycreepers also differ from each other with respect to call. Some of the names given by the Hawaiians were attempts to record the calls: "apapane," for example. *Palmeria* has a vibrating or gurgling sound, while the mamos and apapanes have (or had) short, plaintive calls. Iiwis issue a harsh note. More varied, musical calls are said to characterize the genera of the other subfamily, Psittacirostrinae. The akialoas and ous have been singled out as the possessors of particularly melodious calls. One curious feature said to characterize all honeycreepers is a strong, characteristic odor.

Some of the honeycreepers have survived well: *Loxops, Himatione,* and *Vestiaria* can be seen in wet forests on the largest islands. *Palmeria,* once thought to be extinct, has been rediscovered on Maui. All of the honeycreepers (as well as other birds) ever reported to be on Kauai are claimed still to be extant. *Drepanidis* and *Psittacirostra* have suffered most, *Hemignathus* to a considerable extent, while *Pseudonestor* and *Ciridops* long ago vanished. Most of the honeycreepers which are now extinct can be described as highly specialized ones, and ones which occupied limited areas. Most of them were species or subspecies which existed only in a single area of a single island, and the destruction of forest areas has been a prime cause of honeycreeper extinction. The accessibility of forest areas to man and his pests has perhaps been even more important— rats have undoubtedly killed many honeycreepers. One curious indirect cause of extinction is bird malaria, which causes swelling of the claws. This disease infected Hawaiian birds only after the introduction of the mosquito, which has carried it into wet forest areas not entered by man himself.

The simple cup-like nest of the apapane (*Himatione sanguinea sanguinea*) is constructed from grassy leaves (Kehena, Kohala Mountains). At right, the larger and more complicated nest of *Vestiaria coccinea,* the iiwi (from *Aves Hawaiienses,* by Wilson and Evans).

Clermontia grandiflora

Clermontia hawaiiensis

Clermontia arborescens

Clermontia montis-loa

212 A

Cyanea leptostegia

Cyanea angustifolia

Cyanea aculeatiflora

Cyanea recta

212 B

Rollandia angustifolia

Delissea undulata

Lobelia gaudichaudii var. gloria-montis

212 C

Trematolobelia macrostachys

Brighamia insignis

The ahinahina or
Haleakala silversword
(*Argyroxiphium sandwicense*)

Haleakala crater, Maui

Flowers of the Haleakala silversword

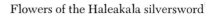

The Kau silversword
(*Argyroxiphium kauense*)

The naenae *(Dubautia plantaginea)*

The Puu Kukui silversword
(*Argyroxiphium caliginii*)

The Puu Kukui greensword (*Argyroxiphium grayanum*)

The iliau *(Wilkesia gymnoxiphium)*

Other Land Birds

What are the competitors of the honeycreepers? One likely to be seen by visitors to the rain forests on Hawaii, Oahu, and Kauai is the elepaio. Although this bird is common on these islands and has a distinct race on each, it evidently never was present on Maui, Molokai, or Lanai. The elepaio tends to follow a hiker, and I have often been approached by one during a momentary stop in a wet forest area. Elepaios watch humans with great curiosity, and chirp actively. The elepaio, scientifically *Chasiempis sandwichensis,* is an Old World flycatcher (Muscicapidae). As that family name suggests, elepaios are insectivorous, and are very agile at catching insects on leaves and stems. The elepaio nest is a remarkable and fragile construction. Formed largely of lichens, it is held together by cobwebs.

Another member of the Old World flycatcher family is the omao thrush, *Phaeornis. Phaeornis obscurus* has races on Hawaii, Lanai, Molokai, and Kauai.

The Kauai race of the elepaio (*Chasiempis sandwicensis sclateri*) is a charming small bird which often approaches one closely. The elepaio's nest is deep, constructed from lichens held together by cobwebs (from *Aves Hawaiienses,* by Wilson and Evans).

An extinct race was once on Oahu and possibly Maui. A second species, *Phaeornis palmeri,* from Kauai is very rare or possibly extinct. This latter species is entirely insectivorous. However, *P. obscurus* is a fruit eater, and likes berries of opiko (*Straussia*), olapa (*Cheirodendron*), pua (*Osmanthus*), and akia (*Wikstroemia*). It also does eat caterpillars, spiders, and various insects, however. A thrush like this might well be responsible for carrying seeds from place to place within the Hawaiian Islands, although other birds may be responsible for introduction of such plants to the Islands from distant source areas.

Miller birds, also members of the Old World flycatcher family, are insectivorous birds native to Nihoa and Laysan, and are discussed and illustrated in Chapters 20 and 24.

If the omao and the elepaio represent insectivore and mixed-feeding competitors of the honeycreepers, members of another family, the honeyeaters (Meliphagidae), are nectar-feeding contenders. This family is predominantly western Pacific in distribution. The Hawaiian representatives fall into two genera: *Chaetoptila* and *Moho. Chaetoptila* is a now-extinct bird from only one island (Hawaii). It was almost as large as a crow. Because it was probably the first Hawaiian bird to have been extinguished, we know little of its habits. It is reported to have liked ohia flowers, the nectar source of so many of the honeycreepers.

The species of *Moho* (Hawaiian name: oo) have been made famous by conversion of certain of their feathers into cloaks by the Hawaiians. *Moho* had four species: *M. nobilis* on Hawaii, *M. bishopi* on Molokai, *M. apicalis* on Oahu, and *M. braccatus* on Kauai. These are apparently all extinct now. Oos were black, with tufts of yellow feathers extracted to make the yellow feather cloaks. This may well have helped to extinguish the oo, but some think that natural rates of reproduction would have replaced individuals taken for their feathers if only the forests where oos lived had been left intact. The oo liked the nectar of lobelioids and various other flowers, although the dwarf oo of Kauai included an appreciable proportion of insects in its diet. The oo nest was a crude collection of twigs, built in treetops.

The Hawaiian crow, or alala (*Corvus tropicus*), is a native only of the island of Hawaii, and is claimed to show relationship to American crows. A forest bird, the alala is fond of fruits of the ieie (*Freycinetia*). Like other crows, it is versatile in diet and has taken to other foods as well.

Two groups of predatory birds are represented in the Hawaiian fauna: the Hawaiian hawk, or io; and the Hawaiian short-eared owl, or pueo. The hawk, like the crow, occurs only on the island of Hawaii. Although the io now catches mice, that food was not available to it in prehuman times and it undoubtedly ate insects and perhaps small birds, both prey it is still known to seek. The io has been alleged to be a close relative of a North American hawk (*Buteo swainsoni*).

The kioea, *Chaetoptila angustipluma,* top, was a honeyeater (family Meliphagidae) much like the oo in its habits. The puaiohi, a thrush (*Phaeornis palmeri*) from Kauai (bottom). It is also now extinct (from *Aves Hawaiienses,* by Wilson and Evans).

Hawaiians hunted the oo, a honeyeater (family Meliphagidae). They used tufts of yellow feathers from these birds in making the famous feather cloaks. These birds are now extinct. At the top, the Oahu oo, *Moho apicalis;* at the bottom, Molokai oo, *Moho bishopi* (from *Aves Hawaiienses,* by Wilson and Evans).

The alala (*Corvus tropicus*), top, is a crow native to only one district of one island: the Kona Coast of Hawaii. At the bottom is the io (*Buteo solitarius*), a Hawaiian hawk, a bird which also has been found only on that island (from *Aves Hawaiienses*, by Wilson and Evans).

The pueo is a short-eared owl which differs only as a subspecies (*Asio flammeus* subsp. *sandwichensis*) from short-eared owls elsewhere in the north temperate zone, and a closely related race occurs on Ponape in the Caroline Islands.

Water Birds

Migratory waterfowl have succeeded in colonizing Hawaiian Islands on several occasions. The Hawaiian goose or nene (*Branta sandwicensis*) is the most conspicuous of these. It is interesting in its adaptations to a nonaquatic mode of life; the loss of webbing on its feet demonstrates its conversion to life on dry land. Characteristically, the nene is found in the high grasslands on Hawaii and (formerly) Maui. It eats various sorts of berries, such as those of the ohelo (*Vaccinium*) and kukainene (*Coprosma ernodeoides*).

All six main islands host the Hawaiian duck, or koloa (*Anas wyvilliana wyvilliana*). The Laysan teal is a distinct subspecies of the same species, and is discussed in Chapter 24.

The rail family is well represented on the Hawaiian Islands, as it is on other oceanic islands. Two races of a flightless rail, *Pennula sandwichensis* were once found on Hawaii and Oahu, but are now extinct. The curious Laysan rail *Porzanula palmeri* became extinct only recently (Chapter 24). Among coots, two species are represented on the Hawaiian Islands by sub-

The nene, or Hawaiian goose (*Branta sandwicensis*), lives on Hawaii and was once on Maui also. It has recently been rescued from near extinction (from a color photograph by Eugene Kridler, Bureau of Sport Fisheries and Wildlife).

The koloa, or Hawaiian duck (*Anas wyvilliana wyvilliana*), is a close relative of the mallard, found on all of the major islands of the chain (from a color photograph by Eugene Kridler, Bureau of Sport Fisheries and Wildlife).

Pennula sandwichensis, called moho by the Hawaiians, is a flightless rail which became extinct early in the history of exploration of the Islands.

The Hawaiian coot, or Alae keokeo (*Fulica alai*), can be found in ponds in low-lands of all of the major Hawaiian Islands. This is also true of the aeo or Hawaiian stilt, *Himantopus knudseni*, at right (from color photographs by Eugene Kridler, Bureau of Sport Fisheries and Wildlife).

species distinct from mainland populations: the Hawaiian coot *Fulica americana sandwichensis* and the Hawaiian gallinule *Gallinula chloropus sandwichensis*.

Likewise, the Hawaiian stilt, *Himantopus himantopus knudseni*, is only slightly different from mainland stilts. One native Hawaiian bird cannot be distinguished from mainland populations even as a subspecies: the night heron (*Nycticorax nycticorax hoactli*).

Shore Birds and Marine Birds

Shore birds which are regular visitors to the Islands include the Pacific golden plover (kolea), bristle-thighed curlew (kioea), wandering tattler (uli-uli), ruddy turnstone (akekeke) and sanderling (hunakai). These birds, which undoubtedly have been important in dispersal of plants and animals to the Hawaiian Islands, are mentioned in Chapter 3.

Marine birds once nested much more widely on the main islands than they do now. When we think of dispersal possibilities of plants due to marine birds, we tend to forget this. Colonies of marine birds, however, may still be seen along some protected or remote shores of the main islands, and on some

The sooty-rumped petrel, or uau (*Pterodroma phaeopygia*), is a marine bird which nests high in mountains, as here in the crater of Haleakala (from a color photograph by James W. Larson, National Park Service).

of the islets which lie near the main islands. Marine birds are still abundant, however, on the Leeward Islands. Consequently, marine birds are illustrated and discussed in Chapters 20 through 27.

In some cases, however, marine birds on the main islands nest well inland. A very good example of this is the sooty-rumped petrel, or uau (*Pterodroma phaeopygia*). This bird nests in deep, crevice-like burrows high in the mountains, such as in the crater of Haleakala. Each day this petrel flies miles out to sea for feeding, returns at dusk. Other marine birds which come inland include tropic birds. These can be seen, for example, soaring in the Kalalau Valley, Kauai. Instances like these show that marine birds can come into contact with inland vegetation, even wet forest vegetation (on cliffs), and thus might disperse plants other than coastal ones.

Chapter 12   *THE LOBELIOIDS*

GARDENERS familiar with lobelias as small but colorful flowers would perhaps never guess how in Hawaii the group to which lobelias belong have unfolded into so unexpected an array of forms, sizes, and colors. These stem from several introductions (at least four) of members of the subfamily Lobelioideae of the family Campanulaceae. Lobelioids, as we can call this group, apparently have reached the Islands easily on account of their small seeds.

Fleshy fruited lobelioids are rare in most parts of the world, but are common in the Islands. *Delissea, Cyanea, Rollandia,* and *Clermontia* are fleshy fruited lobelioids endemic to the Hawaiian Islands and they could have stemmed from a single original introduction—probably from the Andes, where fleshy fruited lobelioids (*Centropogon, Burmeistera*) are well represented.

Delissea

Delissea is a specialized genus, but it may represent some of the features of the immigrants: its large seeds and many-flowered inflorescences suggest this. Also, it characteristically grows—or grew—in dry forest, which appears to have been the site of original colonization for many Hawaiian plants. Most delisseas are rather low plants, but one, *D. undulata,* has attained a curious form, rather like a lettuce plant atop a fishing pole. By this means, the plant can reach up to the light in the shady koa forests of Hawaii, where it grows. The flowers are white, striped green, and fruits are purple-black when mature. *Delissea* can always be identified by two features, the significance of which has not been explained: its large (for lobelioids) wrinkled seeds, and the presence of odd pimple-like projections on the flower.

Delissea undulata may be the last of perhaps seven or eight delisseas which once grew on the Islands. *Delissea undulata* was very nearly extinct when I saw it in 1966, when twenty-three plants were counted in the one cinder cone where it was known to have survived. At that time, one could see plants only recently demolished by cattle or pigs. Most of the remaining plants were fenced off in 1967, and this curious plant may have been saved. The other delisseas, however, may well be entirely gone now.

Cyanea resembles *Delissea* closely, but it is much more common, much more diversified, and is a wet forest group of plants. We can only guess what

Delissea undulata is one of the most curious—and also one of the rarest—of the Hawaiian lobelioids. Its flowers are greenish white, berries are deep purple (Hualalai, Hawaii).

In shady places in wet ohia forest one can find *Cyanea pilosa*. It is relatively inconspicuous in size (less than three feet tall) with small white flowers, small orange fruits (Kulani, Hawaii).

some of the delisseas may have looked like, but many stages in the evolution of *Cyanea* still exist. The gigantic cyaneas seem to be specializations; the primitive cyaneas probably were relatively small. Smallest of the contemporary species is *C. pilosa,* a plant with a stem no more than pencil-thick. Its flowers are white, small and inconspicuous. *Cyanea pilosa,* like *Delissea,* has flowers borne on short lateral shoots, and thus flowering never interferes with upward growth. All cyaneas are built on this plan, so they strongly tend to form rosette plants which grow upward with little or no branching. In general, the taller the stem of a rosette plant, the larger the leaves. There is no obvious feature that limits the tallness of rosette plants, but if a plant is taller and has larger leaves, there is a sort of limit to the size which leaves can attain unless they are "reinforced" in some way to prevent ripping in windy situations. Lobelioids are apparently unable to form tough, leathery leaves; consequently, a limit on leaf size does appear to be operative. The larger-leaved lobelioids appear to inhabit calm, nonwindy localities. Likewise, lobelioids all have very soft wood, so that there is undoubtedly a limit to how tall a rosette tree in this plant family can be.

The increase in size in cyaneas can be represented by *Cyanea acuminata* of Oahu, a species not much larger than *C. pilosa,* and by *C. recta* of Kauai. *Cyanea recta* can become about eight feet tall, although it can flower when it is a small plant that looks much like *C. pilosa. Cyanea recta* departs from the single-stemmed habit, and bears a series of branches each tipped by a rosette of leaves, as it becomes older. The flowers of *Cyanea recta* are unusually attractive—creamy white with a deep purple stripe down the center of each

Cyanea acuminata (left) is larger than *C. pilosa,* but probably closely related (Puna-luu, Oahu). *Cyanea recta,* right, is shown here as a small plant, but it can become a small branched "tree" about eight feet tall (Kokee, Kauai).

corolla lobe (petal). *Cyanea gayana* is probably closely related to *C. recta*, but has larger, smooth leaves and does not tend to branch.

Cyanea marksii is a curious recently discovered species which apparently never reaches what one would call an "adult" condition. Seedlings in a number of the cyaneas begin as very prickly plants, but lose these prickles when they reach adulthood. *Cyanea tritomantha*, discussed below, is a good example of this change. *Cyanea marksii* never loses these prickles, and perhaps this species is thereby permanently juvenile. Even though juvenile, it can flower, of course. Flowers are deep purple in color, and fruits are not prickly.

Cyanea atra is another species with deep purple flowers. Plants can be eight feet tall, and the rosettes of large, crinkly leaves shadow large clusters of flowers in the summer months. The flowers are deep purple outside, white inside, and the leaves are not prickly, but rough with hairs which are like microscopic versions of prickles.

The tendency for cyaneas to grow in very wet, shady locations is shown by *C. solenocalyx*, a vanishing Molokai species. The leaves of seedlings are thin, wavy in outline, and efficient under the very shady conditions in deep gulches. The calyx of the flower is tubular, rather than formed of separate sepals. This tubular calyx might be thought to shelter flower parts from the rains, and prevent them from rotting, although sometimes it appears to have the opposite effect, collecting water which causes the flower to decay. Flowers are purple-striped and would be conspicuous, except for the fact that they are small and thus hard to see unless one looks carefully.

Wet shady gulches are also the habitat for *Cyanea aculeatiflora*, a species

Cyanea gayana is a large-leaved lobelioid related to *C. recta*. Its flowers are white, striped red-purple (Mt. Kahili, Kauai).

Sparsely branched, to about five feet in height, *Cyanea marksii* has very spiny leaves and stems, purple flowers, and nonspiny orange fruits (Honaunau, Hawaii).

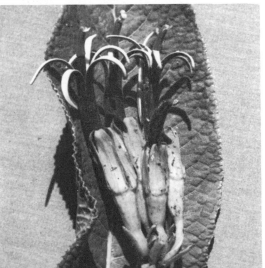

Cyanea atra grows at the margins of the Puu Kukui Bog of West Maui. Its flowers are deep purple outside, white within.

with long leaves and stems six feet or more in height. This plant grows along streams on eastern Maui, streams and gulches where the famous giant-leaved apeape (*Gunnera*) grows. Flowers of *Cyanea aculeatiflora* are purple, and encrusted with prickles or minute teeth. This is surprising, because the remainder of the plant is only sparsely prickly. Why this species, unlike all other cyaneas, should have such bizarre flowers is not at all clear. In the same region, interestingly, there is another lobelioid with warty flowers (*Clermontia tuberculata*).

Cyanea tritomantha, known to the Hawaiians as aku, is a magnificent palm-shaped lobelioid of the forests behind Hilo. Its long leaves—probably larger than those of any other lobelioid—are supposed to have been the source of a spinach-like vegetable for the Hawaiians. The flowers are white and slender. While looking for this species, I unexpectedly found some curious new facts about cyaneas. While hunting for *C. tritomantha*, I was also looking for other cyaneas supposed to grow in the same area. There they were—but also there were stages which connected them and the big palm-like individuals of *C. tritomantha*. *Cyanea noli-me-tangere* proves to be the prickly seedling stage of *C. tritomantha*; it can also occur as a shoot on an injured adult plant of *C. tritomantha*. Even though a seedling, it can form flowers. *Cyanea rollandioides* turns out to be a slightly older juvenile stage of *C. tritomantha*, with leaves not nearly as large as those of adults, but losing the prickly condition. I found the "*C. rollandioides*" stage growing in a cleared area only a few feet away from the deep forest where the adult *C. tritomantha* plants were found. *Cyanea submuricata* is a name that has been given to a seedling stage of *C. tritomantha*, and *Cyanea bryanii* is an older stage, near the adult condition. There may be other juvenile stages referable to *C. tritomantha* which remain to

Deep in shady gulches of Molokai is a very rare *Cyanea*, *C. solenocalyx*. Young plants have thin leaves, wavy in outline. Adult leaves are thicker, with nonwavy margins. Flowers are short and inconspicuous, almost hidden in the tubular calyces.

Cyanea aculeatiflora is restricted to a few gulches on East Maui, where it grows with the apeape (*Gunnera*). The flowers are densely covered with prickles.

One can find the palm-like mature individuals of *Cyanea tritomantha* only in undisturbed ohia forests of eastern Hawaii. Flowers are long and white (Olaa, Hawaii).

Different stages in the development of the aku, *Cyanea tritomantha*, have been called species. These probably include the following. Rosette trees were described as *Cyanea bryanii* (top left). Shorter plants in regrowth areas were called *C. rolland-ioides* (top right) or *C. platyphylla* (bottom left). Seedlings which bear spiny leaves and stems but are old enough to flower were called *C. noli-me-tangere* (bottom right) (all from the same area, Olaa Forest, Hawaii).

be "exposed" for what they are. Possibly *C. fernaldii* and *C. platyphylla* are stages of *C. tritomantha*. In a similar way, other juvenile plants remain to be identified with adult species. For example, the variety *horrida* of *Cyanea ferox* is such a developmental stage, and in turn these might be seedling stages of *Cyanea hamatiflora,* for example. Botanists have not always seen plants in the field when they named them, and they probably had no idea that juvenile stages could look so different from the adults. The spiny nature of seedlings in some cyaneas, as opposed to hairy but not spiny adult plants, is interesting. One can say that the prickles on seedlings are of value for deterring animals—

Cyanea grimesiana grows in deep shady locations like those favored by tree ferns. Its growth form and leaves mimic those of a fern (Waianae Mountains, Oahu).

These individuals of *Cyanea asplenifolia* were photographed in shady gulches of West Maui by Joseph F. Rock (courtesy of Bishop Museum).

but which animals? The only ones concerned would be land snails, or possibly some insects. The very succulent tissues of the lobelioids would certainly be exceptionally inviting compared to the hard tissues of most Hawaiian plants, and these prickles, which represent exaggerated hairs, might be successful in warding off snails or insects.

The adaptation of lobelioids to shady habitats has featured a mimicry of ferns. *Cyanea grimesiana*, which grows deep in gulches of Oahu and Maui, has long pinnate leaves. Flowers are white, with purple streaks within. Fern-like leaves are clearly shown in a related species, *Cyanea asplenifolia* from Maui. In a recently discovered *Cyanea* from Hawaii, however, this fern mimicry reaches its ultimate conclusion. *Cyanea shipmanii* grows in gulches at six thousand feet on the slopes of Mauna Kea above Hilo. The forest here is tall and shady, so that highly dissected leaves are appropriate. The leaves are not merely pinnate; each leaflet is further dissected. The significance of fern-like leaf form in *C. shipmanii* and other species is that leaf tissue is "spread thin"—

Discovered only recently in gulches at six thousand feet on Mauna Kea is this exceptional *Cyanea, C. shipmanii,* which has finely dissected fern-like leaves.

Cyanea fauriei is a woody fountain-shaped tree from Kauai. It is related to *C. angustifolia* from Oahu.

displayed over a wider area, so that the efficiency at picking up light is greater. Plants which have juvenile leaves broader (often wavy in outline) and thinner than those of the adult are also illustrating this principle, and this can be seen in cyaneas such as *C. solenocalyx* and *C. leptostegia*.

Although all cyaneas can be described as inhabitants of the wet forest, and could even be said almost to define wet forests, some do grow at lower margins of the wet forest, where both koas and ohias are dominant trees. A series of very closely related species (which may be merged) grows here: *Cyanea fauriei, C. angustifolia, C. coriacea,* and *C. hardyi.* These are conspicuous by their growth form—rosette shrubs branched from near the base, each branch bearing a rosette of leaves at its tip. In the mountains behind Honolulu, *Cyanea angustifolia* attracts one's attention by its large pendant clusters of curved pinkish white flowers and red-purple fruits.

Truly fantastic among the cyaneas are those species which are extremely tall and palm-like. These species (*C. arborea, C. superba, C. giffardii, C. regina, C. carlsonii, C. leptostegia*) are now very rare or extinct. One which can be seen easily is *C. leptostegia* of Kauai. Plants of *C. leptostegia* never branch, unless because of injury, and even then eventually only one of the shoots survives. The narrow stem progresses rapidly to higher levels of the forest, then grows

Cyanea angustifolia grows in moderately wet forest, and is the *Cyanea* most easily seen on Oahu. It is recognizable by its rosettes of narrow leaves and its pendant inflorescences bearing pale pink or white flowers and purple berries (Waahila Ridge, Oahu).

Cyanea leptostegia (see also opposite page) is one of the great wonders of the Hawaiian flora; it represents an end product in evolution of tall, palm-like trees from small herbs. Seedlings in shady forest locations have leaves sinuous in outline. For flowers, see color plates (Kokee, Kauai).

Cyanea arborea is a giant palmiform lobelioid, now extinct, which grew in moderately dry forests near Ulupalakua, East Maui (photograph by Joseph F. Rock, courtesy of Bishop Museum).

more slowly. Seedling leaves are conspicuously lobed, whereas leaves of the adult plant are long and strap-shaped. Dense clusters of long pink flowers with narrow, spidery sepals are almost hidden beneath the leaf rosette. Fruits are dull violet, and are really hollow and pithy rather than solid and fleshy, as most *Cyanea* fruits are.

Rollandia

Rollandia is a genus very close to *Cyanea*, differing in little more than the fact that in *Rollandia*, stamens are adherent to the floral tube (corolla). Only a single collection of a *Rollandia* (*R. parviflora* from Kauai) was ever made on an island other than Oahu. *Rollandia*, then, is an exercise in adaptive radiation, starting from *Cyanea*-like ancestors, which has taken place on a single island. *Rollandia humboldtiana* is a succulent plant with long stems in wet muddy places, often deep gulches. Its long pendant inflorescences of white flowers are distinctive. *Rollandia angustifolia* grows in almost the same places, but usually on ridges where its rosettes of narrow, glossy leaves reach above or to the same level as shrubs. The leaves are much better adapted to this habitat than those of *R. humboldtiana*, which would probably wilt if similarly exposed. Do these leaf correlations hold true for other rollandias as well? Apparently so. *Rollandia lanceolata*, a rosette tree of the lower wet (or upper dry) forest, has rather wide but markedly hairy leaves. The width of the leaves seems related to shady locations—it grows upward into the koa branches, but does not exceed them in height, does not emerge into open sunshine. Hairier leaves

Seen in shady gulches, *Rollandia humboldtiana* grows in the upper Koolau Mountains behind Honolulu. This species is easily identified because of its long pendant infloresences bearing white flowers (Wiliwilinui Ridge, Oahu).

Rollandia angustifolia can be seen on trails behind Honolulu; its narrow leaves adapt it to sunny places in the rain forest; its flowers are streaked deep purple (Moanalua Trail).

Rollandia lanceolata is a slender rosette tree from koa forest levels of the Koolau Mountains of Oahu.

Rollandia calycina, a species of the wet Koolau Mountain forests, is distinctive because of its rose flowers and wavy-margined leaves.

Deep in gulches of the Waianae Mountains grows *Rollandia pinnatifida.* Young plants bear toothed juvenile leaves for many years, and can flower, while adult plants have nontoothed leaves. These different stages have been described under various names.

often seem adaptations to drier conditions, and this may be true in R. *lanceolata.*

Rollandia pinnatifida is an interesting species from the Waianae Mountains; it also shows correlation between habitat and plant form. A small rosette tree, it grows in deep shady gulches. Younger plants have oddly toothed leaves. These are juvenile leaves but the plant can flower in this juvenile condition. Such leaves, like the juvenile leaves of some of the cyaneas, seem adapted to extreme shade. Adult plants have nontoothed leaves. The occurrence of both

High on the summit ridge of the Koolau Mountains one can find the low, succulent white-flowered plants or *Rollandia st.-johnii,* a distinctive product of adaptive radiation in *Rollandia.*

juvenile and adult leaves, as with the cyaneas, results in confused classification. Juvenile-leaved plants were originally named *Lobelia pinnatifida* in 1833, then *Rollandia pinnatifida* in 1834. That correct name was incorrectly exchanged for *Delissea pinnatifida* in 1836, and *Cyanea pinnatifida* in 1943; the plant was even recently named *Cyanea selachicauda.* Plants with adult leaves were named *Rollandia kaalae* in 1873. Such confusions have occurred largely because lack of field studies permitted authors to think that the juvenile and adult stages are unrelated. The name *Rollandia pinnatifida,* although correct, has not been used since 1834!

No such confusion exists in the case of *Rollandia st.-johnii,* a recently discovered species from the crest of the Koolau Mountains. This *Rollandia* is probably related to *R. angustifolia,* but represents an extreme adaptation to windy, wet ridges. The stems are short, so that the plant does not emerge above the low, windswept vegetation. Leaves, too, are adapted to constant winds: they are curled, and protected by a shiny surface. Flowers are white and succulent.

Rollandias also show diversification with respect to flower color: white to pink or violet, even deep purple.

Clermontia

Contrary to *Cyanea,* clermontias are almost uniform in growth form; they are shrubs, usually between four and twelve feet in height. Branches are few, and the narrow leaves, five to twelve inches long, are glossy and clustered at the ends of the branches. Clermontias are easily recognizable—and were recognized as a group by the Hawaiians, who gave them the name oha kepau.

The diversification in *Clermontia* is in the flowers. Although usually borne in pairs, unlike those of *Cyanea*, *Clermontia* flowers show a gamut from small (one inch or less), as in *C. parviflora* and *C. micrantha*, to large (six inches) in *C. lindseyana*, *C. hawaiiensis*, and *C. drepanomorpha*. Some dangle on long flower stalks (*C. grandiflora*, *C. leptoclada*, *C. drepanomorpha*). Some are markedly curved, some nearly straight; some have markedly ribbed flowers (*C. hawaiiensis*), some have very succulent petals (*C. arborescens*), some flowers are hairy (*C. lindseyana*). Some clermontias have flowers with very short sepals (*C. arborescens*, *C. clermontioides*, *C. peleana*), but most have sepals which are the same length and color as the petals, making the flower look double. One can find both conditions within a species, however, as in *C. caerulea* (Chapter 4). The main variables are those of flower color. *Clermontia* flowers can be white (*C. persicaefolia*, *C. parviflora*), green (*C. kakeana*, *C. oblongifolia*), rose-violet (*C. micrantha*), violet (*C. montis-loa*), purple-streaked (*C. pallida*), or even deep purple-black (*C. kohalae*, *C. drepanomorpha*, *C. peleana*). Some species have a range in color. Specimens of *Clermontia grandiflora* from the Puu Kukui forests, Maui, have green flowers, but those at the margins of the Puu Kukui Bog have rose-purple flowers.

Although wet forest plants, clermontias tend to occupy clearings or open places in a wet forest. Cyaneas rarely occur in disturbed places of that nature. The pioneering characteristics of clermontias make them successful as epiphytes. In wet forests, one can often see a few *Clermontia* shrubs which have taken

Fringing the high bogs of Puu Kukui, West Maui, are the small shrubs of *Clermontia micrantha*, which have diminutive rosy or purplish flowers.

Clermontia lindseyana, shown here with its discoverer John Lindsey, has notably larger bright green flowers (Mauna Kea, Hawaii).

In the Kohala Mountains, one can find a *Clermontia* with deep purple flowers, *C. kohalae* (Kalae, lower Kehena Trail).

These two species of *Clermontia* have flowers borne on long, pendant flower stalks (peduncles). *Clermontia drepanomorpha*, left, has purple-black flowers and is found in the Alakahi Swamp region of the Kohala Mountains. *Clermontia grandiflora*, right, has greenish flowers and occurs in wet forests of Maui.

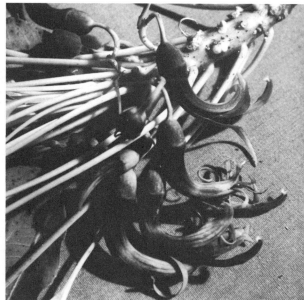

Two clermontias apparently closely related are *C. kakeana*, left, from Oahu and Maui, and *C. pallida*, right, from Molokai. Flowers of *C. kakeana* are light green, while those of *C. pallida* are dull purple.

Along ridges behind Honolulu one can find the low shrubs of *Clermontia persicaefolia,* a white-flowered species.

Clermontia parviflora, a species with small white or purplish flowers, often grows upon branches or trunks of trees and thereby qualifies as an epiphyte. In the ohia tree shown here, two plants have taken root: *Clermontia parviflora* is at left, a *Cheirodendron* at right (Kehena, Hawaii).

Clermontia clermontioides, the only *Clermontia* on Kauai, can grow on the ground, as near Wahiawa Bog. It can also grow—and does so more commonly— as an epiphyte; the shrub shown at right is growing on an ohia tree near Mt. Kahili. Flowers of *Clermontia clermontioides* are pale green.

Clermontia peleana grows only on trees. The only major trees in the area near Hilo where it grows are ohia (*Metrosideros*) trees. The flowers are curved, deep purple.

THE COAST

The white-fruited naupaka kai, *Scaevola taccada,* grows on the Puna District's 1955 lava flow.

THE DRY FOREST

Scrubby vegetation covers the dry, colorful shapes of Waimea Canyon, Kauai.

The lama *(Diospyros ferrea sandwicensis)* forms an open forest, with Mauna Kea in the background.

The wiliwili *(Erythrina sandwicensis)* at Puuwaawaa, Hawaii.

The ohia lehua tree *(Metrosideros)* dominates the wet forest, whether as scraggly trees overlooking Kalalau Valley, Kauai, or as trees covered with bright red flowers at Kilauea. Ohia lehua is phenomenal in its variability: in some places, no two trees are alike.

Puu Kukui (West Maui) has an open bog.

Sedge tussocks (*Oreobolus furcatus*) in the Puu Kukui bog.

The ohelo (*Vaccinium dentatum*).

244 D

Juvenile red-footed boobies at the summit of Necker Island

Egg, chick, and juvenile of the common noddy tern, Necker Island

Fairy tern, Necker Island

Fairy tern in flight, Gardner Pinnacles

Juvenile frigate birds, Necker Island

Blue-faced booby and chick, Gardner
Pinnacles

"South North Island,"
Pearl and Hermes Reef,
covered by mats of the
puncture vine (*Tribulus
cistoides*).

Red-tailed tropic bird, Southeast
Island, Pearl and Hermes Reef.

Sea turtle, Southeast Island, Pearl
and Hermes Reef.

Seal sleeping in lagoon,
Southeast Island, Pearl
and Hermes Reef.

Seal sleeping on shore, Southeast
Island, Pearl and Hermes Reef.

Mother seal and cub, East Island,
French Frigate Shoal.

244 H

root in crotches of trees, or even clinging to bark of ohia trees. *Clermontia parviflora* is almost invariably an epiphyte in the Kohala Mountains, Hawaii, while *Clermontia clermontioides* is usually seen epiphytically in Kauai's rain forests. *Clermontia peleana* has never been found on the ground at all.

One *Clermontia*, now extinct, was the most distinctive in the genus: *C. haleakalensis*, last seen in Puu Nianiau Crater high on the side of Haleakala. Its few branches bore rosettes of large leaves, and the inflorescences had not two, but many flowers each. Some of its floral and fruit details suggested *Delissea*, and it may have been an old relict which could tell us—or could have told us—about the origins of *Clermontia* from related lobelioids.

Lobelia

Oha, or ohawai, is the Hawaiian name for *Lobelia*. The name oha, as in oha kepau (*Clermontia*), suggests that the Hawaiians recognized the similarity between *Clermontia* and *Lobelia*. Unlike the other Hawaiian lobelioids, the genus *Lobelia* occurs elsewhere—it is almost world-wide in its distribution, in fact. Lobelias are typically plants of wet places, and this proves true in the Islands, too. Some lobelias grow only in bogs or equally wet places. *Lobelia gaudichaudii* stands out because of its large leaf rosettes, topped in season by

Lobelia gaudichaudii forms large rosettes in Hawaiian bogs: here is an individual from Wahiawa Bog, where the *Lobelia* population has been called *L. kauaensis*, or *L. gaudichaudii* var. *kauaensis*. The *L. gaudichaudii* flowers shown are from Puu Kukui, Maui, where the plants have been called *L. gaudichaudii* var. *gloria-montis*.

On wet cliffs of Kauai, one can find a smaller species of *Lobelia* with scraggly stems and red-purple flowers, *L. tortuosa*.

Lobelia hypoleuca, a blue-flowered species, grows on Mt. Kaala, Oahu. The lower sides of leaves are covered with a white wool.

gigantic flower stalks; after fruiting, the plant dies. This plant may be seen in the high bogs of Kauai, Maui, and Molokai, and near-boggy areas of Oahu.

Lobelia hypoleuca is a representative of a second group of close species (*L. oahuensis, L. yuccoides, L. neriifolia, L. hillebrandii*) which do not have tall stems, have variously white woolly narrow leaves and blue flowers with petals which curl back tightly. These are wet forest plants and often grow in the shade of trees. Closely related to this group of species is *Lobelia tortuosa*, a magenta-flowered species with smooth green leaves which can be seen on dripping cliffs on Kauai. The two groups of *Lobelia* species mentioned above may represent two colonizations on the Islands.

Trematolobelia

Probably another early colonization by some group in the genus *Lobelia,* or some plant very closely related to *Lobelia,* produced the odd Hawaiian genus *Trematolobelia.* This genus has only one species, but several varieties. Commonly encountered in the wettest forests on all the major islands, *Trematolobelia* is a rosette of wavy leaves atop a pole-like stem; it never branches. As in

Trematolobelia macrostachys bears a single rosette of leaves, and ultimately flowers (see color plates). The fruits look as though they ought to become berries, but the fleshy parts fall away to reveal a porous woody shaker which disperses seeds (Punaluu, Oahu; Moanalua, Oahu; Kokee, Kauai).

Lobelia, flowering and fruiting terminates the life of each individual. The flowers are usually borne on a circle of inflorescence branches, although only a single inflorescence stalk may be present. Flowers are pink or rose-purple. When fruits are formed, they appear fleshy, like those of a *Clermontia* or *Cyanea.* In fact, when fruits are ripe, the fleshy parts break down, rot, and are washed away in the rains which occur almost daily in the regions where *Trematolobelia* grows. Revealed and exposed by the breakdown is a woody skeleton, a spherical structure with holes in it. Inside this is a pair of papery sacs which contain the seeds. The sacs are rainproof, prevent seeds from being wet. On dry days, however, the sacs open, and seeds shake into the woody skeleton, then out through the holes. Thus, a device has been evolved which permits· seeds to be released only during the dry, windy weather which will carry seeds to new localities. On rainy days, the seeds are kept dry and do not rot. This odd fruit was not understood properly until recently. A noted botanist at Kew once even claimed that the holes in the woody skeleton of the fruit are not normal, but are the product of insect boring. This shaker type of fruit, unique among the world's lobelioids, has evolved entirely within the Hawaiian Islands.

Brighamia

Perhaps the strangest of all Hawaiian lobelioids is *Brighamia.* There is only one species, and it grows on steep cliffs of Kauai, Molokai, and (formerly) Niihau. *Brighamia* is perfectly adapted for this mode of life. A single rosette of leaves tops the thick, succulent stem. Roots penetrate cliffs horizontally, and the base of the plant is often rounded, permitting the plant to rock slightly in the wind. The leaf rosette can consist of large or small leaves, depending on the amount of moisture available during various parts of the year. Water stored in the succulent stem assists the plant during periods of dry days or weeks, and offsets the drying effect of an almost constant breeze from the trade winds. At rare intervals, long white flowers are formed just below the leaf rosette. *Brighamia* is strange even when viewed in relation to its supposed relatives: *Isotoma,* from Australia and nearby regions, is claimed to be related; it is only an ordinary herb. Perhaps *Brighamia* is not even related to *Isotoma*—with such strong modifications as it possesses, its relationships are not easy to uncover. Apparently the Hawaiians were much intrigued by *Brighamia,* for they had at least three names for it: puaala, aluli, and ohaha.

Brighamia represents a unique product of evolution, an adaptation to cliff faces. *Trematolobelia* is a unique development also, but one answering a problem of seed dispersal. *Clermontia* has diversified with respect to flower form and color—a development which only events of isolation within the archipelago seem to explain. The nectar-feeding birds in the Islands—several of the honeycreepers and the five species of honeyeaters—represent only a few kinds, a few

Brighamia insignis is one of the strangest of Hawaiian plants. Its tapered succulent stems, · bearing rosettes of leaves, can be seen only on a few virtually inaccessible cliffs (Kauai).

populations of birds compared with the wealth of floral form and color in *Clermontia* (and, for that matter, *Rollandia* and *Cyanea*). If *Clermontia* has evolved so as to attract nectar-feeding birds, why are there so many kinds of *Clermontia* flowers, so few kinds of birds? This is an unanswered question. In any case, the fleshy fruited lobelioids of the Hawaiian Islands are interesting in that each of the genera shows distinctive radiation within it, each of the genera with different emphases. Even within the genera, one can see more than one cycle of radiation. The Hawaiian lobelioids, of course, stem from more than one introduction. But the most amazing example of adaptive radiation—because it stems from a single colonization, and shows a maximum of diversification—is the one in the next chapter.

Chapter 13   *THE SILVERSWORDS AND THEIR RELATIVES*

THE TARWEEDS of California look like poor candidates to be ancestors of the Hawaiian silverswords. The tarweeds are mostly small plants, mostly annuals. None of the silverswords or their relatives are annuals, and the smallest is comparable in size only with the largest of the tarweeds. However, the ancestors of the silverswords need not be picked from today's Californian tarweeds. Indeed, at the same time that this group has evolved peculiar forms in the Hawaiian Islands, it has evolved to suit the California scene, and thereby has formed many annuals there. However, there are still left on the California coast a few tarweeds which hint what tarweeds once looked like, and thereby what sorts of plants were ancestral to the Hawaiian genera *Argyroxiphium* (silverswords), *Dubautia* (including *Railliardia*), and *Wilkesia*. The shrubby hemizonias of California, illustrated in the book *Island Life*, and *Adenothamnus*, a plant found in Baja California just south of the California border, probably represent the appearance of the early Hawaiian colonists. These tarweeds are perennial, narrow-leaved, somewhat sprawling plants, woody at the base, but not quite deserving the title "shrub." They bear clusters of yellow flowers.

Dubautia

These features are not matched by the silverswords, certainly, but they are simulated remarkably well by a few of the dubautias, such as the kupaoas *D. scabra* and *D. linearis*. These live in dry areas of the Islands not unlike the coastal areas of California and adjacent Mexico in climate. Studies of the anatomy of both Hawaiian and Californian tarweeds show even more decisively the relationship. Presuming that the ancestors of the Hawaiian group were as indicated, we can outline a story of adaptive radiation which is probably the most spectacular example of this process in either plants or animals of the Hawaiian chain.

The kupaoas, such as *Dubautia scabra* and *D. linearis*, are plants well suited to lava flows and dry, scrubby hillsides. The narrow leaves present enough leaf surface for efficient utilization of sunshine in these open locations, yet minimize water loss from the plant. The small size of the plants—they are really too small to be called shrubs—correlates well with the dryness of the habitats where

Dubautia linearis grows on dry, barren lava fields or dry scrubby areas of Maui and Lanai.

On recent lava flows of Hawaii, one can find plants of *Dubautia scabra,* the kupaoa.

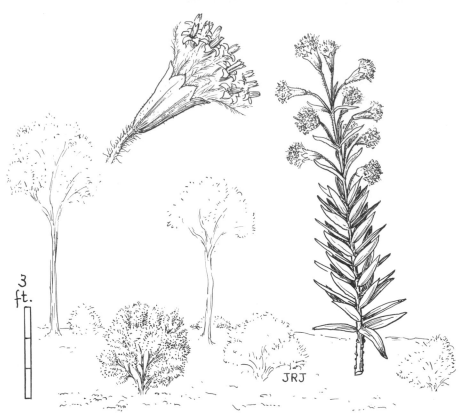

Dubautia ciliolata is a shrub of recent lava in Kilauea and other localities on Hawaii. Its crisp, stiff leaves are arranged in threes.

The naenae, *Dubautia menziesii,* is related to D. *ciliolata* but has larger, thicker leaves. It grows in alpine regions of Haleakala.

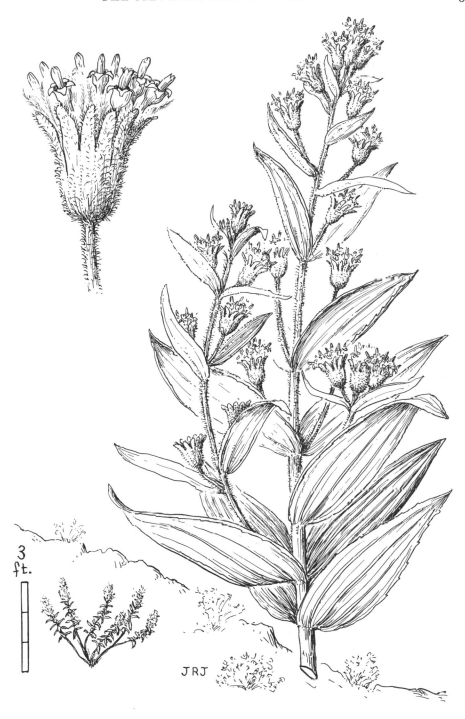

3
ft.

JRJ

Dubautia platyphylla grows in alpine regions of Haleakala, but favors less exposed areas, prefers zones brushed by moist clouds.

they grow. These low, mat-like species have white flowers mostly, unlike the yellow flowers of most *Dubautia* species and of the California tarweeds.

If the ancestors of *Dubautia* were adapted to relatively dry habitats, this group should have been able to evolve easily into most dry habitats. It should come as no surprise, therefore, that dubautias are well represented in the dry alpine regions of the Islands. On Hawaii one can see *Dubautia ciliolata* at Kilauea, Hualalai, Mauna Loa, and Mauna Kea. Its leaves are small, tough, wedge-shaped, borne in alternating groups of three. Shrubs of *D. ciliolata* have a spiky, almost crystalline appearance, although topped by graceful sprays of yellow-flowered heads. A related species on Haleakala, *Dubautia menziesii*, has broader leaves, but they are, in fact, highly succulent and relatively few in number, so that the plant can withstand dry alpine air and brilliant sunshine.

Ranging from low alpine zone into dry forest on Haleakala, *Dubautia reticulata* can be a shrub or tree up to twenty-five feet tall.

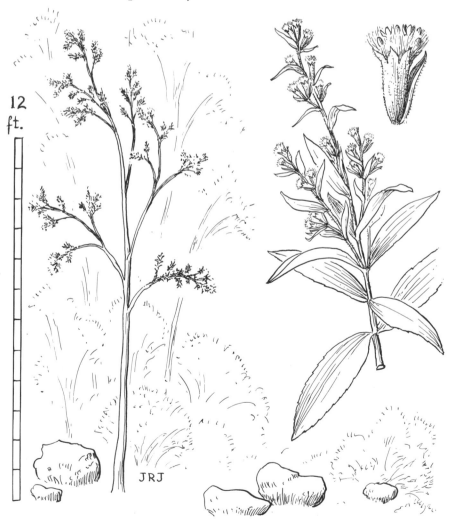

Dubautia platyphylla also grows on Haleakala, but not in the mercilessly exposed sites where *D. menziesii* thrives. Locations favored by *D. platyphylla* are those often bathed by clouds in the afternoon and at night. The broader leaves of *D. platyphylla* suggest a relationship with conditions of at least intermittent cloudiness.

Dubautia reticulata also grows on Haleakala, but in areas of dry forest. Its

Scrambling on cliffs in the Waianae Mountains, Oahu, is *Dubautia sherffiana,* a species notable for having so few flowers in each head.

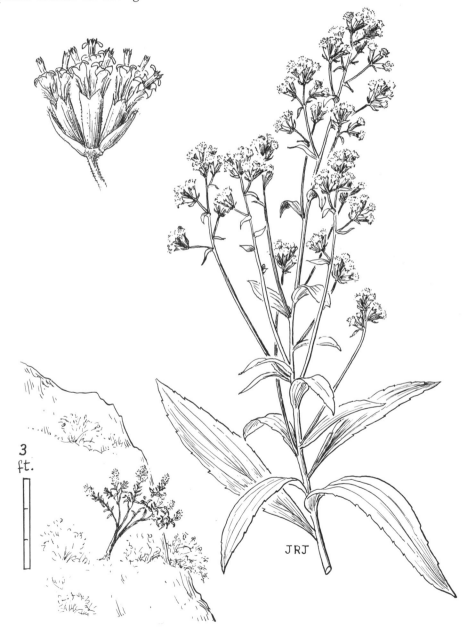

3
ft.

JRJ

The shrubby *Dubautia* common in forest areas of Oahu is *D. plantaginea*. It generally forms a rounded shrub in somewhat open or disturbed areas.

On high, cloudy summits or windy ridges in wet forest is *Dubautia laxa,* a shrubby species with broad leaves and orange to brown flowers.

leaves resemble those of the common dry forest tree, *Acacia koa,* in general size and shape. Although mostly shrubby, *D. reticulata* can gradually attain tree-hood by continued growth. Similarly shaped leaves characterize a rare species from shady but intermediate dry cliffs of the Waianae Mountains, *D. sherffiana.* This species, corresponding to its steep habitat, does not become a tree, but remains a shrub which scrambles through the scrubby vegetation of these slopes. Its leaves are thin, and wilt much more easily than do those of dubautias from exposed locations.

The naenae or *Dubautia* most easily seen in Oahu forests is *D. plantaginea.* Its leaves are moderately narrow, but long, so that each leaf has a considerable area. Leaves are smooth, unprotected by hairs, and would be unsuited for dry forest; they clearly suggest a moderately wet habitat. *Dubautia plantaginea* does grow in areas of about one hundred inches of rainfall per year, but it reveals its derivation from plants of open habitats: it favors sunny ridgetops, cliffs, or somewhat disturbed places. The inflorescence, composed of yellow-orange flowers, is notably large.

Deep in the forests of upper Kauai one can find a tree naenae perfectly adapted to rain forest conditions: *Dubautia knudsenii.*

Probably extinct now is the vining *Dubautia latifolia*, or koholapehu of the Kokee region of Kauai. Both its broad leaves and its vining habit are unique in the genus *Dubautia*.

Adaptation to wet forests can easily be seen in *Dubautia laxa*. The leaves are markedly broader, indicating a link to wet conditions. However, *D. laxa* forms a low, rounded shrub. It is adapted to ridges which are perpetually bathed by clouds, or at least shaded by them. The low stature of *D. laxa* is related to the windy conditions it experiences, since a low, rather flat vegetation is typical of windy (but moist) localities. The summit ridge of the Koolau Mountains is an example of such a location.

If broad leaves are an indication of adaptation to rain forest, *Dubautia knudsenii* ought to grow in wet places. It does. The leaves are smooth, lack hairs, wilt easily. Unlike *D. laxa, D. knudsenii* is a tree. It should be, for the Kauai forests where it grows are tall, protected from the wind. Even the heads of flowers suggest a wet habitat: instead of pointing upward, they are pendant, preventing the flowers from being filled with water during a shower.

Dubautia railliardioides is a large-leaved shrub with a tendency to sprawl through the undergrowth of very wet forest areas on upper Kauai.

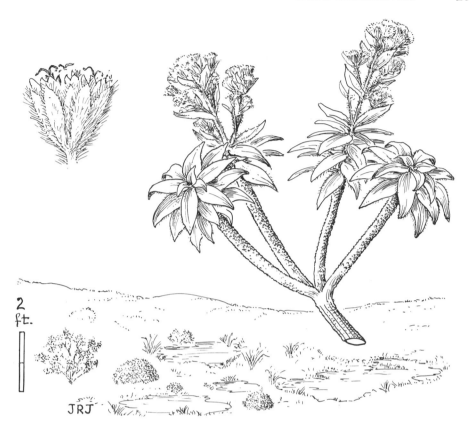

Occupying the wettest place in the Hawaiian Islands, Mt. Waialeale on Kauai, is *Dubautia waialoalae.*

Another broad-leaved *Dubautia* from the Kauai forests is—or was—*D. latifolia.* This remarkable species, not seen recently, was definitely a vine. The vining habit permitted it to reach to the high levels of the koa forest, at which brighter levels it produced masses of flower heads.

Dubautia railliardioides is another unexpected development in the genus. Basically a shrub, its branches are often long and tend to sprawl irregularly on the forest floor, so that it often appears more as a series of rosettes on the ground than a normal shrub.

Atop the high plateau of Kauai, at the almost perpetually rainy and misty summit of Waialeale is *Dubautia waialealae*, which represents a complete about-face from the dry habitats which would seem to have been the primary adaptation of the dubautias. The fact that a *Dubautia* has adapted to the exceptionally wet conditions of Waialeale's Bog shows that this group is in an active state of evolution, and capable of an exceptional degree of adaptation.

Silverswords

If the dubautias represent conquest of many different habitats by means of such features as alteration of habit and leaf form, the silverswords represent amazing adaptation to a few equally divergent habitats, adaptations more amazing the more we study them. The silverswords and greenswords (which collectively form the genus *Argyroxiphium*) and the iliau (*Wilkesia*) are closely related to *Dubautia*, and in fact a hybrid between a *Dubautia* species and an *Argyroxiphium* species has been found.

The Haleakala silversword can be found on cinder cones within the crater of Haleakala, but apparently it favors only certain of these cones. However, the silversword probably could and once did grow in many locations within the crater and around the rim. Haleakala National Park authorities fenced off a small area near the summit of the mountain and planted a few silverswords within this enclosure. In this enclosure, protected from goats, these silverswords not only grew well, they have reproduced abundantly. Probably before goats were introduced by Western man, silverswords dotted the entire summit area and many of the cinder cones within the crater.

The alpine areas of Haleakala where the silversword grows, between seven thousand and ten thousand feet elevation, provide severe problems for any plant, and only a few native Hawaiian plants can cope with this region. Hot during the day, especially in summer, the temperature can fall precipitously at night, often to below freezing in winter. Snowfalls occur during the winter

The Haleakala silversword stays in rosette stage for an unknown period of years before flowering. Seedlings have become increasingly common with protection of the cinder cones favored by this plant.

months. For most of the day, the humidity is virtually zero, and the extreme brilliance of the sunshine is punishing. Precipitation either as rain or snow at these elevations is relatively small, especially within the crater.

The Haleakala silversword can be viewed as a design for withstanding these various conditions. As a rosette plant, it is close to the ground, and its growing point is deeply seated in the rosette, thus avoiding damage from cold. The felt of silvery hairs on the leaves may also help in this regard, but more likely these protect against the excessive sunshine. These hairs are not only very numerous, and lie as a thick covering over the leaf, but they are flat or concave as seen in a section under the microscope. If they were convex in outline (as are most hairs), they might focus the light on the leaf, like lenses, instead of reflecting it. The reflecting quality of the hairs has caused the Hawaiians to name the silversword "ahinahina," the word for "gray" repeated twice, therefore "very gray." (Comparisons with metals and other shiny materials would be unexpected, of course, because the Polynesians did not have these when they came to the Islands.)

Resistance to dryness is achieved by the condensed leaf form. A narrow leaf is capable of absorbing plenty of sunshine under alpine conditions, and the smaller surface area prevents loss of water. The hairs act as a windbreak, preventing breezes from crossing the actual surface of the leaf. In addition to these mechanisms for minimizing water loss, the silversword has a unique mechanism, one otherwise found only in certain California tarweeds, for retaining moisture within the leaf. Cells in a leaf are ordinarily separated by large air spaces. In the silversword leaf these spaces have been filled with accumulations of a gelatinous substance. This gel is capable of absorbing large quantities of water and storing it during the intervals between rains. By breaking a leaf open and squeezing it, one can see these gelatinous accumulations. This stored water is presumably also important when the plant flowers, for the huge inflorescence is produced in a relatively short period of time, and requires large quantities of moisture.

Although the naenaes and kupaoas (*Dubautia*) do not die after flowering, the silversword does. It forms a massive inflorescence, sometimes six feet tall, covered with maroon-colored flowers borne in large heads. These heads are covered by sticky hairs, like those of the California tarweeds. The extraordinary floral display of the silversword (best seen in mid-July) does not last for more than about a month, and soon seeds are formed and the plant dies. The life span of a single plant may be five to fifteen years, although no determination has been made.

Until Haleakala National Park was created, the silversword was very close to extinction. Its chief enemy was goats, although humans also vandalized it. Goats have recently been thinned out in Haleakala, and one may expect the return of more numerous silversword plants. Similar factors apply to the silverswords on the island of Hawaii. These plants are very similar to those of Haleakala, although a little smaller, and belong to the same species (*Argyroxiphium sandwicense*). They once dotted the summit areas of Hualalai, Mauna

Kea, and Mauna Loa. They are all but extinct in these localities now, and no means for saving them has been initiated yet.

There are two other species of silversword, less famous because they grow in remote areas. One, in fact, was discovered only recently and was first named in 1957. This is the Kau silversword, *Argyroxiphium kauense,* which grows at about six thousand feet on the southwestern slope of Mauna Loa. This area looks quite different from Haleakala, and so it is. Although cool, it is almost constantly brushed by moist clouds, so that it is clear only in early morning hours. Although the area is covered by recent lava flows, the constant passage of mist brings considerable moisture, so that in effect the area is wetter than Haleakala. In fact, growing with the Kau silversword are tufts of a sedge, *Oreobolus furcatus,* that one expects to find only in Hawaiian bogs.

The Kau silversword is distinctive in having a short, woody stem on which the leaf rosette is raised. The leaves are much narrower and thinner than those of the Haleakala silversword. The flower heads are smaller, the flower color is much paler, and, like the Haleakala silversword, it dies after flowering. The Kau silversword is known only from one small colony, and it may soon vanish if this area is not protected from pigs and other animals which now roam there at will.

The third species of silversword is quite surprising if one thinks of silverswords in terms of arid alpine localities. *Argyroxiphium caliginii* grows in an area which receives about 375 inches of rain per year, the Puu Kukui Bog of West Maui. This bog is relatively high (about five thousand feet), and is brilliantly illuminated for short periods, although an almost constant drizzling rain is a typical regime. The Puu Kukui silversword is in saturated soil, among tussocks of the sedge *Oreobolus furcatus.* The Puu Kukui silversword tends to form prostrate stems on the bog surface, and these stems can root in the bog. In fact, each older plant generally has produced a series of offshoots at its base, and these soon root, and become independent plants. Thus, although the flowering shoot dies when the plant has flowered, one can say that the entire plant does not die. A plant may branch indefinitely, these branches root in the bog, the connections to the parent rosette rot away, and thus many plants result. Reproduction of the Puu Kukui silversword is mostly in this fashion, evidently. Flowering is rather infrequent. In 1958 I saw only one plant in flower at the right season, while in 1953 and 1966 I saw none, despite the fact that thousands of plants can be seen in the bog. Evidently this silversword compensates for this infrequent flowering by reproducing vegetatively instead of by seeds, a situation that may be related to bog existence. If an almost constant mist covers the bog during the flowering season, pollinating insects may fail to pollinate this plant. Interestingly, the flower heads are inconspicuous in appearance: the ray flowers are short, the disk flowers yellow-brown. The flower heads are somewhat pendant, a position which may prevent flowers from becoming filled with rain.

Although the Puu Kukui silversword has silvery leaves, these leaves are not quite so hairy as those of the Haleakala silversword, and the leaves do not contain as much water-storing gel. Moreover, they have developed a mechanism for jettisoning excess water (hydathodes) that is absent in the leaves of the Haleakala silversword. The fact that *A. caliginii* still possesses a number of the same features as the Haleakala silversword, or relatively small modifications of them, and that these features, like the silvery leaves, appear basically those of a dry alpine plant, suggest that *A. caliginii* is a derivative of an alpine silversword, one which perhaps looked rather like the Haleakala silversword.

The Haleakala greensword, *Argyroxiphium virescens,* is an endangered species of Haleakala now close to extinction (photograph by Joseph F. Rock, courtesy of Bishop Museum).

Greenswords

Another pair of species of *Argyroxiphium* are called greenswords because their leaves are not at all silvery, although these plants belong to the same genus. One of the greenswords, *A. virescens*, is found only on Haleakala, where it is now very rare. This greensword mimics the Haleakala silversword in growth form, for it has a single rosette which dies after flowering. The heads of flowers are yellow.

The Puu Kukui greensword, *A. grayanum,* grows in the Puu Kukui Bog along with the silversword *A. caliginii*. The Puu Kukui greensword resembles that silversword in not dying after flowering. Instead of forming offsets which root in the bog, however, its branches form low shrubs, which tend to grow mostly at the margins of the open bog. It does, however, flower more abundantly than *A. caliginii*. The heads of flowers are light yellow, but formed in a much smaller cluster than those of the other species of *Argyroxiphium*. Flower heads are somewhat horizontal or pendant, and thus avoid filling with water.

Wilkesia

Maui and Hawaii are the islands to which *Argyroxiphium* is restricted. On Kauai, there is a related genus with one species, *Wilkesia gymnoxiphium,* the iliau. Its leaves are arranged in whorls rather than spirals, and are flat and very grass-like, rather than thick. The inflorescence has whorls of heads. The heads of flowers are all disc flowers, and the ray flowers of *Argyroxiphium* are not represented. *Wilkesia* may be more closely related to the greenswords than the silverswords, but differs from both in its manner of growth. The leaf rosette tops a gangling pole-like stem which can be fairly woody at the base and up to ten feet tall. *Wilkesia* is an adaptation to moderately dry scrubby forest regions. The stems place the leaf rosettes above surrounding shrubbery, and this growth form may be related to this vegetation. The species of *Argyroxiphium* grow, in comparison, in open areas. *Wilkesia* plants never branch except by injury, and then usually only one stem persists. After flowering, the entire plant dies.

The iliau grows only in a few pockets on eastern Kauai, and does not seem either common or in great danger of extinction. Preference for certain soil types may limit its range.

If Maui and Hawaii are centers for *Argyroxiphium*, *Wilkesia* is an anomaly, confined to the far western end of the chain of major islands. Kauai has fostered many distinctive evolutionary products. Often one finds, in a genus or family, that the most extreme or most specialized types occur on Kauai. This is clearly true of *Dubautia* and *Wilkesia*. The three genera clearly show the role of isolation and distinctive ecological conditions in promoting the evolution of these exceptional types. The Hawaiian tarweeds have left few habitats unoccupied— only the lower coastal regions. If they have exceeded other Hawaiian plant groups, it is probably because of greater adaptability and evolutionary plasticity.

BIOLOGICAL REGIONS OF THE MAIN ISLANDS

Chapter 14   THE COAST

MOST OF the trees on Hawaiian coasts are introduced by man. For reasons discussed in Chapter 3, ocean currents seem to have deprived Hawaiian shores of many of the seaside trees of the South Pacific, like kamani (*Terminalia* or *Calophyllum*), noni (*Morinda*), mangroves (*Rhizophora*, *Bruguiera*), and others.

The only definitely native tree of the immediate coast is the hala, *Pandanus odoratissimus*. It can also grow well inland, but never seems to occur above about five hundred feet elevation. The long leaves, with their saw-toothed edges, the fragrant male inflorescences, the large, round heads of fruits are

Near the shore of eastern Oahu, one can find a seaside race of the sandalwood, *Santalum ellipticum* var. *littorale*. This race has leaves markedly more succulent than those of the inland sandalwood.

Possibly not native, but brought by the Polynesians, is the noni, *Morinda citrifolia.* Within the Islands, it has dispersed itself by flotation in seawater, and now it can be found at many places along the coast (Puna, Hawaii).

The hala, *Pandanus odoratissimus,* is native to Hawaiian shores and lowlands. The male flowers, left, are grouped with their sheathing white bract leaves and are very fragrant. The fruits, right, shatter into orangeish "keys" when mature. *Pandanus* leaves were used for mats by the Hawaiians, while fruits were eaten when other foods were not available (Puna, Hawaii).

familiar sights on Hawaiian shores. This species of *Pandanus* is native over much of the Pacific.

The wiliwili or Hawaiian coral tree, *Erythrina sandwicensis,* can occur very close to the immediate coast, but it is mostly farther inland (see Chapter 15).

The native Hawaiian coastal vegetation is mostly shrubby or herbaceous. The shrubs are mostly less than three feet in height. Typical of this low stature is the coastal iliahi, or sandalwood (*Santalum ellipticum* var. *littorale*), which is a low, rounded shrub with succulent leaves, gray-green in color. Inland sandalwoods are all trees.

One of the most characteristic shrubs of the coast is *Scaevola taccada,* the beach naupaka (or naupaka kai), a plant illustrated in color. *Scaevola taccada,* which has been burdened with many additional unnecessary names (*S. sericea, S. koenigii, S. frutescens,* etc.), is the most characteristic shrub of atolls and other shores of the tropical Pacific islands.

Most of the common plants of the immediate coast form low mats, or sprawling cushions, or vines trailing on the ground. *Sida fallax* and the nehe, *Lipochaeta integrifolia,* are among the most common of these. Others which can be seen occasionally include some of the akokos such as *Euphorbia degeneri* (Chapter 6), the aweoweo *Chenopodium oahuense* (Chapters 6 and 21), *Schiedea* (Chapter 4), the huluhulu or cotton (*Gossypium sandvicense*), the silvery heliotrope (*Heliotropium anomalum*), coastal kokoolaus (*Bidens*), and *Tetramolopium.*

Sida fallax, the ilima, is a mat with yellow-orange flowers and finely hairy white leaves, common near the shores of all the islands (Koko Crater, Oahu).

Thick whitish succulent leaves and heads of yellow flowers serve to identify the mat-like nehe *Lipochaeta integrifolia* (Waihee, Maui).

A shrubby nehe common along Hawaiian coasts, *Lipochaeta lavarum* usually grows in lava as its name suggests (Papawai, Maui).

Along coastal bluffs just above the sea is a low spreading coastal kokoolau, *Bidens molokaiensis* (left). *Tetramolopium rockii,* right, is a succulent cushion-forming plant with pink flowers, found only on Molokai.

Capparis sandwichiana, the maiapilo, grows on Hawaiian coasts. A low shrub with large white flowers and cucumber-like fruits, it can be found on coral or lava (Ulupalakua, Maui; Barbers Point, Oahu).

The Hawaiian cotton (*Gossypium sandvicense*), known as huluhulu or mao to the Hawaiians, is a yellow-flowered coastal shrub whose seeds have only inconspicuous tufts of brownish cotton (northeastern Lanai).

The silvery beach heliotrope, *Heliotropium anomalum,* grows on the Hawaiian Islands and certain islands of the South Pacific. At right, a blue-flowered beach plant limited to the Hawaiian chain, *Nama sandwicensis;* its closest relatives are in the deserts of California (Makapuu, Oahu).

The pale blue flowers of *Jacquemontia sandwicensis*, the pauohiiaka, reveal that this sprawling plant belongs to the morning glory family. At right, a coastal sedge, *Fimbristylis cymosa* (both from Koko Crater, Oahu).

Lycium carolinianum, the aeae (or ohelo kai), occurs on Hawaiian coasts. Lyciums are plants of dry coasts, even deserts, on mainland areas. *Sesuvium portulacastrum*, at right, is a red-stemmed succulent with pale violet flowers; it can be found on salty flats (Honolulu Airport).

Batis maritima, common along warm coasts of many tropical areas, was apparently introduced to Honolulu. Since that time, currents have spread it to various parts of the Islands, as here at Kealia Pond, Maui.

Some coastal plants are annuals under mainland conditions, but may be of indefinite duration in the Hawaiian climate: *Nama sandwicensis* and *Portulaca oleracea* (see Chapters 3 and 23) are examples.

Vining species mostly belong to the morning glory family. The most common of these is the pink-flowered pohuehue, *Ipomoea pes-caprae* (Chapter 3), and a sprawling morning glory with small pale blue flowers, *Jacquemontia sandwicensis*. One of the naupakas, *Scaevola coriacea* (Chapter 6), is a trailing species.

Sedges are commonly plants of moister areas, but *Fimbristylis* can be found in dry areas. Several grasses are well adapted to coastal localities.

Some plants of the coast are extremely tolerant to and can grow either in salt flats, like *Batis,* or within the reach of salt spray, like *Lycium, Sesuvium,* and many plants of the Leeward Islands (Chapters 20 through 27).

Chapter 15 ❧❧ THE DRY FOREST

COASTAL vegetation can be easily defined as plants that grow near the immediate shore; in describing other regions, however, the vaguest definitions serve best. A number of species "transgress" from one "region" or "zone" or "association" (according to typical ecological usage) into another, especially in the Hawaiian Islands. Detailed analyses of Hawaiian vegetation are very tempting, but often are misleading. The groupings here are entirely arbitrary.

Lower Dry Forest

Areas of lower dry forest are now so few that we have difficulty in constructing a picture of this vegetation. During the human occupation of the Islands, especially that by peoples other than the Polynesians, much dry forest was removed. Grazing by cattle seems largely responsible for this, especially on low areas. Cultivation of sugar cane and pineapples have obviously removed much land from its native state in areas where soil is present. Discovering pockets of dry forest is now even more difficult, and therefore may appeal to some as a challenge. Localities indicated in parentheses under the photographs here will indicate what some of these places are.

The naio, *Myoporum sandwicense,* is a common dry forest tree with relatives in New Zealand and on South Pacific islands (Makulawena, Hawaii; northeastern Lanai).

Light orange (sometimes green) flowers and bright orange seeds characterize the wiliwili (*Erythrina sandwicensis*), a soft-wooded tree which usually flowers during the dry summer months when leaves have fallen (Puuwaawaa, Hawaii).

The lama, *Diospyros ferrea* var. *sandwicensis,* is perhaps the most frequent tree in the dry forest. Its bark is round, its leaves are deep green, and its fruits are orange to red in color (Kaupulehu, Hawaii).

Reynoldsia sandwicensis, the ohe, is a lowland tree with thickish branches which appear to be almost succulent. During dry parts of the year, it may lose a large portion of its leaves (Ulupalakua, Maui; and photograph of fruiting branches by Joseph F. Rock, courtesy of Bishop Museum).

The aiea, *Nothocestrum,* is a genus of trees found only in the Hawaiian Islands; it belongs to the nightshade family. The tubular yellow flowers are notably fragrant. The aiea shown here is *N. latifolium* (Ulupalakua, Maui).

Rauwolfia sandwicensis, the hao, has light green leaves, yellow-green flowers, and two-parted capsules which turn yellow when they release seeds (Ulupalakua, Maui).

Canthium odoratum, the walahee, looks somewhat like *Rauwolfia,* but has opposite leaves, a hallmark of the coffee family (Ulupalakua, Maui).

Sandalwoods (iliahi) are sometimes thought to be rare in the Hawaiian Islands, logged out because of their fragrant woods. Most of the sandalwoods have non-fragrant woods, and some of them are still rather common. The sandalwood shown here is *Santalum paniculatum* (Kilauea; Kaupulehu, Hawaii).

Planchonella of the sapota family was variously called alaa, aulu, or kaulu by the Hawaiians. These trees look somewhat different from locality, and though many species have been named, probably only two or three are justified. Shown here is the most common, *P. sandwicensis*. Aulus are easily recognized by the rusty red color of undersides of leaves, by their milky sap, and by the round yellow fruits. *Planchonella* is native on various Pacific islands (Puuwaawaa, Hawaii).

Hawaiians knew *Nesoluma polynesicum* as keahi. It is a shrub or small tree, found also on South Pacific islands; it resembles the related *Planchonella* (northeastern Lanai).

The kea or uhiuhi, *Mezoneurum kauaiense,* is a tree nearly extinct now in the Hawaiian Islands. Its seeds do not float, but those of other species of *Mezoneurum,* native to the tropical Pacific and to Australia, do float. Seeds probably once arrived on the Hawaiian Islands in this way, then the Hawaiian trees lost seed floatability (N. Kona, Hawaii).

This may be the last individual in the wild of a strange tree cotton, *Kokia rockii*. The genus *Kokia* is found only in the Hawaiian Islands. This species has striking curved red hibiscus-like flowers. Because of these, the tree has been planted as an ornamental in the Kona District, and this may have saved it from extinction (Kaupulehu, Hawaii).

Yellow-green leaves, three-parted capsules, and very hard wood characterize the kauwila, *Colubrina oppositifolia*. It may be closely related to a wide-ranging species with floatable seeds, *C. asiatica*, which also grows in the Islands (Puuwaawaa, Hawaii).

The halapepe, *Dracaena aurea* (or *Pleomele aurea*), ranges from the very dry forest up into moderately moist forest regions. The tree is easily recognized by its distinctive shape and sword-like leaves, by its tubular yellow or yellow-green flowers, and by its brownish fruits (Puuwaawaa, Hawaii; Kokee, Kauai).

Sapindus oahuensis, the aulu, grows only on Oahu. It is unusual in having simple leaves; non-Hawaiian species of *Sapindus* all have pinnate leaves (Waianae Mountains, Oahu).

Dodonaea, the aalii, is a common shrub of dry areas. Leaves bear a sticky varnish-like covering, and fruits have two or three wings, rose in color. Although called *Dodonaea stenoptera* and other names by various authors, the Hawaiian aaliis are a highly variable group which can probably be called part of *D. viscosa,* a wide-ranging species of the tropics (Waimea Canyon, Kauai).

Sida cordifolia can be called a small shrub, although it resembles (and probably hybridizes with) the mat-like ilima of the coast, *Sida fallax* (Lahainaluna, Maui).

The puakala, *Argemone glauca,* is a prickly poppy closely related to species from western North America. It grows as a biennial (or possibly an annual) (Nohonae-hae, Hawaii).

Psilotum nudum, the moa, is an ancient plant of the tropics. It sends up its broom-like shoots from between crevices of lava. The spore cases (sporangia) are three-parted (Kahuku, Hawaii).

"Lower dry forest" here connotes forest of lower, drier elevations, but more particularly the plants which are likely to be found on old lava flows in this region, rather than on good soil. The most common native tree in these low lava-rich regions is the lama, *Diospyros*, a kind of persimmon (but with very small fruits for a persimmon). However, there is also a good chance of finding one or more of the following along with *Diospyros*: hao (*Rauwolfia*); kauwila (*Colubrina*); wiliwili (*Erythrina*); naio (*Myoporum*); iliahi, or sandalwood (*Santalum*); and ohe (*Reynoldsia*). If one is on a leeward coast, plants typical of drier areas occur farther up slopes than on windward coasts. On windward coasts, the ohia (*Metrosideros*), chief tree of the wet forest, can come down to within a few hundred feet of the ocean, as on the Na Pali Kona Coast of Kauai. One might, in such circumstances, find lama growing with ohia.

Upper Dry Forest

The most conspicuous trees between the low, open dry forest and the wet ohia forest are the koas (*Acacia koa*). Koas usually form a broad band on lower slopes. They are easily recognized by their sickle-shaped gray-green phyllodes. Phyllodes, which might be thought mistakenly to be true leaves, are actually leaf-like structures which represent a flattened and expanded version

The koa (*Acacia koa*) dominates upper levels of the dry forest, leads into the wet forest. Acacias are forest trees in the Pacific only on the Hawaiian Islands—and in Australia. Curved phyllodes (leaf-like structures), yellow flowers, and brown pods containing black seeds serve to identify the koa. Koas are sometimes victims of the Hawaiian mistletoe, lower right, *Korthalsella complanata* (Manoa Trail, Oahu).

The koaia (*Acacia koaia*), a close relative of the koa, is a small tree very rare now. It is seen here on the lower slopes of the Kohala Mountains, with Mauna Kea in the background. The leaves and pods are narrower and straighter than those of the koa.

of the leaf stalk (petiole). Koa flowers are lemon-yellow. The pods, resembling those of a lima bean in shape, are flat, curved, and turn brown at maturity. Seeds are flattish and shiny black. Koas tend to form a woodland which is not dense but can be rather open, carpeted by the old phyllodes. When rain falls in the koa forest, or when soil beneath them is disturbed, the roots give off a sharp ozone-like or perhaps faintly skunk-like odor.

Closely related to the koa and not distinguishable from it at a distance is a species from Kauai, *A. kauaiensis;* the true koa is also on Kauai. Somewhat more distinctive is the koaia, *Acacia koaia,* now very rare. It has smaller, straighter phyllodes, and also narrow straight pods.

The upper dry forest is not necessarily a forest of short trees, nor is it necessarily monotonous. *Alphitonia ponderosa,* a kauwila, is reported to have been the tallest tree on Kauai. The koa itself is interesting in this respect, because most acacias, as seen in Australia, are small, short-lived trees. Koas, however, can become quite large. A number of dry forest areas today in the Islands are, or have been, somewhat disturbed, and trees there are not representative of the large dimensions trees in this region can reach, given the chance. Dry forest can occur on broader, lower portions of mountains. However, dry forest species tend to extend well up a mountain on ridges, but not in valleys. Some of the

Inconspicuous tubular green flowers characterize the ahakea, *Bobea elatior*, of the coffee family. Ahakeas grow in upper dry or lower wet forest (lower Kehena Ditch Trail, Hawaii).

Although most of the Hawaiian araliads are wet forest trees, *Tetraplasandra hawaiiensis* succeeds well in lower regions, perhaps aided by the hairiness of the leaves (lower Kehena Ditch Trail, Hawaii).

Pisonia was called papala by the Hawaiians, although they used that name also for a different tree, *Charpentiera* (see Chapter 6). At left is *Pisonia sandwicensis* (also known as *Rockia sandwicensis*). At right, *Pisonia umbellifera* (or *Ceodes umbellifera*). Pisonias are distributed across the Pacific, a fact related to their sticky fruits (see Chapter 3) (Waimea Canyon, Kauai; Kipuka Pualu, Hawaii).

Zanthoxylum (*Fagara*), the heae, ranges to the Hawaiian Islands from Indo-Malaysia and Asia. It is easily recognized by its green capsules, and by its pinnate leaves which usually have three leaflets. Shown here is Z. *hawaiiense* (Puu Lehua, Hawaii).

Alphitonia ponderosa was called kauwila by the Hawaiians, who used this name also for *Colubrina;* both have very hard wood. This tree can be very tall, although scrubby individuals like this one are common in regrowth areas. Rusty-colored hairs and black woody fruits distinguish *Alphitonia* (Kokee, Kauai).

A common tree of the koa forest is the olopua, *Osmanthus sandwicensis.* It looks like—and is related to—the olive, and probably has its closest relatives in Indo-Malaysia (Kokee, Kauai).

Kauai's iliahi, or sandalwood (*Santalum pyrularium*), has large purplish red flowers, large red-purple to purple-black fruits the size and shape of an olive. A small rounded tree, it is common in koa forests of Waimea Canyon, and may be partly parasitic on roots of koa trees.

Most of the Hawaiian species of hoawa, *Pittosporum,* are inhabitants of the wet forest. A few, like this *P. terminalioides* from the dry part of Hawaii Volcanoes National Park, grow in downslope localities. Lowland hoawas probably resemble Indo-Malaysian ancestors of Hawaiian pittosporums most closely.

scrubby ridge species can be alpine shrubs also: the pukiawe (*Styphelia*) and aalii (*Dodonaea*), for example.

Frequently seen in dry forest is the mistletoe *Korthalsella*, which can grow on various kinds of woody plants, and which has flattened stems, sometimes markedly so, with a tape-like appearance. Dry forest is the habitat for the iliahi or sandalwood, *Santalum*. Not generally known perhaps is the fact that sandalwoods are semiparasites. They manufacture their own food, but they do not grow well unless they form root connections with other plants in their vicinity. Legend has it that sandalwoods are extremely rare or extinct in the Islands, that they vanished after being cut down for their fragrant wood. Not so. Fragrance of wood varies within the Hawaiian sandalwoods, and many trees have nonfragrant wood. Oahu sandalwoods were cut most extensively and have not recovered to their former abundance or stature yet. Perhaps they never will, for the upper dry forest is not likely to be allowed to grow back over large areas. Sandalwoods are easily found in some places on the other islands, particularly Kauai and Hawaii.

The dry forest is not rich in lobelioids, but some do characteristically grow there. There is a possibility that the fleshy-fruited lobelioids might have originated in dry forest and evolved into wet forest, so that the dry forest species are relicts. All the species of *Delissea* were probably primarily dry forest plants. Some of the cyaneas, such as *C. leptostegia, C. angustifolia,* and *C. arborea*, are koa-forest species, and some clermontias, such as *C. kakeana* and the odd extinct *C. haleakalensis*, are characteristically koa forest species.

The trees with an aberrant method of wood formation (known to botanists as anomalous secondary thickening) are all dry forest plants. The kului (*Nototrichum*) and the papala (*Charpentiera*), discussed in Chapter 6, are characteristic of dry forest; *Charpentiera* and another "anomalous" tree called papala, *Pisonia*, may prefer shady places, such as gulches, within a dry forest area.

Other Hawaiian plants of dry forest considered in detail elsewhere in this book include some of the alanis (*Pelea:* Chapter 5), some akokos (*Euphorbia:* Chapter 6), some naupakas (*Scaevola:* Chapter 6), some violets (*Viola tracheliifolia:* Chapter 6), the mahoe (*Alectryon: Chapter* 8), and a few of the naenaes (*Dubautia:* Chapter 13).

The undergrowth of the dry forest can be tangled with vines such as maile, *Alyxia*, famed for the fragrant foliage from which the most noble leis are made, and the huehue *Cocculus*. Legume vines include the bright-flowered *Strongylodon,* or kaiwi; *Mucuna;* and some species of *Canavalia*. Clumps of the uki, *Dianella*, are common. The mat-like tangles of the uluhe fern, *Dicranopteris*, may grow in dry forest, although it is more often a wet forest fern. The dry forest is not as rich in ferns as wet forest, although some, such as *Sphenomeris chusana, Adiantum hispidulum,* and a rare endemic genus, *Diellia*, are characteristically dry forest ferns. In shady and wet places within the dry forest, a number of ferns might be found.

Barely saved from extinction by cultivation of a few individuals is *Hibiscadelphus hualalaiensis*, a relative of *Hibiscus*. This species has curved green flowers which probably represent adaptations to pollination by nectar-feeding birds with curved beaks. This species, as well as the two others, is restricted to the island of Hawaii, and this genus is not found anywhere else in the world.

Among the few plants with large, colorful flowers in the native Hawaiian flora are a number of species of *Hibiscus*. Here are two from dry forest areas: *H. brackenridgei*, left, and *H. st.-johnii*.

Endemic to the Hawaiian Islands, the genus *Pteralyxia* is probably an "old" Hawaiian resident. The three species occur on the older islands, Kauai and Oahu. *Pteralyxia macrocarpa* has oblong, plum-sized scarlet fruits, each of which contains a large winged seed about two inches long. Flowers are yellow-green (Waianae Mountains, Oahu).

Hesperomannia, a rare endemic Hawaiian genus from dry forest areas, has orange thistle-like heads of flowers. Its relatives are in the New World, probably in South America, and it may be a relatively early immigrant to the Islands. Illustrated here is *H. arbuscula* subsp. *oahuensis* (Waianae Mountains, Oahu).

One of the curious features of the dry forest is the number of plants in it which probably owe their arrival to flotation in seawater, and which have evolved into inland situations following their original seaside colonization. Such a tendency is represented very little or not at all on other Pacific islands. Hawaiian dry forest trees which probably have this mode of origin include the koa (*Acacia*), the wiliwili (*Erythrina*), various species of kokio (*Hibiscus*), genera allied to *Hibiscus* such as *Kokio* and *Hibiscadelphus,* a legume, *Mezoneurum,* the kauwila (*Colubrina*), the papala (*Pisonia*), and an endemic Hawaiian genus, *Pteralyxia.* Vines of the dry forest which probably represent this mode of origin include *Strongylodon, Mucuna,* and *Canavalia,* which are legumes. There is even a possibility that others could be added to this list, but it seems obvious that some of the more important plants of the dry forest are derived from seeds which once floated ashore. This phenomenon is a curious one, and

A shiny-leaved akia with drooping spikes of yellow flowers and orange fruits, *Wikstroemia elongata* grows in open places in forest (Kalalau Valley, Kauai).

Although the rare *Exocarpus sandvicensis* is mostly broom-like in appearance, it also bears a few broad, flattened leaves. This shrub of ridge and dry forest areas is related to plants from Indo-Malaysia and Australia (Waianae Mountains, Oahu).

This tree from the Kona Coast was named *Neowawrea phyllanthoides* by botanist Joseph F. Rock, but it proves to be a member of the genus *Drypetes*, an Indo-Malaysian group of trees and shrubs.

Phyllanthus sandwicensis is a small shrub, belonging to the spurge family (Euphorbiaceae). Its relatives are found in tropics of the Old World and the New (Waianae Mountains, Oahu).

A sprawling shrub with white flowers and white fruits, the uulei (*Osteomeles anthyllidifolia*) is a Hawaiian representative of the rose family, and may be related to South American species of *Osteomeles*. It is a common sight on dry ridges (Lahainaluna, Maui).

Prized by the Hawaiians as the noblest of all lei materials is the maile, *Alyxia olivaeformis*, a woody vine which ranges from dry to wet forests. *Alyxia* is Indo-Malaysian, extends from Madagascar to the South Pacific and to the Hawaiian Islands (Waianae Mountains).

Small red fruits, narrow, sharply tipped leaves, and minute white flowers distinguish the pukiawe, *Styphelia tameiameiae*. This is a very common shrub of dry ridges, from low elevations to the alpine zone. *Styphelia* ranges from Australia to the Hawaiian Islands (Waimea Canyon, Kauai).

Sagebrushes from western North America colonized the Hawaiian Islands in pre-human time, producing several endemic species which grow on cliffs. Here is *Artemisia australis* from Nuuanu Pali, Oahu.

probably has the following explanation. As we saw in Chapter 3, some plants which have arrived by means of oceanic drift may have arrived on only a single occasion, owing to the fact that the North Pacific, whose few islands are relatively poor in tropical beach plants, is cut off from the South Pacific and its wealth of shore plants by contrary currents—such as the equatorial currents which sweep eastward and westward but break the path from south to north. Let's suppose that an *Acacia* from Australia or another South Pacific island managed to reach the Hawaiian Islands and establish there. This *Acacia* might evolve races suited to inland areas, and eventually might die out in beach areas. Certainly the suitable areas for trees inland are much greater in extent and offer more opportunity than the narrow strips of beaches, which are harsh localities for trees. The *Acacia*, if it remained on the beach, might stay as a small colony, too small for long-term survival, for reasons mentioned in Chapter 4. If the same *Acacia* drifted in from the South Pacific a second time, a population living exclusively on a beach would be "'saved" by the infusion of "new blood" (cross-pollination between old and new colonists), but then its preferences for the beach habitat would be "reinforced," and races which might adapt to inland areas would be prevented by reintroduction of dominant genes dictating beach preference. The failure of any introductions after the first one would, on the contrary, permit evolution of inland dry forest races. If a second event of dispersal was delayed long enough, the original beach

Most of the Hawaiian species of *Bidens* (kokoolau) grow on dry ridge sites, and form shrubs or "miniature trees." They are good example of the tendency toward arborescence, of which other examples are given in Chapter 6. Here is *Bidens waianaeensis*, a kokoolau with odd spiral fruits illustrated in Chapter 8. Hawaiian species of *Bidens* are related to species in the southeastern Pacific and the Americas (Waianae summit ridge, Oahu).

Sprawling under shrubs in dry areas is the huehue, *Cocculus ferrandianus*. It has minute white flowers, small green fruits (Ulupalakua, Maui).

Ancestors of the kaiwi, *Strongylodon lucidus*, probably floated ashore. Now this vine ornaments dry forests with its bright scarlet flowers (Waianae Mountains, Oahu).

Dianella sandwicensis, the uki, is common in the undergrowth of dry forests. Its flowers are small, bluish white, and the fruits are bright blue. *Dianella* is distributed throughout the South Pacific (Waianae Mountains, Oahu).

Hawaiians called *Peperomia* ala-alawainui. This species, *P. reflexa,* has yellowish leaves and grows on rocky outcrops. It is not restricted to the Hawaiian Islands but is found widely in the tropics (Waianae summit ridge).

Adiantum hispidulum is a maiden-hair fern which grows in shady places of the dry forest (Pololu Valley, Hawaii).

The finely dissected but tough fronds of the fern *Sphenomeris chusana* are a common sight in open places of the dry forest (Konahuanui Trail, Oahu).

colonist might already have evolved well inland and be unaffected by the new beach colonists. Plants which float ashore consistently, year after year, such as the beach morning glory (*Ipomoea*), the naupaka kai (*Scaevola taccada*), etc., cannot form inland races. These float ashore consistently every year because they are represented on various of the Hawaiian Islands, but, more importantly, they are represented on tropical coasts of the northern hemisphere, so there is great likelihood of a naupaka kai seed from some other part of the Pacific floating ashore.

If the Hawaiian dry forest were, during its early history, filled with numerous successful trees which arrived in some fashion other than oceanic drift, evolution inland by beach plants would probably not be possible, it would be inhibited by the "pre-empting" of the trees already in the dry forest. However, the Hawaiian Islands are so remote that for much (or perhaps all) of their history, many niches remained open, unfilled, or occupied by fewer species than one would find on a rich tropical island close to Asiatic source areas. This relative impoverishment, known as disharmony, would be much less on Fiji, for example, and in fact the Fiji flora contains very few inland elements derived from beach-inhabiting ancestors.

A number of the dry forest trees did not have this ancestry in the Hawaiian Islands, and were derived from dry forests of continents or other islands. The aiea *Nothocestrum*, for example, probably was derived from *Cestrum* of rather dry areas in the Andes. The kului *Nototrichum* probably stemmed from *Ptilotus* in Australia.

Chapter 16 🙟 *THE WET FOREST*

DURING the winter, the high Hawaiian forest is pervaded by clouds of the kona storms that make the mountain areas forbidding and gloomy, misty or rainy, for days at a time. During the remainder of the year, a clear morning in the mountains may give way in the afternoon to a gentle shower. Only on an occasional day does bright sunshine penetrate into the tangle of wet forests for most of a day. Rainfall is sufficient to support a luxuriant growth, and the persistent cloud cover intensifies the value of the rain, as it lessens evaporation. During the summer months, only occasional light sprinkles may occur for periods of days or even weeks, and one can visit forests with little or no discomfort. Summer seems to be the time when much of the flowering occurs in wet forests, although one certainly can find a number of

On most of the Hawaiian Islands, rain forest covers a highly sculptured landscape, as these cliff areas at Kehena, on the Kohala Mountains, Hawaii, show.

Valleys and gulches, almost perpetually cloudy and wet, offer vistas of wet forest in the Waikamoi region of East Maui.

the native plants in flower at any season of the year, and some flower continuously during the year.

The wet forest is a forest of more than about seventy inches of rain per year, and can be said to have one common denominator: the ohia lehua (*Metrosideros*), featured in Chapter 4. Endlessly varied in its foliage, the ohia lehua lends a somber air to wet forests because of its dark green foliage, dark gray bark, and often gnarled branches. Roots are formed on the sides of trunks of ohia trees, and older trunks can bear a tangle of roots. In such matted roots, ohia seedlings or other plants can take root, and the forest can be an infinite series of plants-upon-plants.

Ohia forest can be very tall, exceeding fifty feet. Surprisingly, deep good soil is not a prerequisite for a tall ohia forest, as one might imagine. The tallest ohias are on the island of Hawaii, where they grow on relatively recent lava with little soil accumulation. The most magnificent *Metrosideros* forest easily accessible by road at present is along the Kulani Road behind Hilo. Some of the Kona District ohia forests are also notably tall. Curiously, the ohias of Oahu are scrubby in comparison with those of Hawaii, despite the better soil conditions on Oahu.

Within the ohia forests are many kinds of trees and shrubs. Some are prom-

A loulu palm, *Pritchardia macdanielsii*, emerges from low wet forest on the windward crest of the Koolau Mountains (Punaluu, Oahu).

Pritchardia martii dots the ridges and valleys on the leeward side of the Koolau Mountains. In full bloom, the masses of yellow flowers make a conspicuous display. Fruits are green, turning brown as they dry. Although many species of loulus have been recognized, many represent minor differences; perhaps all of the short, stubby loulus should be included in *P. martii* (Wiliwilinui Ridge, Oahu).

Tall species—or races—of loulus grow in tall rain forest; here is *Pritchardia beccariana* (Kulani Road, Hawaii).

inent, and equal ohias in height; others are shrubby. In no case, however, does any other group of trees exceed ohias in abundance. Among the most common trees intermixed with ohias are the araliads: *Tetraplasandra* (in which is included *Pterotropia* and *Triplasandra*), and the olapa or lapalapa *Cheirodendron*. Depending on the location, members of the coffee family may be abundant: kopiko (*Straussia*), pilo (*Coprosma*), *Hedyotis*, *Gouldia*, and *Gardenia*. Various kinds of koleas (*Myrsine*) abound; they are easily recognizable when they bear young shoots because their young foliage is a bright magenta color. The alani (*Pelea*: see Chapter 5), hoawa (*Pittosporum*), and hame (*Antidesma*) are abundant in wet forests. In quite wet localities, one is very likely to see the kawau, (*Ilex*), a kind of Hawaiian holly. Most of the kinds of naupaka (*Scaevola*: see Chapter 6) are natives of wet forest. One of the most common shrubs, however, is the kanawau, *Broussaisia* (Chapter 4), which looks much like a hydrangea, to which it is related. Several of the dubautias (Chapter 13) are characteristically shrubs of this zone, and the lobelioids (Chapter 12) are more numerous in wet ohia forest than in any other vegetation type.

In deep gulches, an introduced tree, the kukui *Aleurites moluccana*, is likely to be quite abundant. It is mentioned here only because it virtually appears as a native, so frequent and characteristic is it. Kukuis can easily be sighted in vistas of mountains and valleys, because they invariably occupy the valleys, and have a very pale green foliage. One could mention other common introduced plants of wet forest areas, such as strawberry guava (*Psidium cattleianum*), mountain apple (*Syzygium jambos*), and Brazilian pepper (*Schinus terebinthifolius*), but the list is literally endless.

Deep gulches are likely to contain native members of the nettle family (none of which have stinging properties), such as the mamaki, *Pipturus*, easily recognized because the backs of its leaves are whitish. Cyrtandras (Chapter 5) are likely to be found in most gulches of wet forest areas. Only in very wet areas, particularly bottoms of deep valleys and sides of ravines, will one find the curious apeape (*Gunnera*) with its giant round leaves, however.

Probably the most common native plant of the wet forest, other than the ohia, is a fern, and a very strange one: *Dicranopteris*, the uluhe. It has trailing underground stems, wiry leaf stalks. Leaves are rather large, repeatedly forked, and form a dense tangle. *Dicranopteris* mats, often about three feet high, cannot be eradicated quickly; ohia trees and other plants will eventually cover over and shade out uluhe and form a forest—or re-form one. Uluhe usually indicates a former area of forest destroyed by grazing, landslides, or some human activity. *Dicranopteris* can be seen at a distance, identifiable by its yellowish green leaves. It belongs to a family (Gleicheniaceae) of ferns which is exclusively tropical, and is interesting on account of its curiously forked leaves.

Less common relatives of the uluhe, *Sticherus* and *Hicropteris*, can be found in a number of Hawaiian localities, usually wetter than the ones *Dicranopteris* occupies.

The Islands are famous for tree ferns, although there is only one genus of true tree ferns, the hapu *Cibotium*. These are a series of very close species, not easily distinguished; the one seen in most localities is *C. chamissoi*. Tree fern forest is very wet forest, and in general occurs in areas of more than a hundred inches of rainfall per year.

The amau, *Sadleria*, is not so restricted ecologically. Recognizable by its bronzish or orangeish new fronds subdivided only once (pinnate) instead of twice (bipinnate) like those of *Cibotium*, sadlerias occur in rain forest, on lava flows, or in alpine situations. Most common of sadlerias is S. *cyatheoides*. Looking like S. *cyatheoides*, but with more scaly hairs on the leaves, is S. *pallida*, which can be found near Kilauea. One *Sadleria* quite exceptional in size and form is S. *squarrosa*, which is adapted to dripping cliffs in wet forest. Its leaves tend to lie flat, or droop against, these cliffs; the leaflets are cupped, looking like a mosaic or a series of beads. The genus *Sadleria* is endemic to the Hawaiian Islands, so the various species have undoubtedly developed within the confines of the Islands.

The wet forest is quite rich in ferns, only a few of which can be shown here. One can say that because fern spores disperse more easily than seeds,

Tetraplasandra meiandra from the Koolau Mountains has fragrant greenish purple flowers and deep purple fruits (Moanalua Trail, Oahu).

The oblong fruits and pinnate leaves of *Tetraplasandra waialealae* from Kauai are notably large, providing an instance of seed and fruit gigantism described in Chapter 8 (Mt. Kahili, Kauai).

a higher proportion of ferns to flowering plants is native to the Hawaiian Islands than would be true in continental rain forest. Only a few of the native ferns can be shown here. Ferns, mosses, liverworts, fungi, and lichens of the Islands would all make interesting subjects for a botanical hobbyist, however.

The ohia forest probably contains the richest assemblage of genera and species, compared with other regions of the Islands. Some people have thought that the dry forest was richer, but this is really not true. The larger plant genera—*Cyrtandra, Cyanea, Clermontia, Pelea*—are wet forest plants, and the largest genera of insects are centered in the wet forest—the native fruit flies,

The olapas form rounded trees in the rain forest; leaves are light green in color, berries purple. Here is *Cheirodendron trigynum* var. *acuminatum* (Kehena, Hawaii).

for example. The dry forest, at least the upper dry forest, might be the site of most colonizations but plant and animal groups appear to have evolved into and diversified within the wet forest. The reasons for supposing this are as follows. Most of the source areas for the Hawaiian flora (and fauna) are areas drier than wet Hawaiian forest. Wet forest, then, represents an area relatively unoccupied at first on the Islands, and if evolution involved ecological shift, in most cases it was into areas of greater rainfall. Because wetter areas are more favorable for plant growth, this transition was undoubtedly accomplished easily. That it happens readily is evident in such an example as the Puu Kukui silversword, a relatively recent bog derivative of the dry alpine silverswords; *Dubautia* also illustrates this trend (Chapter 13). Wet forest is, however, an ecological extreme, and tends to be a "dead end." That this is true is illustrated by the loss of dispersibility and flightlessness which so often accompany evolution into the wet forest (Chapters 7 and 8). In addition to the visible changes evident in loss of dispersal mechanisms and loss of flying ability, there are invisible changes in the physiology of plants and animals, changes which are evidently irreversible.

On the high ridges of Oahu, the quivering pale green foliage of the lapalapa, *Cheirodendron platyphyllum,* is easily recognizable (Konahuanui summit, Oahu).

The wet forest appears more exclusively Indo-Malaysian in the affinity of its species, with relatively few American elements. This is entirely logical. Even if most source areas for the Hawaiian flora and fauna are drier than wet Hawaiian forest, Indo-Malaysian forests are more nearly similar: those of Queensland, New Guinea, the Philippines, Indonesia, Fiji, and other Pacific islands, for example. American source areas, on the contrary, are relatively dry: the Andes, Mexico, western North America.

Straussia mariniana, the kopiko, is a glossy-leaved shrub or tree with white flowers, oval fruits which turn orange at maturity (Kalalau lookout, Kauai).

A kopiko with depressed veins on its dark green leaves, *Straussia faurioi* grows on wet ridges of Oahu. *Straussia* is a Hawaiian genus extremely close to *Psychotria,* a genus (belonging to the coffee family) which ranges throughout the islands of Indo-Malaysia and the Old World tropics.

Flowers of the pilo, *Coprosma*, are male on some plants (left), female on others (right). Shown here is *Coprosma longifolia,* one of many species of this genus native of the Hawaiian Islands. Coprosmas range from Australia, New Zealand, and New Guinea through the high islands of the Pacific (Wiliwilinui Ridge, Oahu).

Bright orange fruits characterize most pilos: *Coprosma stephano-carpa* (Puu Kukui, West Maui).

Although a common shrub in the rain forest, *Gouldia terminalis,* the manono, is inconspicuous because of its greenish flowers and green fruits which turn purple at maturity (Konahuanui Trail, Oahu).

Gardenia, or nanu, is a characteristic, although somewhat rare, shrub of Pacific islands. Hawaiian species include the small-flowered G. brighamii, (left) (cultivated, Manuka Park, Hawaii), and the larger G. mannii (Waikane Trail, Oahu) (right).

Although some of the Hawaiian species of Hedyotis have inconspicuous green flowers, H. fluviatilis has large white ones. Hawaiian species of Hedyotis were formerly called Kadua. They belong to the coffee family (Punaluu, Oahu).

The olomea, Perrottetia sandwicensis, is a very common tree or shrub of the wet forest; its reddish-veined leaves and numerous small flowers aid in identifying it (Konahuanui Trail, Oahu).

The hame, *Antidesma platyphyllum,* is one of the commonest shrubs or trees of the wet forest. It is seen here in the misty Punaluu forests of Oahu.

Spindly stems and dark green leaves mark the poola, *Claoxylon sandwicense* (Kokee, Kauai).

Xylosma hawaiiense, the maua, mimics *Antidesma* very closely; it is less common, however (Punaluu, Oahu).

Kalia, *Elaeocarpus bifidus,* is a common tree in wet forest areas of the Islands. It has fruits similar to olives in appearance. Another feature by which one can recognize it is the all-but-universal occurrence on this tree of galled growths, which can be called "witches'-brooms" (Kokee, Kauai).

Ilex anomala, the kawau, is a kind of holly which occurs in very wet forest areas as a shrub or small tree (Puu Kukui, Maui).

Most species of the hoawa, *Pittosporum,* are shrubs or trees of wet forest. Here the large leaf rosettes of *P. dolosum* overhang the Kaluanui Stream, above Punaluu Valley. Fruits of this species are deeply wrinkled.

One of the most common genera in wet forest is *Pelea,* the alani. At left, *P. clusiae-folia;* at right, *P. wawreana* (both from Moanalua Trail, Oahu).

Platydesma campanulata, the pilokea, is related to *Pelea,* and grows in wet forest of Kauai, Oahu, Maui, and Hawaii. Flowers are up to an inch long, and white. Fruits are four-parted (Punaluu, Oahu).

Kolea, *Myrsine lessertiana,* is one of the most frequently encountered trees in the wet forest. Large leathery leaves of various shapes characterize this species. Fruits are clustered along the main stems; young leaves are bright magenta. Myrsines occur on various high Pacific islands (Kipuka Pualu, Hawaii).

Kolea laulii, the "small-leaved *Myrsine*," *M. sandwicensis*, is a shrub or small tree on all five major islands (Kilauea).

Eurya sandwicensis, the anini, has fruits which look like those of *Myrsine*, but this tree, now rather rare, has toothed leaf margins. The genus *Eurya* is Indo-Malaysian in distribution, and belongs to the tea family (Kulani Road, Hawaii).

Kokia keokeo is the Hawaiian name for *Hibiscus arnottianus,* whose striking white flowers stand out clearly in the rain forest (Punaluu, Oahu).

A red-flowered kokio, *Hibiscus kahili,* forms scraggly trees near Wahiawa Bog, lower Kauai.

The mamaki, *Pipturus albidus,* is a small tree or large shrub in wet forest of all the islands. *Pipturus albidus* is the most common Hawaiian *Pipturus;* other species have been named, but some of these should probably be called *P. albidus.* Hawaiian mamakis are close to those of other Pacific islands, such as Samoa. Shown here is a typical mamaki shrub (Honaunau, Kona, Hawaii); a branch with male flowers (Waikolu, Molokai); and a branch with female flowers (Puna, Hawaii).

Neraudia melastomaefolia forms a vine-like, or straggling plant in wet forest areas, the flowers (males shown here) clustered at leaf bases. Fruits (not shown) have a conspicuous pink cup-like appearance (Waianae Mountains, Oahu).

Urera sandwicensis, the opuhe, grows in wet places on all of the larger islands; the small fruits are orange in color. Plants were used by the Hawaiians as a fiber source (Koolau Gap, Maui).

Touchardia latifolia, the olona, was sought by the Hawaiians because it was the source of a strong fiber, good for fishnets (Waikane, Oahu).

Labordia, the kamakahala, has yellow-orange flowers, leaves which are glossy above, pale below. This genus, endemic to the Hawaiian Islands, is related to *Geniostoma* of the South Pacific. Shown here are *L. baillonii* (left), from Kulani Road, Hawaii; *L. waialealae*, right, is a small-leaved species from high, wet areas on Kauai. The fruits are from *L. kaalae*, a species of the Waianae Mountains, Oahu.

Most kinds of the ohelo (*Vaccinium*) grow in open places, such as bogs, of wet forest or in alpine country. However, the large-leaved *V. calycinum* is common in the undergrowth of wet forest (Kilauea).

The naenae, *Dubautia plantaginea*, grows on ridges and open places in the lower wet forest of Oahu and the other islands (Konahuanui Trail, Oahu).

Dubautia laxa is a naenae which grows on wet, windblown ridges. Its flat-topped clusters of flower heads are purplish orange in color (Konahuanui summit, Oahu; Mt. Kahili, Kauai).

Lysimachia of the primrose family is represented on the Hawaiian Islands by a number of interesting purple-flowered shrubby species. At left, *L. hillebrandii* (Koolau Gap, Maui); at right, *L. rotundifolia* (Mt. Kaala, Oahu).

Restricted to the Hawaiian Islands (except for one species in Tahiti) is the genus *Phyllostegia*, which forms sprawling stems, tipped by white flowers, in the undergrowth of wet forests. Shown here is *P. lantanoides* (Konahuanui summit, Oahu).

Phytolacca brachystachys is a purple-fruited Hawaiian pokeweed seen sometimes straggling, sometimes climbing, in wet forest areas (Kehena, Hawaii).

The giant-leaved apeape is a plant of deep shady wet gulches at left, Waikamoi Gulch, Maui; or on cliffs perpetually brushed by clouds, as at Alakahi, Hawaii, right. Although several species have been described, all the Hawaiian apeapes may perhaps be called *Gunnera petaloidea*. The long inflorescences bear inconspicuous reddish flowers, then small orange fruits. If one cuts open stems of the apeape, one can find numerous colonies of blue-green algae, which form a symbiotic relationship: these algae fix nitrogen, and help supply nitrates to the apeape, which lives in wet, nitrogen-poor conditions.

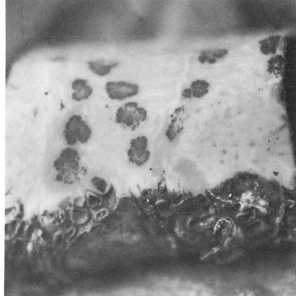

Hillebrandia, a genus of the begonia family, is limited to the Hawaiian Islands. In wet shady localities one can find *H. sandwicensis* with its pale pink flowers,
grouped into nodding inflorescences (photo of male flowers
above, female flowers at left).

Luzula campestris var. *hawaiiensis* has gray, silky leaves and can
be found in open places in the
wet forest, as here at Kilauea.

Forming tangled vines over shrubs in wet forests from Kauai to Maui is the uhi (or ulehihi), *Smilax sandwicensis* (Wiliwilinui Ridge, Oahu).

Astelia menziesiana, the painiu, has bright orange berries and silvery leaves. Painius are conspicuous plants in wet forests (Kilauea, Hawaii).

The ohe, *Joinvillea gaudichaudiana*, is a rare clump-forming plant in wet forests. Its flowers are very inconspicuous. The fruits are also small, but turn bright orange when mature. Leaves are distinctively deeply grooved. *Joinvillea*, like many other Indo-Malaysian genera reaches its easternmost point in the Hawaiian Islands (Waianae Mountains, Oahu; Olaa forest, Hawaii).

Although many sedges can be found in the Hawaiian Islands, *Cladium angustifolium* is one of the most conspicuous (Konahuanui Trail, Oahu).

Native orchids are very few in the Islands: only three species, all with very small, inconspicuous flowers, are native. Here are *Liparis hawaiiensis*, left (Puu Kukui, Maui); and *Anoectochilus sandwicensis*, right (Nuuanu, Oahu).

Pendant spikes of sporangia of this club moss, *Lycopodium cernuum,* were commemorated by the Hawaiian name "wawae iole," which means "rat's foot" (Kalalau lookout, Kauai).

Lycopodium venustulum trails on the ground in wet places (Kahuku, Mauna Loa, Hawaii).

Selaginella arbuscula is an inconspicuous primitive land plant from wet Hawaiian forests (Waianae Mountains, Oahu).

The pala fern, *Marattia douglasii*, is now rather rare because it is readily eaten by pigs. It grows in deep shade, can form a rosette of large leaves, deep green in color, with curious swellings at the bases of leaflets (Waianae Mountains, Oahu).

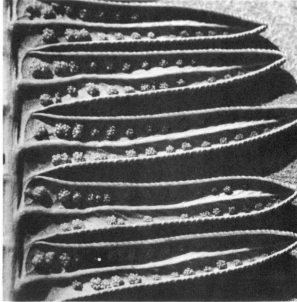

Dicranopteris linearis, the uluhe, is the commonest and most conspicuous fern of wet forest areas. Pale green mats of it cover open ridge areas, steep cliff sides, and devastated forest areas in moist regions of all the major islands (Kalalau, Kauai).

Sticherus owyhensis is related to the common uluhe, but differs in leaf shape (Kalalau, Kauai).

Hicropteris pinnata, in the same family as the uluhe, grows in wet forest areas; its leaves are forked into only two large halves (Honopue, Hawaii).

Most filmy ferns are small and grow on trees, but this one, *Callistopteris baldwinii,* occurs on the ground in shady areas of wet forest (Punaluu, Oahu).

Cibotium glaucum, with whitish waxy undersides of leaves, is the hapuu, or tree fern, which can be found at Kilauea. Scaly hairs on the young fronds are abundant and have been used for stuffing pillows. The greatly enlarged leaf undersurface shows cupules which contain the minute spore cases (sporangia), and represents the species most common in the Islands, *Cibotium chamissoi,* the hapuu iii (Humuula Saddle Road, Hawaii).

Several species of amau (*Sadleria,* an endemic Hawaiian genus) have evolved into distinctive situations. In wet forest, as at Kilauea (upper left), the scaly S. *pallida* can be found. *Sadleria cyatheoides,* upper right, can form a trunk; this species is the commonest one in the Islands. From specimens in a different locality (Kehena, Hawaii), young fronds and greatly enlarged leaf undersurfaces, showing arrangement of sporangia, are shown.

Sadleria squarrosa is a very small amau which grows on dripping slopes and cliffs. Leaf segments are cup-like (Kehena, Hawaii).

Doodia kunthiana, the pamoho, forms rosettes on the floor of moderately moist forest areas. Closely related species grow in the South Pacific (Kokee, Kauai).

Athyrium microphyllum is a "miniature tree fern" with a trunk up to two feet tall and a rosette of finely dissected leaves. It grows in shade of wet forests (Pihea, Kauai).

Asplenium falcatum is one of many species of this fern genus in the Islands (Manoa Trail, Oahu).

Athyrium sandwichianum is a rather common Hawaiian fern, identifiable by the characteristic pattern of sporangia on undersides of leaves (Konahuanui Trail, Oahu).

Microsorium spectrum is a polypody fern distinctive because of its creeping habit and ivy-like leaves (Punaluu, Oahu).

The ear fungus (*Auricularia*) is only one of many interesting fungi in the Hawaiian Islands. Hawaiian mushrooms tend to be very small and inconspicuous, but bracket fungi are abundant and easily found (Waianae Mountains, Oahu).

Chapter 17 🙢 *THE EPIPHYTIC VEGETATION*

EPIPHYTES, the "plants upon plants," merit discussion as a separate habitat, even though this habitat is, in fact, tree trunks within the wet forest. A tree trunk is a pioneering habitat, because it has no soil, yet it is within a rain or cloud forest, so the roots of plants which grow on those tree trunks will not become excessively dried.

The Hawaiian Islands have extremely wet areas, and would be expected to contain many epiphytes, which require frequent rainfall to counter the natural evaporation from tree trunks. Epiphytes tend to show that moisture, not sunlight, is the limiting factor for plant growth in a forest, and that additional tiers of plants could grow successfully, even if the forest were quite shady, provided that enough rainfall and cloud cover were available. Epiphytes are conspicuous in the Hawaiian Islands, but there are only a few kinds. Bromeliads, the pineapple family, are a group of epiphytes all but universal in forests of the New World, but none are native to the Hawaiian Islands. Dispersal has evidently not favored introduction of the bromeliads. Orchids are also notably absent from the Islands, although one would have guessed that the minuteness of orchid seeds would make them excellent candidates for long-distance dispersal. Only three species of orchids are native to the Islands, and these are all terrestrial (ground inhabiting). While the trees of wet Indo-Malaysian forests are clotted with epiphytic orchids, those of wet Hawaiian woods are covered mostly with mosses and liverworts. Evidently epiphytic orchids, like the bromeliads, are not as good at dispersal or establishment as might be expected. The difficulty of establishment might be the clue, for many orchids have intricate pollination relationships with particular insects, and if the insects did not establish on the Islands concomitantly with the orchids, no seed would be set.

There are a few true epiphytic flowering plants in the Hawaiian flora. Most frequent and characteristic of these is the alaawanui, *Peperomia*, of which there are about fifty native species. Peperomias are typically epiphytes wherever they grow, but the other flowering plant epiphytes are not. These include *Astelia*, the painiu, most species of which are terrestrial, although the genus seems to slip into epiphytism easily enough in rain forests. *Plantago* and *Nertera* occur as epiphytes, although they are most common in bogs, and are discussed in that connection in the next chapter. A few species of *Clermontia* (Chapter 12) are characteristically epiphytes. These clermon-

Wet forest trees are coated, sometimes very densely, with mosses, liverworts, and lichens. These are epiphytes which aid the larger epiphytes—ferns and flowering plants—in establishing upon tree trunks. The tree illustrated here is an olapa (*Cheirodendron*) on Puu Kukui, West Maui.

tias may form the only case of plants which have evolved into true epiphytes within the Hawaiian Islands. Obviously there is a "vacuum" where epiphytes are concerned, and mosses, liverworts, and ferns partly fill this vacuum, but a few flowering plants—mostly just chance seedlings from the terrestrial flora, except for those noted above—accept this opportunity. One such frequent epiphyte is *Cheirodendron*, the olapa. The ieie, *Freycinetia arborea*, perhaps qualifies more as a climber than as an epiphyte, but it combines qualities of both; most of its roots penetrate, cling to, the bark of the tree on which it grows.

Because such typical epiphytes as orchids and bromeliads are not present, and flowering plants other then *Peperomia* are mostly epiphytes-by-chance, ferns appear to assume an important role as epiphytes. Some of these ferns are those familiar as epiphytes in other tropical countries—for example, the bird's-nest fern (*Asplenium nidus*), *Vittaria elongata*, and *Elaphoglossum*, the tongue fern. *Elaphoglossum* is the largest group of epiphytic ferns in the Islands, in numbers of species. However, in number of individuals, *Amphoradenium* ex-

An ohia tree, subjected to the constant mists rising from the pali on Oahu, has collected a thick coating of mosses and liverworts, in which numerous ferns have taken root (Konahuanui summit, Oahu).

A single ohia tree can host many large epiphytic shrubs. *Clermontia* and *Cheirodendron* can be seen on this ohia, in addition to tree ferns (*Cibotium*) and smaller plants (Honaunau, Kona, Hawaii).

ceeds the others. Hawaiian amphoradeniums may be closely related to epiphytic polypody ferns of the South Pacific, like *Polypodium samoense*. However, *Amphoradenium* can be considered an endemic genus in the Islands. It has diversified, and done so very largely within the epiphytic realm. Some of the amphoradeniums do grow in bogs, but the difference between bog and epiphytic habitats is not very great: a fern growing on a fallen log in a bog region can just as easily grow in the bog itself. *Amphoradenium montanum, A. haalilioanum,* and *A. pumilum* can be found within bogs occasionally. Among amphoradeniums, *A. hymenophylloides* is distinctive in its delicate, much-dissected drooping leaves, which are pale green in color. *Amphoradenium tripinnatifidum* is essentially a race of *A. tamariscinum* in which leaves are larger, more dissected. Curiously notched leaves characterize *A. pinnatifidus* and *A. haalilioanum;* the notches cut down close to the leaf midrib in leaves of *A. sarmentosum.* The significance of these various leaf forms in *Amphoradenium* poses an interesting evolutionary problem.

Epiphytism in the Hawaiian Islands is, as we have seen, not a matter of plants which are always epiphytic, while others are always terrestrial. In the wet forest, we see minute epiphytic assemblages of mosses and filmy ferns, but we also see larger plants, and almost any plant in the wet forest can occasionally be seen as an epiphyte, part of an endlessly complex and irregular arrangement.

The ieie (*Freycinetia arborea*) is a common vining epiphyte in the wet forest. It takes root as it climbs, so it can be regarded as an epiphyte (Honaunau, Kona, Hawaii). Along the summit ridge of the Koolau Mountains, Oahu, ecological conditions are right for the ieie, but there are no trees on which it can climb, so it lies on the ground (Moanalua Trail, Oahu).

The flowers of the ieie are surrounded by short leaves bright
orange in color. These flowers
probably attract bats, which are
known to pollinate such flowers
(Honaunau, Kona, Hawaii).

The painiu can grow on the ground or on trees, and often can be seen in both
localities at once. This narrow-leaved species is *Astelia argyrocoma* (Pihea, Kauai).

Plantago hillebrandii grows epiphytically in mosses on ohia trees at the summit of the Koolau Mountains. Most Hawaiian species of Plantago could be called bog plants, and the occurrence of P. hillebrandii as an epiphyte shows that the epiphytic habitat in very wet forest is not unlike the bog habitat.

This alaalawainui, Peperomia leptostachya, is native in the Hawaiian Islands, but is also native elsewhere in the Pacific: the Marquesas Islands, Society Islands, and tropical Australia (Mt. Kaala, Oahu).

The pendant moa, Psilotum complanatum, is almost always found growing epiphytically. The plant at left occurs on a tree fern (Cibotium) trunk (root of an epiphytic Clermontia parviflora to the left) at Kehena, Hawaii. The P. complanatum at right is surrounded by a tuft of mosses on a tree on Puu Kukui, Maui.

Lycopodium phyllanthum is a club moss which grows epiphytically, its stems pendant (Puu Kukui, Maui).

The laukahi, *Ophioglossum pendulum*, is a peculiar fern, belonging to a family of primitive ferns. Its sickle-shaped leaves bear pendant tongue-like groups of sporangia (Wiliwilinui Ridge, Oahu).

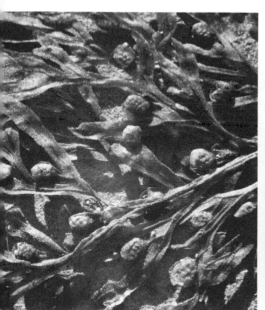

The most common filmy fern in the Hawaiian Islands is *Mecodium recurvum*, (left) a very small fern often hidden among mosses on tree trunks. *Sphaerocionium lanceolatum*, (right) is also a small filmy fern, which can be identified by its hairy fronds (Kehena, Hawaii).

Amphoradenium tamariscinum is almost always found as an epiphyte in the mountains of all the major islands. The Hawaiian name, "wahine noo mauna" ("lady of the mountains"), indicates how characteristic it is of the Hawaiian forests. The leaves are typically bipinnate, with sporangia at the tips of the numerous segments (Konahuanui summit, Oahu).

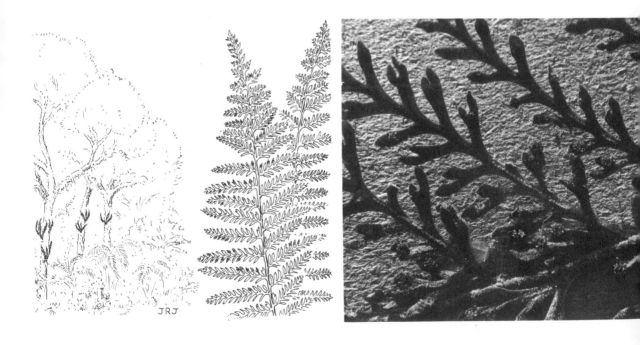

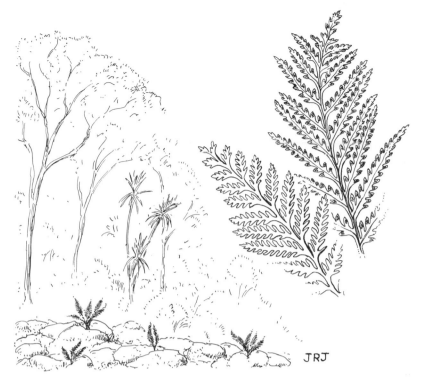

Amphoradenium hillebrandii is occasionally epiphytic but tends also to grow on ground in the lower forests.

Amphoradenium montanum grows in bogs or as an epiphyte in nearby woods in extremely wet localities, such as Waialeale, Kauai, or Puu Kukui, Maui.

Much-divided leaves characterize *Amphoradenium tripinnatifidum,* a sort of exaggerated A. *tamarascinum.*

Leaves of *Amphoradenium haalilioanum* are only notched along the edges, and represent a condition opposite from that of *A. tripinnatifidum.*

Amphoradenium hymenophylloides has small, delicate drooping leaves and is always epiphytic (Kehena, Hawaii).

Amphoradenium sarmentosum is a conspicuous epiphyte with pinnate leaves (Mt. Kahili, Kauai).

Amphoradenium pinnatifidum has long, pendant leaves, the longest of any *Amphoradenium*. Once this species was common, now it festoons only a few trees.

Grammitis tenella is a very common fern epiphyte. It can easily be recognized by its narrow leaves, which bear dots of sporangia (sori) wider than the leaf itself (Punaluu, Oahu).

The giant rosettes of the bird's-nest fern, *Asplenium nidus,* form a magnificent sight in shady valleys (Waianae Mountains, Oahu).

The tongue fern, *Elaphoglossum,* is represented by many species in the Hawaiian Islands. These individuals, growing on a log in the Olaa forest, are *E. alatum* var. *parvisquameum.*

 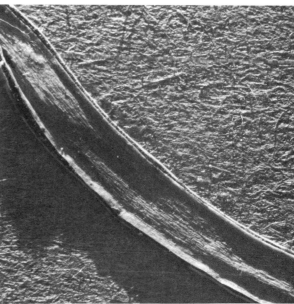

Vittaria elongata is a common epiphytic fern of moderately moist forest. It can be recognized by its strap-like leaves, about a quarter of an inch wide, which have sporangia set in a groove along each margin (Pauoa, Oahu).

Chapter 18 THE BOGS

HAWAIIAN bogs are surprising if one is acquainted with bogs elsewhere. Despite many areas of high rainfall in the Islands, Hawaiian bogs are mostly relatively small in number and area. A map of Kauai usually labels the high plateau "Alakai Swamp," and decorates this area with the tuft-like symbols cartographers place on swamp areas in maps. However, Alakai is not a swamp at all. There are very few areas of standing water, or ponds. Most of the "Alakai Swamp" is simply an ohia forest. The "Swamp" covers rolling country and is mostly well drained. There are, however, small pockets of open bog in several parts of the Alakai.

If topography aids bog formation, bogs ought to be a feature of lower elevations, where flatlands would make bogs more likely. Only one Hawaiian bog is at a lower elevation, and it is a relatively small one: Wahiawa Bog ("Kanaele

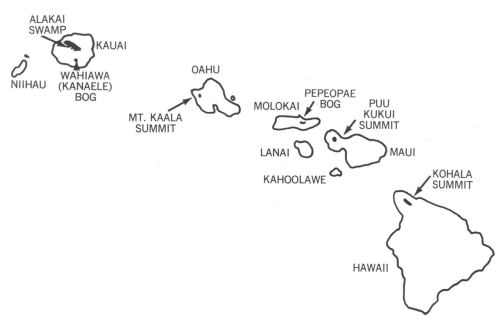

Open bogs in the Hawaiian Islands are few, mostly small (much smaller than areas indicated on this map), and mostly in remote localities difficult of access. Development of bogs depends on heavy rainfall, but also on suitable terrain.

Wahiawa Bog (Kanaele Swamp on some maps) on Kauai is the only low-elevation bog in the Islands. It has occurred from natural damming of a valley, apparently.

Swamp" on some maps), at about a thousand feet on southern Kauai. The other bogs in the Islands are all high elevation bogs. The reason for this appears to be that the porosity of Hawaiian soils is so great that only in areas of greatest rainfall can runoff be exceeded. Reasonably level land in these wet areas is small in extent. The largest area is that of the Alakai plateau, an unusual "cap rock" formation discussed in Chapter 1. Bogs on islands other than Kauai are on summit areas of old volcanic domes, and are limited by steep slopes which drop off away from them. Apparently only peculiar conditions, such as a natural damming which permits clay-like soil to accumulate, permit bogs to form even in these summit areas.

Another common criterion of bogs in various parts of the world is the presence of *Sphagnum* moss. This moss, which acts as a sort of wick drawing water from a pond and permitting enlargement of the bog, is absent from Hawaiian bogs with one exception. Only in the Kohala bogs can one find *Sphagnum,* and even these areas do not remind one of typical *Sphagnum* bogs. They are only small mats of *Sphagnum* on slopes, among ohia trees. The Alakahi area of the Kohala summit dome is not really a swamp or a *Sphagnum* bog—merely an area of rather level wet vegetation.

The common denominators of the Hawaiian bogs are mud, very small pockets of standing water, and tussocks of *Oreobolus. Oreobolus furcatus* is a sedge which forms deep green, rounded tussocks. Another tussock-forming plant in

One interesting plant visible in Wahiawa Bog is the sundew, *Drosera anglica,* an insectivorous plant which can also be found in bogs elsewhere in the northern hemisphere.

Cheirodendron fauriei forms a small tree in Wahiawa Bog, illustrating that the bog habitat tends to dwarf woody plants. A large rosette of *Lobelia gaudichaudii* (*L. kauaensis* of some authors) is not dwarfed; species of *Lobelia* typically grow in very wet places.

Myrsine angustifolia is a kolea which forms a spindly shrub with willow-like leaves in the Wahiawa Bog. It is seen here growing with uluhe, *Dicranopteris*.

Pelea waialealae is a distinctive plant which grows in the summit bog of Kauai and also in Wahiawa Bog.

Nertera granadensis var. *insularis* is a small trailing plant with orange fruits which grows in bogs or as an epiphyte (Wahiawa Bog, Kauai).

Hawaiian bogs is the grass *Panicum*, of which several closely related species have been distinguished. Several kinds of mosses tend to infiltrate into the sedge or grass tussocks, or to lie between them, sometimes forming tussocks themselves.

Many Hawaiian bog plants tend to form trailing stems which root in the bog: *Viola mauiensis* (Chapter 6), *Lagenophora mauiensis,* and *Geranium humile,* for example. This habit has been adapted, in a rather gross way, by the Puu Kukui silversword (Chapter 13) also. The ohia forms roots easily along stems, and so it is pre-adapted to bog life. Most surprising is the way in which ohias are greatly decreased in stature in Hawaiian bogs. Many of them mature, even flower, when they are less than a foot in height—and some plants never exceed that height. These ohias are probably the same kind as those which grow at the margins of the bogs, but are severely stunted in the bog conditions. Similar stunting occurs in the case of ohelo (*Vaccinium*) and pukiawe (*Styphelia*), which provide miniature growths often no higher than the sedge tussocks. In the Puu Kukui Bog, the pilo (*Coprosma ochracea*) is markedly dwarfed.

Drosera, the sundew, is a bog plant in various parts of the world. In the Hawaiian bogs *Drosera anglica,* a widespread species in the northern hemi-

The summit bog of Waialeale, wettest place in the Hawaiian Islands, is an open bog dotted with clumps of a grass, *Deschampsia ambiguua* (photography by Melvern Tessene). A typical scene in the central part of Alakai Swamp, right, shows standing water, low vegetation, and pockets of ohia forest.

Plantago krajinai, left, a strange plant found only at the summit of Mt. Waialeale, has white wool on both surfaces of leaves. At right, *Plantago nubicola* grows as clusters of numerous small rosettes (photographs by Melvern Tessene).

sphere, can be found. It has oblong leaves, with glistening drops on the tentacle hairs. Sundews are insect-eating plants, a habit which has been interpreted as a compensation for the low nitrogen content of bogs.

The painiu, *Astelia,* is common in Hawaiian bogs. Most bogs contain *A. forbesii.* However, *Astelia nivea* with its strikingly white, almost silvery leaves is a conspicuous sight in the high Puu Kukui bogs. Another typical Hawaiian bog plant is *Plantago.* Various species occur in the bogs, notably *P. hillebrandii* and *P. melanochrous.* The summit area of Waialeale, Kauai, is a center for these rosette plants. The large leaves of *P. glabrifolia* contrast with the miniature rosettes of *P. nubicola.* Although some of the Hawaiian plantagos have woolly hairs on the undersides of leaves, *P. krajinai* is also woolly on upper surfaces of leaves as well. This is indeed a curious development, because hairiness in leaves is often associated with dry, sunny locations.

Plantagos are relatively small rosette plants. Among the striking features of Hawaiian bogs are the giant rosette plants: *Lobelia* and *Argyroxiphium.* *Lobelia gaudichaudii*, described in Chapter 12, appears in bog and near-bog areas on Kauai, Oahu, Maui, and Molokai in the form of varieties. The variety *gloriamontis* on Puu Kukui sends up striking tower-like or candelabra-like inflorescences of white flowers. Populations of *L. gaudichaudii* in the other bogs may have white flowers streaked purple, or reddish flowers. Rosettes of the silversword

The suitability of Waialeale's wet conditions for *Plantago* species is illustrated here by a largish species, *P. glabrifolia,* growing among clumps of *Deschampsia ambiguua* grass. The Waialeale naenae, *Dubautia waialealae,* right, is a species found only in the summit bog of Kauai (photographs by Melvern Tessene).

The Puu Kukui Bog contains a colony of the bog silversword, *Argyroxiphium caliginii.* Ohia forest is seen in the background. Standing water is not common in the Puu Kukui Bog (with the exception of small pockets), but there is a pond known as Violet Lake.

Argyroxiphium caliginii and the greensword *A. grayanum* are exclusive features of the Puu Kukui Bog, and make this bog perhaps the loveliest in the Islands.

The bog habitat is a difficult one: waterlogged soils are poor in nitrogen compounds, and roots under water become starved for oxygen. In the high bogs, moments of bright sunshine alternate with cool misty showers; nights are cold. It is surprising that there are as many plants in the bogs of the Islands as there are. Some of these (*Oreobolus*) appear to be bog plants from other regions, some appear to be Hawaiian wet forest plants (*Vaccinium, Metrosideros*) which can grow, although not very luxuriantly, in the bogs, and do so perhaps in the absence of other groups. Some plants appear to be adaptations of alpine plants (*Geranium, Argyroxiphium*), for which tolerance to extreme temperature and sunlight conditions pre-adapts them in part for life in the high bogs. Some are merely plants of wet places in the north temperate zone, which of course has relatively cool temperatures like those of alpine Hawaii: *Viola, Lobelia*. Collectively, these plants form a curious plant assemblage.

The dark green tussocks of the Puu Kukui Bog (left) are a sedge, *Oreobolus furcatus*. Among these, various plants, some of them diminished version of plants seen in wet forest, can be found. The uluhe, *Dicranopteris*, is seen below the tussock; two rosettes of *Argyroxiphium caliginii*, left; and numerous ohia plants. In photo at right is an *Oreobolus* tussock in front of which is the bog pukiawe, *Styphelia douglasii*, right, and the oalii makalii fern, *Schizaea robusta*, left.

A daisy-like composite, *Lagenophora mauiensis,* grows in the Puu Kukui Bog. Other species of *Lagenophora* grow on mountains of the South Pacific and cooler parts of South America. At right, a *Plantago* seen in several Hawaiian bogs, *P. melanochrous.*

One of the Hawaiian geraniums, *G. humile,* is restricted to the Puu Kukui Bog. Its stems trail and root in the bog. Also seen in the photo at left is a rosette of *Argyroxiphium grayanum,* the Puu Kukui greensword, and some ohia plants.

The silvery Puu Kukui painiu, *Astelia nivea*, bears purple flowers. Growing with the *Astelia* is a pilo, *Coprosma ochracea*, shown enlarged at right.

Growing among tussocks of the Puu Kukui Bog can be found *Selaginella deflexa*, left; and the oalii makalii fern, *Schizaea robusta*, right.

Close views of tussocks from the Pepeopae Bog, Molokai: at left, a tiny ohia plant in flower, with clumps of a white moss, left. In photo at right, the bog *Plantago, P. hillebrandii,* surrounded by various tussocks—at lower right, a grass (*Panicum isachnoides*).

The two chief tussock plants from Hawaiian bogs are *Oreobolus furcatus,* left, and *Panicum isachnoides,* right (Pepeopae Bog, Molokai).

The painiu from Molokai's Pepeopae Bog is *Astelia forbesii*. It has purple flowers. Unlike woody plants, which are stunted by bogs, the herbaceous bog plants appear to grow at near-normal stature.

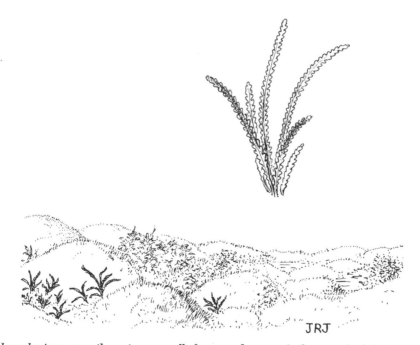

Amphoradenium pumilum is a small fern, and one of the amphoradeniums which seems to grow in bogs more than as an epiphyte.

Most of the world's bogs feature *Sphagnum* moss, but this is absent from all Hawaiian bogs except for those at Kehena, in the upper Kohala Mountains.

Chapter 19   THE ALPINE ZONE

THOSE accustomed to alpine vegetation in other areas will find the vegetation of the high Hawaiian summits surprising. Most typical alpine plants are absent. Instead, some Hawaiian alpines are the same as plants one finds at lower elevations on dry, exposed ridges: pukiawe (*Styphelia tameiameiae*), aalii (*Dodonaea*), sagebrush (*Artemisia*), iliahi (*Santalum*), akia (*Wikstroemia*), and *Exocarpus*. Other alpine plants belong to groups which appear at various levels in the Islands: naenae or kupaoa (*Dubautia*), pilo (*Coprosma*), *Hedyotis*, ae (*Polypodium pellucidum*), and amau (*Sadleria*). The mamani (*Sophora chrysophylla*) grows in lower forest occasionally, as on Kauai, but mostly grows in high dry forest.

In addition to varied types of lava and cinders, Haleakala offers varied climatic conditions. Here, clouds filtering up Koolau Gap can be seen.

A scattering of Hawaiian alpines occurs exclusively in this zone, or nearly so. *Geranium* cannot be found in the lowlands; while one species (*G. humile*) has adapted to the high bogs of Maui, the remainder are in drier high elevation localities. Other plants which are "true" alpines or nearly so include catchfly (*Silene*), ahinahina (*Argyroxiphium*), strawberry (*Fragaria*), pawale (*Rumex*), *Sisyrinchium,* and, with few exceptions, the ohelo (*Vaccinium*).

At the summit of Haleakala one can find an aster relative, *Tetramolopium humile*, which forms a miniature shrub in crevices of lava.

The Haleakala naenae, *Dubautia menziesii*, is a low shrub with stiff yellowish succulent leaves and yellow-orange flowers (from color photographs by James W. Larson).

Appropriately, many Hawaiian alpines are representatives of north temperate zone groups. For example, the strawberry, *Fragaria chiloensis*, is apparently identical with the coastal strawberry of North America and Chile. At the higher latitudes, cool temperatures occur at the coast; similar temperatures occur at the lower latitudes of the Hawaiian Islands only at higher elevations. Other north temperate zone representatives include *Artemisia, Sisyrinchium, Silene, Dubautia*, and *Vaccinium*. On the other hand, *Coprosma, Santalum, Wikstroemia*, and probably *Sophora* are from the south temperate zone. Geraniums are found in both north and south temperate zones, and the Hawaiian species are not readily linked with a particular site of origin because they are so distinctive. The veins in leaves of Hawaiian geraniums run almost parallel, and the leaf terminates in a series of teeth.

Alpine localities in the Hawaiian Islands can be thought of as levels of six thousand feet and above. Thus only four mountains qualify: Haleakala on Maui, and Mauna Kea, Mauna Loa, and Hualalai on Hawaii. However, the saddles between Mauna Kea and Mauna Loa and between Mauna Loa and Hualalai are themselves high enough to support alpine vegetation. Kilauea, at about four thousand feet, contains a number of alpine species. In part, alpine plants may be adapted to growing in barren cinders at intermediate to high altitudes, and

Mainland species of *Silene* ("catchfly") never become woody miniature shrubs like *S. struthioivides* of Haleakala. Flowers are pale purple-brown.

barren cinder areas at Kilauea may prove suitable for alpine plants partly because of these soil conditions. Four thousand feet elevation, however, is rather
cool in the Hawaiian Islands.

Haleakala has a striking collection of alpine plants. One thinks first of the
silversword and greensword (*Argyroxiphium*), as well as the related naenaes
(*Dubautia*), all of which are described in Chapter 13. Within the crater, two
distinctive species of *Coprosma* can be seen: the orange-fruited mountain pilo,
C. montana, is related to species of the wet forest, but *C. ernodeoides* is a
distinctive species with black fruits, not closely related to other Hawaiian coprosmas. The silvery *Geranium tridens*, a striking plant whose silvery leaves
suggest alpine adaptations like those of the silversword, is found only on Haleakala, but is not far from the species *G. cuneatum* on Hawaii. The red-flowered
Geranium arboreum (Chapter 4) is a quite distinctive plant from low alpine
regions of Haleakala. At the low alpine zone, as at the National Park headquarters, one can find shrubby or tree-like individuals of the mamani (*Sophora
chrysophylla*) and an endemic sandalwood or iliahi (*Santalum haleakalae*). The
aalii (*Dodonaea*) and pukiawe (*Styphelia*) are common shrubs at this elevation.

Two species of *Coprosma* common in Haleakala Crater are the orange-fruited
mountain pilo, *C. montana*, left, and the trailing black-fruited *C. ernodeoides*,
right, variously known as kukainene, punene, or leponene—all names which imply
that its fruits are sought by the Hawaiian goose, the nene. *Coprosma* is a Pacific
genus best developed in New Zealand and the Hawaiian Islands.

The silvery Haleakala *Geranium, G. tridens,* was known to the Hawaiians by the same name as was the silversword, ahinahina, because both have shimmering leaves.

The Haleakala iliahi or sandalwood, *Santalum haleakalae,* has massive clusters of brick-red flowers, purple-black olive-shaped fruits.

Two ohelos can be found on the floor of Haleakala Crater: *Vaccinium reticulatum*, left, and *V. berberidifolium*, right.

Sadleria cyatheoides, the amau, grows on alpine slopes along the Halemau Trail of Haleakala. These slopes are on the windward side of Haleakala, so that clouds occasionally rise to this height (ca. eight thousand feet), providing enough moisture for ferns.

Ferns favoring high elevations are well represented at Haleakala. At the summit area, only a few plants can be found—most notably *Tetramolopium humile* and *Dubautia menziesii*. On cinder cones within the crater, the silversword *Argyroxiphium sandwicense* is found, and with it the odd shrubby catchfly, *Silene struthioloides*.

Hualalai does not have as varied a summit area as Haleakala, but it has virtually as many interesting plants. Counterpart to the silver *Geranium* of Haleakala is *G. cuneatum*, which is also silvery but has five, rather than three, teeth at the tip of each leaf. *Exocarpus gaudichaudii*, a curious broom-like shrub, is frequent. It could, by a stretch of the imagination, be regarded as a counterpart to the Haleakala sandalwood, because both belong to the sandalwood family. Akia (*Wikstroemia*), uulei (*Osteomeles*), aalii (*Dodonaea*), and pukiawe (*Styphelia*) are other shrubs easily seen at the summit area. The herbs *Sisyrinchium acre*, *Fragaria chiloensis*, *Tetramolopium humile*, *Dubautia ciliolata*, and *Stenogyne diffusa* are less common but can be found in a few places. The mamani, *Sophora chrysophylla*, becomes abundant below the summit area.

Alpine Mauna Loa offers much the same range of plants as Hualalai. However, a *Geranium* with leaves silvery below but green above (*G. cuneatum* var. *hypoleucum*) may be found. A race of the Haleakala silversword, *Argyroxiphium sandwicense*, may still be found at the summit, while the Kau silversword, *A. kauense*, grows at the lower margins of the alpine zone.

Alpine plants on Hawaii may be seen conveniently on the Humuula Saddle Road. On the Hilo side of the summit of the road, old flows bear such typically alpine plants as ohelo (*Vaccinium*), kukainene (*Coprosma ernodeoides*), *Hedyotis centranthoides*, as well as pukiawe (*Styphelia*) and aalii (*Dodonaea*), various ferns, and a magnificent display of the lava lichen, *Stereocaulon vulcani*.

Kilauea is basically a rain forest area, but alpine plants enter the region. Kilauea plants which could be regarded as alpines include ohelos (*Vaccinium reticulatum*, *V. pahalae*), kupaoa (*Dubautia ciliolata*), Kilauea catchfly (*Silene hawaiiensis*), and pawale (*Rumex giganteus*).

Reviewing alpine plants, we find that the dry habitat preferences of tarweed ancestors probably have pre-adapted their descendants—*Argyroxiphium* and *Dubautia*—for alpine conditions. *Coprosma* is perhaps a more surprising entry into the alpine habitat, but there are alpine coprosmas on South Pacific islands, such as New Zealand and New Guinea. These groups, however, are distinctive for extending into the alpine zone, whereas most groups represented in the rain forest do not.

In addition, *Dubautias* are exceptional alpines in the fact that different species occur in the alpine zone of different mountains: *D. menziesii* (and several others) on Haleakala, *D. struthioloides* on Mauna Kea, *D. ciliolata* on all four volcanoes of Hawaii, etc. The only examples of speciation in Hawaiian alpine areas at all comparable to this are in *Geranium*, and, to a lesser extent, *Vaccinium* and *Silene*.

Polypodium pellucidum, the ae, grows with other ferns high on Haleakala.

Asplenium trichomanes from alpine Haleakala (Halemau Trail) has leaves highly reduced compared to those of forest aspleniums.

Pellaea ternifolia, or kalamoho laulii, can be found in various alpine localities in the Islands, as here at Halemau Trail, Haleakala.

The summit of Hualalai consists of numerous cinder cones, sparsely dotted by shrubs.

Stenogyne diffusa var. *glabra* has leaves much smaller than stenogynes of rain forest, although its red-orange flowers are similar (Hualalai).

Geranium cuneatum from Hualalai has five-toothed leaves covered with silvery hairs on both surfaces.

Exocarpus gaudichaudii is a broom-like shrub of the sandalwood family. It grows in cinders at the summit area of Hualalai. Its leaves are scale-like and vestigial; seeds are enclosed by a fleshy white cup.

The mamani, *Sophora chrysophylla*, grows in dry forest, but is perhaps most characteristic of high areas rather than low. Its flowers, like those of peas, lupines, and beans, reveal that it is a legume; they are yellow. This species may be closely related to sophoras from New Zealand.

An alpine akia, *Wikstroemia phillyreaefolia*, has elliptical leaves and tubular yellow flowers (Hualalai).

Sisyrinchium acre represents an American element in the Hawaiian flora. Other species are found in the New World (Hualalai).

A wild strawberry, *Fragaria chilo-ensis,* is native to the Hawaiian Islands as well as coastal areas of North and South America (Huala-lai).

Geranium cuneatum var. *hypoleu-cum* has silvery hairs on the lower leaf surfaces, but the upper surfaces are smooth and green. This variety comes from Mauna Loa.

Along higher elevations of the Humuula Saddle Road are recent lava flows which bear plants typical of alpine areas. This is not surprising, because the road rises above six thousand feet. The distinctive purple-leaved plant shown here is *Hedyotis centranthoides* (or *Kadua centranthoides*) of the coffee family.

An ohelo, *Vaccinium reticulatum,* can be seen as a markedly woody shrub on the Humuula Saddle Road.

Lava in moist or even relatively dry areas is often covered by a white lichen, *Stereocaulon vulcani* (Humuula Saddle Road).

In Kilauea, one can see individuals of a giant dock, the pawale *Rumex giganteus.*
The stems and fruits of the pawale are orange-brown.

The kupaoa *Dubautia ciliolata* forms spiky shrubs in Kilauea. It is closely related
to other alpine dubautias, such as *D. menziesii* of Haleakala.

Silene hawaiiensis, a catchfly of Kilauea, differs from S. *struthioloides* of Haleakala. *Silene hawaiiensis* is not shrubby; instead, it branches from a parsnip-like tuberous root.

THE LEEWARD CHAIN

"Leeward" is a misnomer for the lesser islands of the Hawaiian chain, which stretch westward beyond Niihau. They are not in the "lee" of anything; their relative dryness simulates a leeward coast, and probably accounts for the name. The islands are relatively small, which accounts for their dry climate: they total only about ten square miles, or two thousand acres.

These rocks and atolls, now worn down to vestiges of their ancient estate, support only a limited assortment of plants and animals. The Leewards flora is basically that of a tropical beach, and virtually all of the plants can be seen on shores of the main islands—with a few exceptions, of course. The fauna is very largely a shore fauna, too. Nonetheless, a rich assortment of marine and shore birds is crowded on the islands. A few land birds are native. Laysan was (and to some extent, still is) a unique museum of birds, and would be worth description for that alone.

The very poverty of the flora and fauna is interesting. These islands support miniature assemblages of organisms, and the problems of life on small land areas are, in fact, quite interesting ones.

Because their land areas are limited, the animals and plants of the Leeward Islands are potentially endangered: any disturbance will be more drastic there than on a large land mass. For this reason, protection has been necessary. In 1909 President Theodore Roosevelt proclaimed the islands from Nihoa to Kure the Hawaiian Islands Bird Reservation. It is known today as the Hawaiian Islands National Wildlife Refuge. Military installations on French Frigate Shoal, Midway, and Kure must be counted a loss of potential refuge area, but the remaining areas are being wisely and carefully managed and studied. Access to these islands is restricted under the terms of the Refuge, and under this protection we can look forward to preservation of these vulnerable areas indefinitely. Curiously, the attitude of many on learning of the existence of these tiny islands is, "How can they be used?" To such people, the preservation of an island is a waste. Fortunately, though, the commercial value of the Leeward Islands is minimal. They can, however, serve as perfect examples of small islands and their wildlife.

The marine birds of the Leeward Islands are much the same from island to island, with certain exceptions. This is also true of the atoll plants. Therefore, marine birds or beach plants shown here for a particular island could just as well have been shown for others in most cases. Readers interested in finding precise and full records of which animals and plants have been recorded for which islands will want to consult the references.

Chapter 20   NIHOA

A MERE one hundred and seventy acres, Nihoa is nevertheless the largest of the lava islands west of Niihau. It is only a small fragment of a volcanic cone—perhaps a southernmost piece of such a former cone. The northern edge of Nihoa is a vertical cliff, the result of action of waves driven onto the island by the trade winds. These cliffs contain some spectacular examples of successive lava layers and of volcanic dikes.

The northern edge of Nihoa is a steep cliff. The entire island slopes into Adams Bay on the south side (U. S. Navy photo).

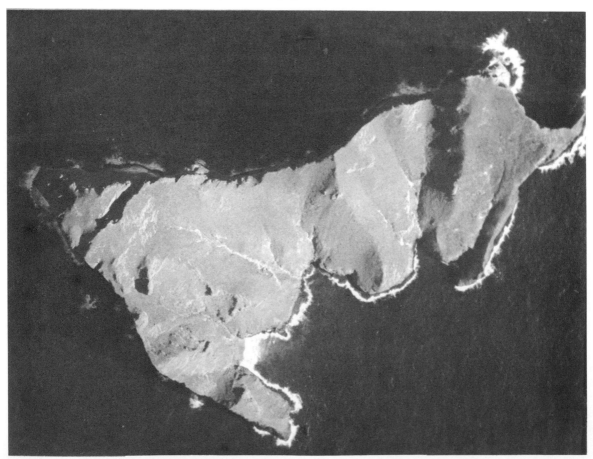

From the south, the valleys leading to Adams Bay can be seen. Cliffs surround the island except for the center of the south side (photograph by Eugene Kridler, Bureau of Sport Fisheries and Wildlife).

An aerial view of Nihoa from the east end shows the northern cliffs, with the small spire of Miller's Peak at far right (photograph by Eugene Kridler, Bureau of Sport Fisheries and Wildlife).

The most conspicuous plants on the island are the loulu palms, *Pritchardia remota*. This species is unusual among Hawaiian loulus in its dry habitat. Perhaps the rain forest is a specialized habit for *Pritchardia*, and *P. remota* represents a relict of coastal species which were once widespread in the Hawaiian Islands. (For a possible piece of evidence, see the fossil palm stems in Chapter 1, from near sea level on Oahu.) *Pritchardia remota* is restricted to Nihoa. Other plants endemic to Nihoa include *Amaranthus brownii, Portulaca caumii,* and *Schiedea verticillata.*

Many marine birds can be found on Nihoa, including the Bulwer's petrel and Christmas Island shearwater shown here. Other marine birds present in large numbers include frigate birds and the various kinds of boobies and terns. Two land birds have been found on Nihoa: one of the parrot-billed honeycreepers (*Psittacirostra cantans*) and the millerbird (*Acrocephalus familiaris kingi*). The honeycreeper is described and illustrated in Chapter 24: the Laysan birds are very similar to those of Nihoa.

The millerbird was also native to Laysan, but that race (illustrated in Chapter 24) is now extinct. The Nihoa millerbird has survived. Millerbirds are members of the flycatcher family, Muscicapidae. It was apparently named millerbird be-

An aerial view of Nihoa from the west reveals steep cliffs with a prominent series of dikes. The island summit is Tanager Peak (photograph by Eugene Kridler, Bureau of Sport Fisheries and Wildlife).

In the shallow valleys of Nihoa, a few palms have a foothold. This loulu, *Pritchardia remota*, is restricted to Nihoa; it grows in a much drier location than do any of the loulus of the main islands (photograph by Eugene Kridler, Bureau of Sport Fisheries and Wildlife).

cause it eats the moths commonly called millers. The Nihoa millerbird is one of the world's more recently discovered birds: it was discovered in 1923, by the Bishop Museum's Tanager Expedition. The speckled eggs of the millerbird may be found in a small cup-like nest, made from leaves of the grass (*Eragrostis variabilis*) common on Nihoa, among branches of the shrubs ilima (*Sida*) and aweoweo (*Chenopodium*). The number of plant species known from Nihoa is approximately twenty. Nihoa is the highest of the Leeward Islands; it reaches 895 feet. However, this elevation is not sufficient to increase precipitation beyond what would fall on a virtually flat island.

The Hawaiians knew Nihoa and occupied it at some remote time. Over a hundred terraces thought to be house foundations have been uncovered. Nihoa possesses only very small seeps, probably not enough for a permanent population of more than a few people, certainly not enough for agriculture. Very likely the colony was a short-lived one.

The Nihoa millerbird (*Acrocephalus familiaris kingi*) is a rare land bird which has managed to survive on Nihoa, although a close relative on Laysan did not. It nests among bushes of ilima (*Sida fallax*) and aweoweo (*Chenopodium oahuense*) (photograph by David B. Marshall, Bureau of Sport Fisheries and Wildlife).

The Bulwer's petrel, *Bulweria bulweri,* can be seen on the slopes of Nihoa, mostly under the shelter of rocks or shrubs (photograph by Eugene Kridler, Bureau of Sport Fisheries and Wildlife).

The Christmas Island shearwater (*Puffinus navitatis*) has a wide range in the Pacific and can be found on the Hawaiian Leeward chain, but it has been seen on an islet off Oahu, Moku Manu, also (photograph by Eugene Kridler, Bureau of Sport Fisheries and Wildlife).

Chapter 21   NECKER

NIHOA is one hundred and seventy acres in extent; Necker is only forty-five. This difference is in proportion to the number of flowering plants native to the two islands: twenty on Nihoa, five on Necker. The minimum number of flowering plants on an island would be one, and that condition is reached on Gardner Pinnacles (six acres). Gardner Pinnacles may be regarded as a "more minimal" island, but Necker is a close approach, and tells us about the effects of small island size. Necker has, for example, less than the minimum area on which land birds can persist: Nihoa has two species of land birds, Necker has none.

This diminution of species numbers with diminishing area may seem strange at first. If one lopped forty-five acres off of the eastern end of Oahu, a part of Oahu which looks much like Necker, one would probably find at least thirty kinds of plants. Why only five on Necker?

A population of an animal or plant species must consist of a certain minimum number of individuals. The reasons for this lie in genetics: if a population becomes too small, inbreeding occurs, fatal defects become common, and the population becomes weakened, is unable to compete, and vanishes.

Necker Island stretches from west to east, and is only about thirteen hundred yards long.

Suppose that a population of a particular animal or plant must have a thousand individuals to stay genetically "healthy." Can it survive on Necker Island? Yes, if a thousand individuals can be "fitted" onto Necker. The answer would clearly be "yes" for insects. In fact, about thirty-seven species of insects have been found on Necker.

Trees could be ruled out as suitable for Necker—too few individuals would be able to grow on such a small island, even if there were trees suited to the Necker climate. A few shrubs and herbs do qualify, however. The two shrubs, *Chenopodium* and *Sesbania,* are relatively small ones. The three other plants are all herbs: *Sesuvium, Panicum,* and *Portulaca lutea* (the last-named not illustrated here: see Chapter 23).

One can guess that if thirty-seven kinds of insects can survive indefinitely on Necker, those that we find are probably going to be the thirty-seven which are (a) best adapted to Necker's particular climatic conditions and food supplies for insects; and (b) best suited to dispersal to this remote island. The same is true for the five flowering plants: all, as one might imagine, can tolerate salt spray and low rainfall; two are wind-pollinated, the remainder can probably self-pollinate.

Why are there no land birds on Necker? Land birds tend to have territories, and perhaps there is simply not room for, say, a thousand territories for a

Seen from the southwest, Necker appears as a series of hills. The highest point of the island is 276 feet.

particular land bird on Necker. Territories are related to food supplies: a territory of, say, forty square yards might be required to provide a food supply for one bird. If territories had to be smaller, the birds would eat themselves out of food, the number of birds would shrink, and, according to our principle above, they would fall below a minimum number required for a continuing population and would die out. This apparently is exactly what happened to a colony of rabbits introduced to Lisianski Island (see Chapter 25); it very nearly happened (and eventually might have happened) to a rabbit colony on Laysan (see Chapter 24). Plants, of course, generally occupy areas smaller than animal territories, and thus two kinds of shrubs can easily live on Necker while a land bird might not.

Shark Bay, looking toward the northwest: the slope of lava beds can be seen on the tip of the island.

This juvenile red-footed booby (*Sula sula rubripes*) at the summit of Necker is changing from a brown-feathered juvenile phase to the white-feathered mature phase. Although it can fly at this stage, it does so very little, because its parents will still bring food to it.

This red-footed booby is losing its down, gaining its brown juvenile feathers. The parents are out at sea feeding, so it is alone during the day.

A mature red-footed booby with a young chick still in its white down. The nest is a crude flat construction of sticks.

There is a loophole in the case of marine birds, however. For them, Necker is not an island of forty-five acres. It is an island which extends far out to sea, as far out as a bird can fly for feeding yet still return by nightfall. For marine birds, Necker is an island of perhaps hundreds of square miles of ocean, and so the limitation is not, in the case of Necker's marine birds, not so much the availability of food as the availability of nesting space. Large numbers of marine birds can, in fact, crowd onto a small island.

There is also a second loophole where marine birds are concerned. Unlike land birds, a certain proportion of the marine birds on an island will leave for another island each year. These migrations seem to affect all islands on which marine birds live. Even if, say, only one blue-faced booby from another island arrived on Necker every five years, the Necker blue-faced boobies would be provided with "new blood," and the dangers of inbreeding would be avoided. In this case, the population could fall below, say, a thousand without harm. If no immigrant blue-faced boobies did come for a long period of years, the Necker population might suffer from inbreeding and die out, or die from

The blue-faced booby (*Sula dactylatra personata*) is named for the bluish base of the bill, which is yellow at the tip. The wing coverts are dark brown or blackish, but the remainder of the feathers are white

A juvenile frigate bird (*Fregata minor*) with brownish head, black feathers, cannot fly yet but can snap at an intruder. Younger chicks still retain their white down. Adult frigate birds leave the chick during the day while they obtain food—often by harassing other marine birds and forcing them to yield a catch of fish.

The common noddy tern (*Anous stolidus phileatus*) is a dark brown color, almost black on the wings and tail. Its nest is a flat pile of sticks on any convenient lava surface. The common noddy is widespread in the Pacific.

The blue-gray tern, or Necker Island tern (*Procelsterna caerulea saxatilis*), occurs on Necker and occasionally several atolls of the central Pacific, such as Johnston, Enderbury, and Howland (photograph by Eugene Kridler, Bureau of Sport Fisheries and Wildlife).

The sooty tern (*Sterna fuscata oahuensis*) is one of the most common birds on Necker, as it is on the other Leeward Islands (photograph by Eugene Kridler, Bureau of Sport Fisheries and Wildlife).

some other reason (competition from other birds, for example); however, a new colony of blue-faced boobies might eventually develop on Necker from immigrant individuals.

The same loophole, that of a steady immigration rate, is open to plants which disperse repetitively. Both *Portulaca* (Chapter 3) and *Sesuvium* are plants which float in seawater, can wash ashore and establish. *Portulaca* from other islands probably wash ashore on Necker occasionally and provide the "new blood" needed to maintain this plant. For this reason, *Portulaca* on Gardner Pinnacles may be able to persist, though it might not be able to if *Portulaca* plants from other islands never washed ashore there.

Would the same be true of humans? We know that both Nihoa and Necker were occupied once by humans. On Necker, there are thirty-four ceremonial or religious platforms called maraes. Curious stone figures as well as artifacts of a useful nature have been found. Did a group of early Hawaiian people colonize Necker? Evidently so, if they stayed long enough to manufacture these articles and platforms. I would guess that they were marooned, unable to sail for another island (there are no really woody plants on Necker, so even a raft could not be constructed). They might have survived for a while on birds and eggs and the small seeps of water, but perhaps they eventually died, building their maraes as a sort of desperate symbol of hope. A human colony could not exist isolated on Necker for long. Too little water is available, and the land is unfit for agriculture. Even if it were, inbreeding of a small human population would devastate such a hypothetical colony in a few generations.

Necker can be used as a good example that the interest in the Leeward chain can be in the poverty, simplicity, and clarity of their plants and animals, their graphic illustrations of the processes of life.

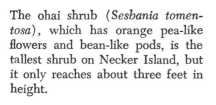

The ohai shrub (*Sesbania tomentosa*), which has orange pea-like flowers and bean-like pods, is the tallest shrub on Necker Island, but it only reaches about three feet in height.

Chenopodium oahuense is the only shrub other than *Sesbania* on Necker Island. Its leaves can be somewhat succulent.

Sesuvium portulacastrum can withstand saltiness and grows closer to the surf than do other plants on Necker.

Tufts of a grass, *Panicum torridum,* can be found in a few places on Necker Island.

Chapter 22 ✦ FRENCH FRIGATE SHOAL

FRENCH FRIGATE SHOAL is an exceptional atoll in representing the last stage in degradation of a high island. A typical atoll with barrier reef and sandy islets is present, but southwest of the atoll is a mere flake of a lava island: La Pérouse Pinnacle (La Pérouse Rock).

Within the reef is a shallow lagoon: the aerial photographs show that neither beaches nor reef are sharply defined. Waves break on the reef as though it were—as it is—a series of coral heads adjacent to the gradual dropoff from the atoll margins. There are coral heads scattered within the shallow lagoon, so that even in a shallow boat one must take care to avoid corals which rise to a short distance below the surface. The islets are formed from coral sand and rubble: bits of various sizes, broken loose from the reef and disintegrated by wave action. The coral sand is relatively light, and currents or exceptional wave action within the lagoon can carry portions of the islets away, pile them up in other places within the lagoon. Disappearing Island in French Frigate Shoal is well named for this reason. The two islets named Whale and

Messerschmidia argentea, a shrub with white flowers and fruits that float, belongs to the heliotrope family. It is favored as a roost by various kinds of marine birds. The grass is *Lepturus repens* (East Island).

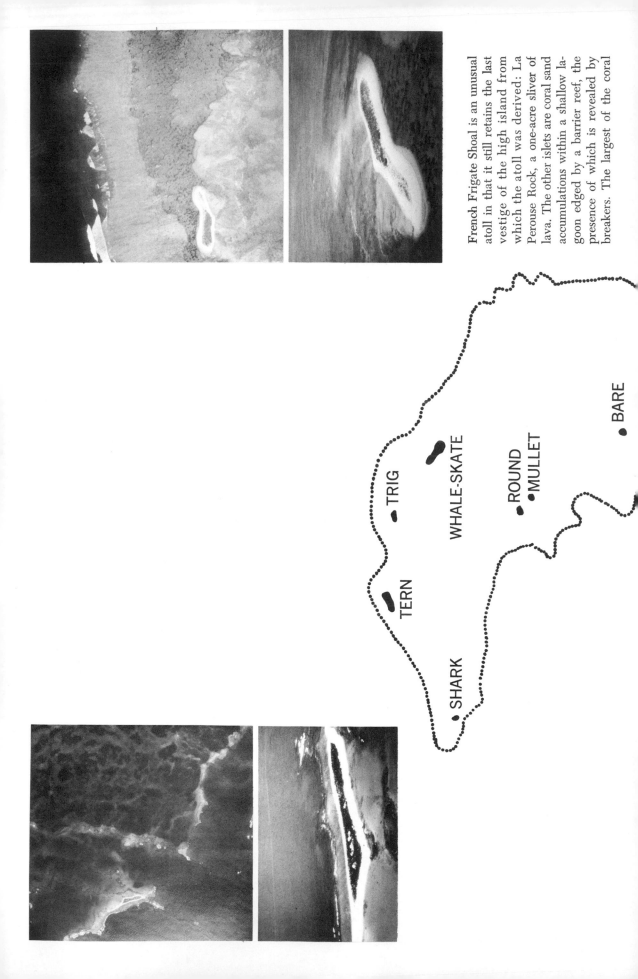

French Frigate Shoal is an unusual atoll in that it still retains the last vestige of the high island from which the atoll was derived: La Perouse Rock, a one-acre sliver of lava. The other islets are coral sand accumulations within a shallow lagoon edged by a barrier reef, the presence of which is revealed by breakers. The largest of the coral

SHARK

TERN

TRIG

WHALE-SKATE

ROUND
MULLET

BARE

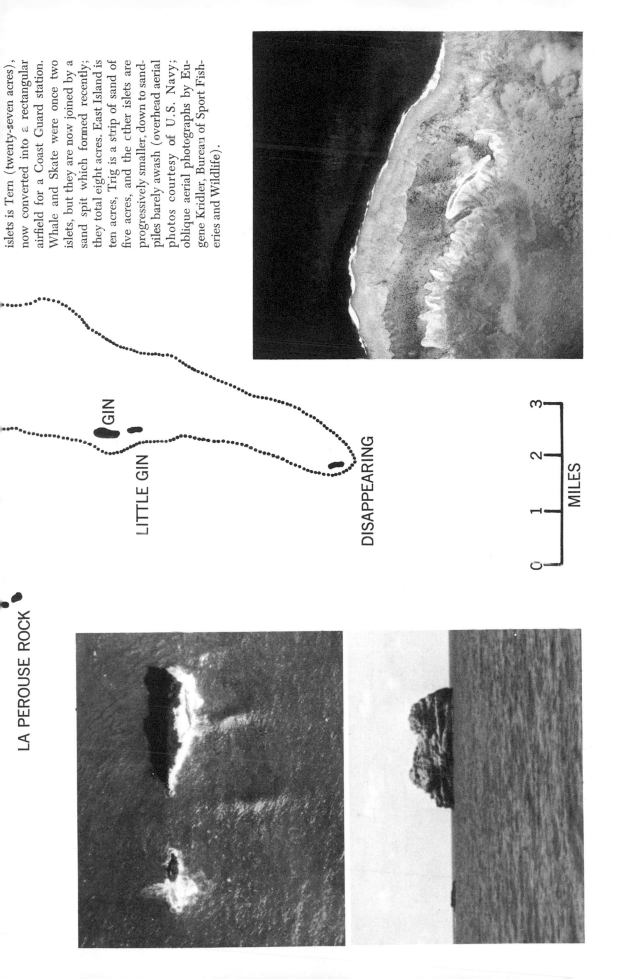

islets is Tern (twenty-seven acres), now converted into a rectangular airfield for a Coast Guard station. Whale and Skate were once two islets, but they are now joined by a sand spit which formed recently; they total eight acres. East Island is ten acres, Trig is a strip of sand of five acres, and the other islets are progressively smaller, down to sandpiles barely awash (overhead aerial photos courtesy of U.S. Navy; oblique aerial photographs by Eugene Kridler, Bureau of Sport Fisheries and Wildlife).

LA PEROUSE ROCK

GIN

LITTLE GIN

DISAPPEARING

0 1 2 3
MILES

Frigate birds are conspicuous on French Frigate Shoal. During the fall months, downy chicks and brown-headed black-plumaged juveniles may be seen sitting on the islets, waiting for parents to bring them food. During the spring months, male frigate birds are conspicuous because of their large red throat pouches, a display device which attracts females. Frigates are conspicuous in flight because of their black color, large size, and forked tails (photographs of male frigate birds by Eugene Kridler, Bureau of Sport Fisheries and Wildlife).

Skate must now be called "Whale-Skate" because they have become joined by a sand bar.

On the islets of French Frigate Shoal are no plants or animals not found on several or many other islands of the Pacific—a feature typical of atolls. Atoll plants are mostly plants distributed by seawater and ocean currents. Those not dispersed in this fashion are probably carried by marine birds. Marine birds definitely do migrate from one island to another, even though most individuals tend to stay on a single island. For example, of the red-footed boobies banded on French Frigate Shoal, 255 were seen again on French Frigate Shoal, but eighteen were seen on Johnston Island, one on Wake, two on Kure, three on Midway, one on Pearl and Hermes Reef, eight on Laysan, two on Kauai, and two on Oahu. Some of those seen on Johnston Island were later seen back on French Frigate Shoal. With frequent migratory movements like these, any plant which can travel on bird feathers is likely to be transferred from one atoll to another with great regularity.

Likewise, there are no birds or insects on French Frigate Shoal that are not also on other islands. However, French Frigate Shoal is a good place to see the animals and plants typical of Hawaiian shores. Animals formerly seen on the

A pair of adult blue-faced boobies stand on the shore of East Island; another soars above. The dark band of wing-covert feathers serves to identify this booby.

main islands, such as the sea turtle or the Hawaiian monk seal, can be seen frequently on French Frigate Shoal. With luck, you might see a nest of hatching baby turtles, or a mother seal with a cub, and over the coral islets the endless wheeling of frigates, terns, and boobies as they leave for and return from their distant fishing grounds.

The members of our party, while visiting East Island, discovered a nest of hatching sea turtles. There were about forty in the nest, and as they crawled into the warmth of the sunlight they became active and unerringly clambered down to the shore and swam off.

Chapter 23 ❧ *GARDNER PINNACLES*

AN ISLAND as small as Gardner Pinnacles would not rate mention, perhaps, if it were a short distance from the shore of Oahu or Molokai. That it is more remote does not really make it more interesting, although seals and sea turtles, rarely seen on the main islands, can be seen resting on a crevice or shelf of Gardner Pinnacles. The most interesting feature is the obvious geological one: it is the farthest west of the lava islands, perhaps the oldest piece of lava still above the ocean surface in the Hawaiian chain.

It is surprising that colonies of several marine birds can exist on such a small piece of ground. Common noddies, sooty terns, wedge-tailed shearwaters, frigate birds, Bulwer's petrels, red-tailed tropic birds, blue-faced boobies, fairy terns, and blue-gray terns were all sighted during our 1966 visit. None of these is represented by a really large colony, but the island is, in fact, quite crowded with birds. Although marine birds customarily build some kind of nest with twigs, there is, in fact, no such nesting material on Gardner Pinnacles. The bare, whitened slopes offer only one kind of plant: *Portulaca lutea.* The succulent stems of this plant are excellent in their ability to resist salt spray and low rainfall, but they are not usable as nesting material.

Gardner Pinnacles, a six-acre remnant of a volcano, is rarely visited. Landing is difficult because a high surge almost perpetually breaks on the steep slopes of this island.

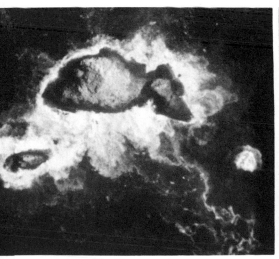 

A ninety-foot pinnacle lies a short distance away from the main segment, 170 feet high, of Gardner Pinnacles.

In a saddle on the main part of the island, one can see clearly a volcanic dike, which stands above the bedded lava; evidently the dike has eroded more slowly than the lava beds.

The only plant species on Gardner Pinnacles is *Portulaca lutea,* a succulent mat-like plant with yellow flowers opening only at midday in full sun.

As suggested in Chapter 21, Gardner Pinnacles is probably too small to support any species of plant or animal indefinitely without the aid of a trickle of immigrants from other islands. The desolation of a small rock like Gardner Pinnacles is illusory where marine birds are concerned: it is surrounded by seas full of fish. This rich harvest will be taken, if only by a constant, if gradual, migration of marine birds to tiny, isolated Gardner Pinnacles.

Although several kinds of marine birds can be seen on Gardner Pinnacles, fairy terns (*Gygis alba*) are particularly picturesque. They nest in crevices and holes of the rocks, pockets which would be too small and precarious for other birds. Chicks are covered with soft down. Fairy terns eat small sardine-like fish, and can carry several in their beaks at once.

Chapter 24 🙰 *LAYSAN*

LAYSAN is an atoll, but with a difference: it is a raised atoll. What would be a lagoon within a barrier reef is mostly land, some of it thirty to fifty feet above sea level. There is, however, a depression in the center of the island which is a shallow lake, saltier than the ocean. The raised-atoll plan of Laysan gives it a larger land area than most atolls. In fact, Laysan consists of one thousand and one acres, which is roughly half of the total land area of the Leeward Islands combined.

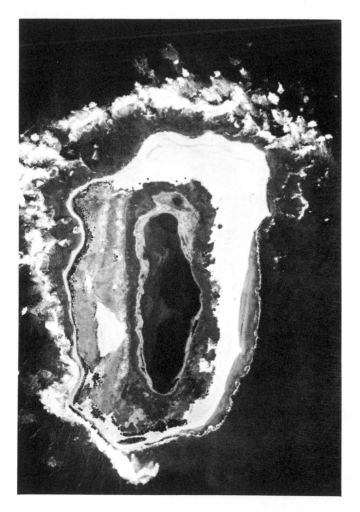

An overhead aerial view of Laysan shows the central lagoon and various zones of vegetation on the broad ring of coral sand.

The central lagoon of Laysan expands if a heavy rain falls, but most of the year it is shrunken. The lagoon is saltier than the sea, and the dry margins bear a crust of salt.

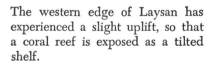

The western edge of Laysan has experienced a slight uplift, so that a coral reef is exposed as a tilted shelf.

The relatively large area (for an atoll) and the isolation of Laysan have permitted it to acquire a number of interesting animals and plants. Of greatest interest among these are the birds. A surprising number of land bird species (three) and water bird species (two) are present; these have become different from their relatives elsewhere in the Hawaiian chain to the extent of being called distinct subspecies.

The millerbird, an insect-eating bird related to Asiatic flycatchers, is perhaps a logical resident of Laysan, for of course insects are present. However, the two representatives of the Hawaiian honeycreepers—the Laysan honeyeater and the Laysan parrot-billed honeycreeper ("Laysan finch")—seem out of place, since on the main island these are forest birds. The Laysan rail was a flightless bird; the Laysan teal, although capable of flying, flies little. The interesting qualities of bird life on Laysan made it the focus of two works: Walter Rothschild's *The Avifauna of Laysan and the Neighboring Islands,* and Alfred M. Bailey's attractive *Birds of Midway and Laysan Islands.*

About twenty-five species of flowering plants colonized Laysan in prehuman times. Five of these became slightly different from their relatives on the main islands—like the land birds, they are distinct subspecies. Two Laysan plants are unexpected ones for an atoll: a loulu palm (*Pritchardia*) and a sandalwood (*Santalum*): plants one would see in upland forests on the main islands. The various adaptations by birds and plants are unusual ones for atoll residents, and may have been caused, in part, by the fact that Laysan received some of its colonists from the main islands, not just other atolls. That they have been able to live on an island with such unvaried topography is interesting.

Laysan came very close to almost total devastation not long ago. The abundance of bird life gave Laysan guano deposits of commercially usable extent. Exploitation of these deposits meant human occupation, and human occupation meant the introduction of plants and animals. For example, tobacco plants were grown and went wild on the island. They still can be found, and may persist indefinitely. Another pest, the rabbit, has now been exterminated. Before it was, it occupied the entire island, and literally reduced it to a desert. Those who saw Laysan at that time have expressed surprise that any of the native plants and animals survived at all. Of the approximately twenty-five native plant species, only four were found in 1923. The Laysan honeyeater, the Laysan rail, the loulu palm, and the sandalwood did not survive this devastation. Probably the rabbits themselves were reduced in numbers as food vanished; the Bishop Museum's Tanager Expedition in 1923 was able to kill all of the remaining rabbits. During that visit, the last three individuals of the Laysan honeyeater were seen one day, then were extinguished the next as a wind blew the surface of the island into a vicious sandstorm.

If one did not know of these events, or of the two extinguished birds and the two now-vanished plants, one probably would not know now that anything had happened. The island has become revegetated and has much the same

The beach morning glory, *Ipomoea pes-caprae,* is a common plant both along the coast and along the lagoon of Laysan.

Along the lagoon, *Ipomoea* stems trail toward the water. In this morning glory tangle, Laysan teals (*Anas wyvilliana laysanensis*) can be found (closeup of teal by David B. Marshall, Bureau of Sport Fisheries and Wildlife).

appearance it probably had in prehuman time. Few indications of human occupation remain, and these will disappear into the sands before long.

Of the birds which survived, the Laysan teal probably experienced the
narrowest escape. In 1911 only six individuals were left. The census today runs
at about two hundred—a number which may seem perilously small, but which
is perhaps greater than at any time since 1900. Actually, the teal is limited
to only part of the island—the lagoon and part of the lagoon's shore—so its
numbers would never be expected to be very great. As one walks through
the pink-flowered morning glory east of the lagoon, one nearly steps on some
of the teals, and they flutter off, almost reluctantly. The teals fly only short
distances. If one sits still for a short while beside the lagoon, the teals will

Much of Laysan is covered by
clumps of the grass *Eragrostis
variabilis.*

Scattered in various parts of the
island are tufts of the sedge
Fimbristylis cymosa, whose seeds
are eaten by the Laysan "finch."

The Laysan "finch"—actually a parrot-billed honeycreeper (*Psittacirostra cantans cantans*)—can be seen feeding on the seeds of the *Eragrostis* grass (photograph by David B. Marshall, Bureau of Sport Fisheries and Wildlife).

The nest of the "finch" is made from *Eragrostis* grass, and can be found within a clump of grass (photograph by Walter K. Fisher, courtesy of Denver Natural History Museum).

approach within a few feet. The fearlessness and unwillingness to fly are not typical of teals and ducks, and not typical of the koloa (Hawaiian duck), a bird of the main islands which differs from the Laysan teal only as a subspecies.

Living in and among the clumps of *Eragrostis* grass and *Fimbristylis* sedge is a bird that also probably escaped extinction narrowly: the so-called Laysan finch. This name is misleading, for this bird belongs to the same genus as the parrot-billed honeycreepers (*Psittacirostra*). It was probably able to survive the years of the rabbit plague because it accepts varied food articles. *Psittacirostra cantans* can eat large, tough seeds, such as those of the nohu or puncture vine, *Tribulus*, as might be inferred from the shape of its bill. It also eats smaller seeds, however, and is often seen feeding on the spikes of the grass and the sedge. However, the "finch" also eats eggs, dead birds, probably

The Laysan honeyeater, *Himatione sanguinea freethii,* is closely related to the apapane of the main islands. It became extinct as a result of Laysan's rabbit plague. The historic photo of a singing honeyeater is from a motion picture taken by Donald Dickey in 1923; the photograph of the honeyeater nest was taken by Walter K. Fisher in 1902 (courtesy of Denver Natural History Museum).

various articles of sea food washed ashore. Today, it is in no danger of extinction, and numbers in the thousands. *Psittacirostra cantans* differs from main-island psittacirostras in its longer legs, which are stronger and suited to hopping on the ground rather than perching in trees.

The scarlet Laysan honeyeater, *Himatione sanguinea freethii,* also nested in the grass clumps. Its counterpart on the main islands, the apapane (*H. sanguinea sanguinea*), feeds on ohia nectar. These flowers are absent on Laysan. Consequently, it sought the only substitutes possible: nectar from the pink-flowered morning glory and other flowers.

The Laysan rail was also an inhabitant of the grass clumps. Decidedly flightless, this bird had fewer primary feathers than any other bird in the world. Superficially, the Laysan rail looked entirely wingless. The rail was well suited to life on Laysan, because it could eat almost anything: eggs, seeds, bits of vegetation, moths, and other insects. These curious, fearless birds did not survive Laysan's denudation, however. An attempt to introduce the rail to Lisianski

The only known photographs of the flightless Laysan rail (*Porzanula palmeri*) are these, taken before the rail vanished during Laysan's rabbit plague. The photograph of the rail with its nest was taken in May 1902 by Walter K. Fisher; the photograph of the rail walking was taken in December 1912 by Alfred M. Bailey (courtesy of Denver Natural History Museum and Mrs. Patricia Witherspoon).

The Laysan millerbird (*Acrocephalus familiaris familiaris*) became extinct before 1923. This photograph was taken by Walter K. Fisher in May 1902 (courtesy of Denver Natural History Museum and Mrs. Patricia Witherspoon).

was ill-timed, because that island was also on its way to devegetation by rabbits. Rails introduced from Laysan to Midway in 1891 did, however, multiply. The rails would probably be there now, but the accidental introduction of rats during the Second World War proved fatal to them. Rails were last seen on Midway in 1944.

Although the Nihoa race of the millerbird has survived, that on Laysan has not. The millerbirds evidently nested in the *Eragrostis* clumps, were abundant and quite fearless. When vegetation disappeared on Laysan, so did the insects, and this undoubtedly accounted for extinction of the millerbirds.

Probably all the marine birds recorded on the Leeward chain can be seen on Laysan, with the possible exception of the blue-gray tern, which is native to Necker and has been seen on a few other islands. Tropic birds, fairy terns, noddy terns, sooty terns, grayback terns, and the three species of boobies

A juvenile red-tailed tropic bird (*Phaethon rubricauda rothschildi*) has white feathers banded black, and a bright red beak. An egg of this tropic bird is beige, speckled brown.

can be seen abundantly. Shearwaters are present in tremendous numbers; their burrows are everywhere. Shearwaters are not evident during the day, for they stay on land during the dark hours.

The most conspicuous of the marine birds—during their breeding season —are the two species of albatrosses. The Laysan albatross is much more abundant than the black-footed albatross. Although these albatrosses look quite distinct, they must be closely related, for hybrid individuals have been seen on several occasions. Laysan is the chief breeding ground for both. Although many individuals may be seen during the breeding season, albatrosses are not as abundant now as they once were. Photographs from 1893 show huge numbers of the birds. Albatrosses seem an unlikely bird to be victimized, but they were sought both for their feathers and for their eggs. Albatrosses lay only a single egg each year, so obviously any increase of albatrosses is very slow. Probably the Laysan populations are on the increase now. Albatrosses have been known to live as long as thirty-five years, so even low rates of reproduction might permit increase. Infant mortality can be high, however. For reasons difficult to understand, parents may abandon chicks, occasionally in large numbers. In recent years, chick fatality appears to be caused when parents feed them large indigestible articles: floating plastic and charcoal picked up at sea, apparently because of their conspicuousness. The central lagoon of Laysan has

The Laysan albatross (*Diomedea immutabilis*) constructs a shallow crater of sand as a nest. Albatrosses arrive on Laysan in October; the breeding season ends in June (photograph by Eugene Kridler, Bureau of Sport Fisheries and Wildlife).

The black-footed albatross (*Diomedea nigripes*) is also commonly found on Laysan. During the breeding season, large colonies of this and the Laysan albatross can be seen (photograph by Eugene Kridler, Bureau of Sport Fisheries and Wildlife).

Wedge-tailed shearwaters (*Puffinus pacificus cuneatus*) return to the island at dusk, leave early in the morning. Their burrows undermine much of Laysan and other coral islands, and make walking hazardous.

Nama sandwicensis var. *laysanicum* is a mat plant endemic to Laysan, but it is not very different from *N. sandwicensis sandwicensis* on the main islands. It has pale blue flowers and grows on sand dunes.

been known to expand during heavy rains, and at such time inundates albatross nests. Albatrosses are very conservative about nesting sites, and usually return to the same nesting place they occupied the previous year.

Marine birds, when they are protected, offer no serious conservation problems. If Laysan has lost some of its birds and plants, it has retained others, and we can expect that this island can increasingly become a most interesting showcase of atoll life.

Chapter 25 🌺 LISIANSKI

AN AERIAL view of Lisianski shows it to be, like Laysan, an upraised atoll. Lisianski, although it has a central depression, does not have a central lagoon. Perhaps it did, in prehuman time. The 382 acres of Lisianski make it the second largest of the Leeward Islands. However, Lisianski does not now, nor apparently did it ever, rival Laysan in its animal or plant life. Its flowering plants and birds include none endemic only to Lisianski; they are all typical atoll species. However, the island is a verdant one, and marine birds are abundant.

This was not always true, for Lisianski suffered as much as Laysan. The attractions for commercial usage were the same, the exploitation and destruction identical. Lisianski was occupied by guano diggers, and likewise rabbits were introduced (via Laysan) and allowed to go wild. Terns were killed in large numbers by Japanese poachers. Reports of the latter incursions caused President Theodore Roosevelt to proclaim the Leeward Islands a bird refuge in 1909. The rabbits, however, continued to reduce Lisianski to a barren plain. In 1923 the vegetation was said to have been reduced to a single patch of tobacco and a couple of *Ipomoea* vines. Even the rabbits were reduced to cannibalism. When the Tanager Expedition called at Lisianski later that year to exterminate the rabbits, they found that the rabbits had extinguished themselves.

Recovery of plants and marine birds has taken place in a relatively short time. However, this recovery is probably still occurring. In 1931, only four kinds of flowering plants were reported on Lisianski. Now there are at least eight, plus coconuts planted intentionally. One can expect that additional plants dispersed by seawater and by marine birds will reach Lisianski. Vegetation on the Leeward Islands is not static; it is perpetually in the process of changing. Some species appear, then vanish, and are replaced by others. The tenure of many beach plants may be cyclical in this fashion. If so, Lisianski will be a good place to watch.

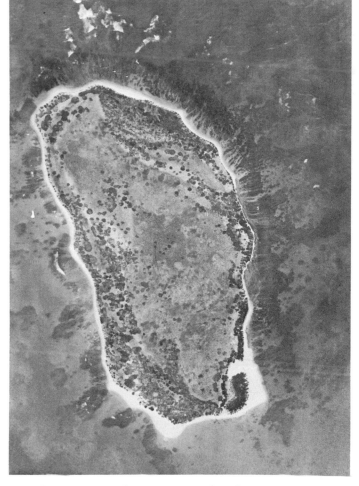

An overhead aerial view of Lisianski reveals it to be a flat coral island with a depressed center. Most of the shrubbery is located at the periphery of the island.

Scaevola taccada, with its fan-shaped white flowers and leathery, semisucculent leaves is a shrub found on many Pacific shores.

Common on Lisianski is a blue-flowered morning glory, *Ipomoea indica*. It climbs on clumps of grass.

Tribulus cistoides, a puncture vine, is found close to the shore, where it forms a sprawling mat. Its flowers are bright yellow.

Lisianski's broad shores provide excellent places for the Hawaiian monk seal to rest after long periods of feeding at sea. Left, a moulting seal on the western shore; at right, a seal on the upraised coral shelf along Lisianski's eastern shore.

Chapter 26   *PEARL AND HERMES REEF*

Too often, an expedition biologist visiting a remote and small island has time only to snatch a few specimens before returning to his ship. In September 1966 the cruise schedule of the Coast Guard cutter *Ironwood* allowed me and the others of the scientific party to spend a week on Pearl and Hermes Reef. This time might seem almost too long for the few, small coral islets of this atoll. However, such a length of time permits, perhaps even enforces, an appreciation of this environment.

A coral islet is a mid-ocean beach, the sun's glare doubled by the flat expanse of coral rubble. That anything grows in this white desiccation is surprising. The dryness is perhaps not as extreme as it seems. At intervals of several days or a week, moist trade winds that drift down from the North

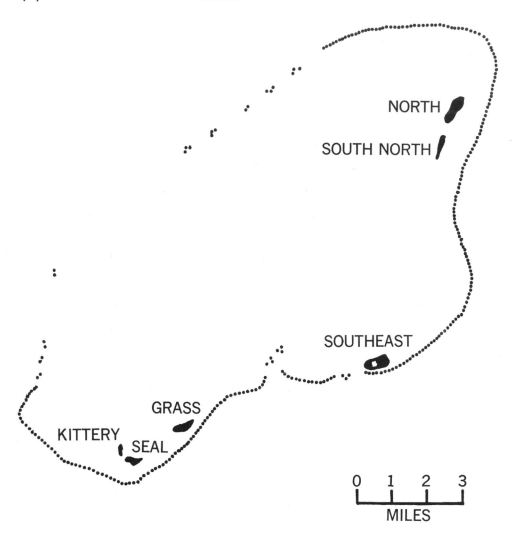

Pearl and Hermes Reef is an atoll with a barrier reef which is vaguely defined or absent on the northwest side. It contains six coral islets which lie close to the reef.

Pacific accumulate lines of clouds that group into a brief, drenching squall and then pass on. These showers are local, and may miss one islet yet wet other within an atoll. Between these scant rains, the atoll is bared to the sun, and plants on the islets must be able to resist it.

Leaf surfaces hint how dryness and sun are counteracted. The amaranth *Achyranthes splendens* and the nightshade *Solanum nelsoni* have leaves that are gray-green with an ashy velour of very fine hairs. The puncture vine *Tribulus* has leaves shiny with a felt of hairs, hairs that can be a "microscopic windbreak" preventing the wind from drying the surface of the leaf, and that also

Southeast Island, the largest islet in Pearl and Hermes Reef, has thirty-one acres. It consists of two halves connected by a sand spit.

Seen from the lagoon a short distance from shore, Southeast Island is a uniformly flat coral platform.

reflect the sunlight, shade tissues of the leaf, and reduce the burning of the sun. The mats and sprawling stems of *Portulaca* and *Sesuvium* have an obvious defense: succulence. They rapidly absorb moisture from the rain squalls, and store it indefinitely. Even the pepperweed *Lepidium* proves to have thickish water-rich leaves. Leaves of *Boerhavia* (shown in Chapter 3) are not so succulent, perhaps because this plant has an alternative storage system. Trailing stems of *Boerhavia* grow from a turnip-like succulent root.

The grasses *Eragrostis* and *Lepturus* are narrow-leaved, exposing a minimum surface, especially to the midday sun; their leaves, like those of a palm, have shiny surfaces that prevent loss of water. All of the above plants belong to groups notable for adaptation to dry, even salty, localities, and one might find representatives of these groups in inland Australia or the California deserts.

Sand bars come and go in Pearl and Hermes Reef, and new ones can provide occupiable ground for these plants. South of North Island is a new sand bar, which has been called "South North Island." It has now acquired plants (*Lepturus, Tribulus, Boerhavia, Lepidium*); perhaps these four have the greatest pioneering ability—at least of those easily able to arrive on the island.

The coral sand of the atoll can gradually turn to soil, and can become packed. In this sand shearwaters dig their burrows, often undermining plants. Perhaps only the number of burrows which can be dug into the atoll surface limits the number of shearwaters which can live here.

On Southeast Island of Pearl and Hermes Reef, one can see the debris of human occupation still. Wartime buildings have now collapsed, and gradually are rusting, rotting, falling into unrecognizable shape. This debris proves ideal for the nesting of Bulwer's petrels: these petrels, adapted to niches and caverns in cliffs, easily accept the similar shelter of crumbling sheets of corrugated iron.

Adaptability is great in atoll life. All atoll plants and animals are pioneers, weeds that will secure some unlikely foothold here. A sphinx moth caught my eye on Grass Island. Sphinx moths, giants among Lepidoptera, are ideally designed for extracting nectar from long tubular flowers with their agile, wire-like tongues. On Pearl and Hermes Reef, no such flowers exist. The sphinx moths appeared to be hovering meaninglessly until I noticed the extremely small pale violet flowers of *Boerhavia*. The moths were indeed feeding on these, and with their typical posture of tongues well extended, even though there were no floral tubes into which to place their tongues. Thus, they had to hover several inches away from flowers when feeding—a tongue's length away. The only other open flowers on the islet were those of the puncture vine, *Tribulus*—saucer-shaped yellow flowers as much as an inch across. Would the sphinx moth feed from flowers with shapes so "wrong" for them? No, but the moths did notice the buds of the puncture vine flowers, and unerringly picked buds just open enough to permit their tongues to enter, a habit which seemed to express that a broad flower in bud stage simulates a tubular flower enough to attract the moths. Perhaps other cryptic pollination relationships are also

Although formerly on some of the other Leeward Islands, *Achyranthes splendens* is an amaranth which now can be found only on Seal Island of Pearl and Hermes Reef. Atoll plants tend to come and go.

Solanum nelsoni, a nightshade, is currently found in the Leeward Islands only on Nihoa and the various islets of Pearl and Hermes Reef (Southeast Island).

Lepidium owaihense of the mustard family has seeds which develop a coat of mucilage when wet. In this way, they can stick to bird feathers and reach remote islands such as those of Pearl and Hermes Reef (North Island).

Grayback terns (*Sterna lunata*) in flight present a graceful sight. They are abundant on Southeast Island.

represented on Pearl and Hermes Reef. Minute flies could be seen in the puncture vine flowers; thrip-like insects were evident inside the nightshade flowers. Such flowers may self-pollinate much of the time, but probably even clumsy visits by nonpollinating insects might serve for occasional cross-pollination.

On Southeast Island, an area of several acres could be said to belong to brown boobies. I did not notice this at first, for many of the boobies were at sea, fishing. The downy chicks, however, proved to be good indicators of the colony. Seated on rude nest-like accumulations of twigs, they aimlessly raised and lowered wings too heavy for flight, and signaled alarm with bills that opened and closed without emitting a noise. Eggs and featherless chicks could be seen in other nests. A booby usually raises only a single chick each year, although a pair of eggs may be laid.

The chick of a brown booby soon loses the fluffy white down, and mottled brown juvenile feathers are exposed. Day after day during our visit to Pearl and Hermes Reef, we noticed a particular juvenile standing by the shore. It was old enough to fly, and on occasion did so. However, usually it did not fly, but waited for parental feeding—and received it.

Boobies seem tremendously vulnerable birds. They are fearless—all of the accompanying photographs were taken by an ordinary lens. Boobies are awkward on the ground. They are efficient in flight, however; they can catch flying fish, and are even adept at diving well beneath the surface in pursuit of a fish.

A prolonged stay on an atoll permits one to scan the beaches for whatever may be cast ashore. For the botanist, this means seeds. Some seeds and fruits wash up fragmented, scoured and killed by seawater. Others, like the various kinds of "sea beans" (legumes with floating seeds: *Mucuna, Canavalia,* etc.) are ideally suited to oceanic drift. Some of these can even be found germinating on the beaches of Pearl and Hermes Reef, but none survive to flowering age. They are a graphic example of how dispersal takes place, and colonization almost—but only almost—succeeds.

The bare foreshore, sloping into the water, is not without interest. Exhausted by hours or days of feeding at sea, the giant sea turtles and Hawaiian monk seals doze. Sea turtles sleep close to the sea, often half immersed, and are more skitterish; they sense human presence easily, and swim off.

The monk seals often haul themselves farther inland, and may slumber on a mat of puncture vine. One can walk past seals without disturbing them, but if they are touched, they lumber off into the surf. Only a mother with a cub is aggressive, and this is mostly a defensive show of teeth and barking, with a tendency to stand her ground rather than run away. In a shallow lagoon on Southeast Island, monk seals sleep half immersed. When they do so, their wet fur appears green—a color which is, in fact, the result of a growth of algae. They stay at sea for so long that certain algae are able to colonize on their fur.

The Hawaiian monk seal lives perhaps more than thirty years. Numbers of

In September on Southeast Island, one can see stages from egg to adult in the brown booby (*Sula leucogaster plotus*).

Bulwer's petrel (*Bulweria bulweri*) nests in crevices, if they are available. On Southeast Island, sheets of corrugated iron provide this habitat.

Downy gray chicks of the wedge-tailed shearwater (*Puffinus pacificus cuneatus*) can be seen on Southeast Island.

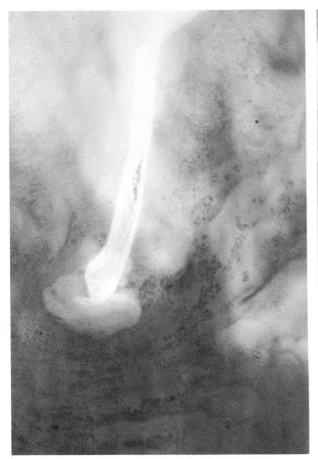

Seen from the air, "South North Island" looks like a strip of sand flowing southward into the lagoon. It is an island which has only recently emerged and stayed dry so that now plants have colonized on it. At the south end of the island is a dense mat of puncture vine (*Tribulus cistoides*).

monk seals are not very great, although the species is probably not seriously endangered. It will probably persist as long as the atolls of the Leeward chain remain unmolested. The monk seal is a curiosity to biologists, because there are only two tropical seals. One is the Hawaiian monk seal, limited to the Leeward chain; the other is the Mediterranean monk seal, limited to the Mediterranean Sea and in danger of extinction.

Atolls are not rich in numbers of individuals or of numbers of species. The number of species on small islands is directly related to the size of the island. The tiny coral islets of Pearl and Hermes Reef are not showcases of diversity, but they are sites crowded with plants and animals—species almost pitifully vulnerable. Although these organisms are adapted to the sun and salinity of atoll life, and are sturdy, they occupy tiny areas which can be all too easily taken from them by man. The islets of Pearl and Hermes Reef are a living museum, one which shows that the nonuse of land can be the best, the most elegant use.

At the north end of "South North Island," a scattering of clumps of an atoll grass, *Lepturus repens,* can be found. When mature, the inflorescence of this grass breaks into seed-bearing segments which float.

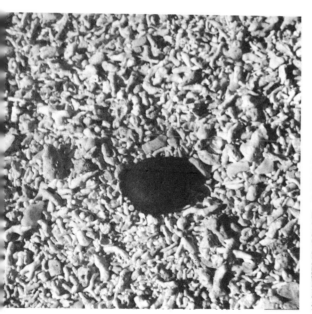

Seeds of *Mucuna* and other large legume seeds float ashore on Pearl and Hermes Reef. They sometimes germinate, but soon die, an example of dispersal which is very nearly—but not quite—followed by successful establishment (Southeast Island).

On shores of Pearl and Hermes Reef, giant sea turtles come ashore after feeding at sea; they sleep for hours or even days. Fortunately, sea turtles are protected on Pearl and Hermes Reef—as they are in very few places in the world (Southeast Island).

The Hawaiian monk seal (*Monachus schauinslandi*) is a marine mammal found only on the Hawaiian chain. Hunted by the ancient Hawaiians on the main islands, it has disappeared on those shores and now appears only on the Leeward Islands. Although its numbers are rather small, it is not seriously endangered (Southeast Island).

Chapter 27   MIDWAY ISLANDS AND KURE

MIDWAY is an atoll which has the largest flat sand islet at the western end of the Hawaiian chain. Such an islet in such a position between Honolulu and the Orient virtually invites a role in history or commerce, and so Midway has a name more familiar than that of any of the other Leeward Islands.

As early as 1870, human influence began to be felt. Dredging was begun. In 1903 a cable station was established, and this precedent made the addition of a station for seaplanes natural. Beginning in 1935, Midway became known to passengers on the Clipper, a craft of such modest speed that overnight stops at Midway, Wake, and Guam were required on the route from Honolulu to Manila. The existence of the Pan American station led logically to the use of Midway as a military base. The Battle of Midway left a devastated island, but, surprisingly, not only was the damage quickly repaired, many new buildings were added. Midway is today more important than ever before, because it is a link to the vast oceanic sprawl of Micronesian atolls currently administered by the United States as the American Trust Territory.

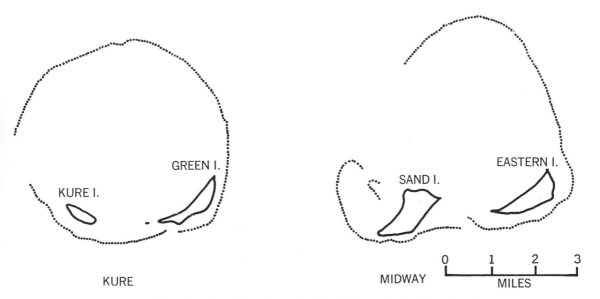

The westernmost island in the Hawaiian Islands is Kure; it is fifty-six miles west of Midway Islands. The two atolls are remarkably similar; each has a pair of coral islands inside the southern part of the reef, a large break in the western part of the reef and a smaller one in the southeastern part.

Nooks on ledges in coastal caves are the preferred nesting sites of the Hawaiian tern, or whitecap noddy (*Anous minutus melanogenys*). On Midway, there are no such places, so it nests on a branch of a *Casuarina* tree (photograph by Eugene Kridler, Bureau of Sport Fisheries and Wildlife).

Chicks of fairy terns (*Gygis alba*) on Midway somehow manage to stay in the crotch of a tree without falling (photograph by Eugene Kridler, Bureau of Sport Fisheries and Wildlife).

The Laysan albatross in flight above Midway shows characteristic patches of dark feathers on the undersides of its wings (photograph by Eugene Kridler, Bureau of Sport Fisheries and Wildlife).

A pair of black-footed albatrosses perform a courtship dance on Midway Island (photograph by Eugene Kridler, Bureau of Sport Fisheries and Wildlife).

With the intensity and duration of human activity, the persistence of any wildlife on Midway is surprising. Even if good intentions are honored, space does not permit an albatross to retain its nesting site if a house is to be built there. For the "gooneys," as albatrosses on Midway are called, Midway becomes less tenable each year. Because albatrosses return annually to their exact nesting site, extinction is inevitable as land is developed. Conflicts between aviation and the albatross are virtually insoluble. Airport authorities regard albatrosses as a hazard. Moreover, the albatrosses do not seem to be able to adjust to the radio towers, and fatally injure themselves on the guy wires.

Similar considerations apply to Kure, where there also is an airstrip. We can only hope where the albatrosses are concerned, that areas currently left as good nesting territories will not be disturbed. Perhaps the best hope—a defeatist one—is that albatross colonies on Laysan, Lisianski, and the other atolls will thrive.

As might be imagined, many plants have been introduced to Midway. The most successful of trees introduced is the *Casuarina*. Some of the smaller marine birds have adapted to nesting in these trees, as well as in a few man-made structures.

Curiously, Midway and Kure never had any endemic species or even sub-species of birds or flowering plants. Both Midway and Kure did have moderately rich floras and faunas for atolls, however.

FOR YOUR INFORMATION

Chapter 28 🌿 *FIELD TRIPS*

THE HAWAIIAN ISLANDS offer many interesting areas that are accessible by foot and by car. The climate is favorable in most areas for field work without special equipment or clothing. Light rainwear is advisable in some areas, although first-time visitors may be surprised to discover that a light shower of short duration is often ignored by Hawaiian residents; such a shower can be pleasant, in fact. Field work in wet and cold areas will require special precautions. My own approach to an area of notoriously heavy rainfall is to abandon the field trip if the day is too rainy.

There are no plants likely to be skin irritants, like poison ivy or nettles; no such plants are native, and fortunately none have been introduced. The most noxious encounters on a hike might be the thorns of blackberries, an introduced plant which has gone wild in a few areas; or bites of mosquitoes, which are a problem in only a few areas in the Islands, and are absent from most regions.

For the amateur naturalist or enterprising tourist, a combination of travel by car (or, in a few cases, bus) and on foot can be recommended. Car rental may seem expensive, but it may permit you to see many areas not otherwise visible, or to view them at your own pace. At present, commercial tours can be said to ignore Hawaiian natural history completely. If natural history interests you, you would do well to organize your own travels. Those who say that "Hawaii is too commercialized" have never availed themselves of the many beautiful natural areas, some of which even have excellent accommodations. The Hawaiian Islands are either a beautiful wilderness area or a concrete sprawl, depending how *you* do your travel. Information and help are always available. Notable among the agencies that help tourists is the Hawaii Visitors Bureau, offices of which are conveniently located at airports, and near major hotels in cities and towns. If the native plants and animals are your goal, be sure to specify precisely this. Many attractive forest regions are nothing but groves of introduced trees such as strawberry guava; on trails, you must not be discouraged by seeing a high proportion of weeds at lower elevations; upper regions are almost always freer from weedy trees and herbs. Local information is often advisable.

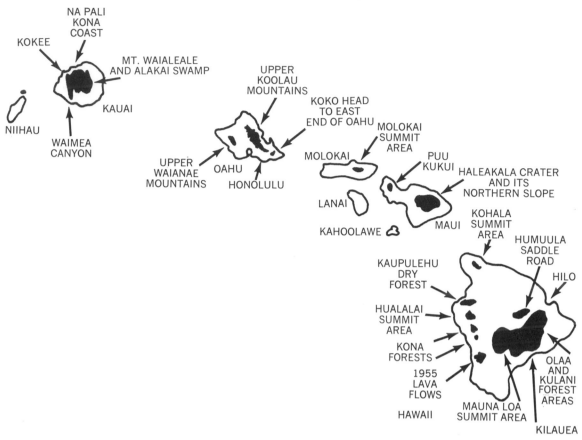

Areas shown black on this map can be called natural or seminatural. Even in the areas indicated, some introduced species are to be expected. In areas left white, a very few native plants and animals can be found, however. Some of the natural areas are very difficult of access, others can be visited easily.

Travel on foot is the best tactic in some regions, although a car is an adjunct and can be very important. On Oahu, for example, one sees the Koolau Mountains well by motoring to the base of a trail, then climbing. In Kokee, Kauai, a d in Kilauea, Hawaii, a great variety of regions may be seen close to roads. There are very few hikes on Oahu or elsewhere that require more than a single day. Helicopter charter is available on several of the islands, but it is of advantage to the amateur or professional naturalist in only a few cases, although it may be widely used for sightseeing.

When hiking in the Hawaiian Islands, the usual cautions prevail. Straying from trails is very unwise. One can become lost very easily, and feasible alternative routes once one has left a trail are few or none. Every year, a few hikers get into difficulty attempting to go cross-country without trails. Do not

The small proportion of land left as wilderness is hinted by this photograph of Lanai, most of which is pineapple fields or grazed lower hill slopes. The summit ridge still has some native plants, but even that area has been seriously, perhaps permanently, damaged.

attempt to ascend or descend steep slopes. Although rock on the Hawaiian Islands looks solid, it usually is not: old lava is weathered and crumbles easily, so that typical alpinism and alpinist equipment is inappropriate. There are very few plants, animals, or vistas not easily reached on a trail, or within a few feet of a trail. Horses are not generally available for hire, and would be a poor plan for most natural history excursions in any case.

Unless you must see particular species or particular areas, go to places of

Many trails in the Hawaiian Islands follow ridges. Here is such a trail in the
Koolau Mountains—Moanalua Trail.

easy access if your visit must be brief. Many excellent areas can easily be
reached. There are, to be sure, areas of difficult access, or where access lies
over private land, behind locked gates, etc. While some of these pique the
curiosity, they in fact offer very little that cannot be seen better in accessible
areas. The fact that the island of Niihau is private property and thus off limits
to virtually everyone seems to make it more alluring for some; if they visited it,
they would find it is only a dry, weedy cow pasture.

When you go hiking, or driving, you may wish to go with others. Sharing
car costs for economy and hiking with others for safety have obvious advantages.

In addition to native plants, plants brought by the ancient Hawaiians and now growing wild in the forests will interest visitors. The green (rarely purplish) rosettes of the ti (ki), *Cordyline terminalis,* are common at intermediate levels of the mountains.

The kukui tree (*Aleurites moluccana*) was almost certainly brought by the Hawaiians. Known also as candlenut, it provided an illumination source for the Hawaiians: the oil-rich seeds, strung together, provided a kind of lantern in which one seed, as it burned out, set fire to the next. Kukui looks like a native tree because it is almost universally present in valleys of mountains, and is easily recognized by its pale green, almost white, foliage.

I must admit that I have taken many hikes alone in the Islands, however, as have many other biologists, but I have never gone into these areas without maps or equivalent advance information.

Oahu

It may seem obvious, but, above all, visit the Bishop Museum in Honolulu. This museum has done an excellent and courageous job of fostering studies, providing exhibits of Hawaiian natural history and anthropology, serving these areas despite modest funding.

Forests of the Koolau Mountains can only be seen via trails. For a map of Oahu trails, see the Department of Forests in Honolulu. Only a few trails enter the Waianae Mountains.

The eastern end of Oahu, from Hanauma Bay to Makapuu, is an interesting area because of its varied geological formations and because it contains some good examples of coastal vegetation. This tour can be made by car, in which case you will probably want to begin from Honolulu, go to the eastern end of the island along the southern coast, and return to Honolulu via Nuuanu pali (or do the tour in the reverse direction).

Hawaii

A museum of recent geology and lava flow vegetation, this island offers good areas that are easily visited by car. Because of the distances involved, cars are to be preferred to hikes, although walks within the Kilauea region are worth while.

Hawaii Volcanoes National Park (Kilauea) has fascinations that a single day's visit is unlikely to exhaust. Kipuka Pualu ("Bird Park") offers birdwatching, an interesting forest, and a self-guiding trail. Forests near the Park Headquarters are interesting; the dry areas in and near the Kau Desert offer a remarkable contrast. Kilauea and the various calderas of the Chain of Craters are, of course, magnificent volcanic areas.

Kulani Prison Road (behind Hilo) offers good examples of wet ohia forest.

South Kona District (along the main highway): recent lava flows, lava flow vegetation, moderately dry ohia forest are well illustrated here.

North Kona Coast (north of Kailua): between Kailua and Kamuela, the highway passes through good dry forest at Kaupulehu and Puuwaawaa. Relatively old, but still nearly bare lava flows may be seen.

Humuula Saddle Road goes through many interesting lava flows, and shows kipukas well (Hilo side of summit) and alpine vegetation at higher elevations.

Maui

Haleakala National Park offers the best display of alpine vegetation to be seen in the Islands via a paved road, and has a number of points of geological interest. If time permits, you can hike into the crater and stay overnight in one or more of the cabins (arrangements must be made in advance; secure information well ahead of proposed visit). Other readily accessible areas on Maui may offer some points of geological interest, but little of the original flora and fauna.

Kauai

The forest of the upper plateau, Kokee State Park, is a lovely area with a cool, pleasant climate. Because it is a varied area, from dry Waimea Canyon to the spectacular Kalalau pali or the wet Alakai Swamp margins, a stay of several days is advisable, and good accommodations exist (consult Hawaii Visitors Bureau or other sources of information).

The Na Pali Kona Coast is beautiful, although the number of native plants is limited.

Molokai

An unpaved road (slippery when wet) leads to the summit area of eastern Molokai. Roads and trails in this area lead to some interesting patches of native vegetation, although much of Molokai's forests has been destroyed.

Other Islands

Lanai has been badly devastated, and may be disappointing where botany and zoology are concerned. Kahoolawe is a bomb impact area, definitely "off limits." A few smaller islets off the main islands might be fun to visit but would probably offer very little, if anything, not seen well elsewhere. This applies to the Leeward Islands also: as a Wildlife Refuge, the area is restricted to professional biologists. Only a very few plants and animals not represented in coastal areas of the major islands are to be seen in the Leeward Islands, and coasts of major islands offer many things not seen in the Leeward Islands.

Chapter 29 ❦ REFERENCES

OBVIOUSLY only a selection of references can be included here. The ones cited are those which are more important, more interesting and readable, or which have exceptionally good listing of books or papers in one or more fields. If one consults the bibliographies in some of the more important books and papers listed here, one can quickly find one's way to virtually all the significant literature on Hawaiian natural history.

References are arranged here according to chapters with three exceptions: (1) general references on plants and animals are listed in a special section after the references for Chapter 2. These general biological references contain some important titles, and special attention is called to them; (2) plant groups typical of one region are often found in several zones, so references for Chapters 14 to 19 are grouped together; (3) literature on the Leeward Islands is grouped together under the heading "Chapters 20–27."

Chapter 1. Geology

BRIGHAM, WILLIAM T. 1909. *The Volcanoes of Kilauea and Mauna Loa on the Island of Hawaii.* Mem. B. P. Bishop Mus. 2(4):1–222 (or 2:379–600).

HERBERT, DON, and FULVIA BARDOSSI. 1968. *Kilauea: Case History of a Volcano.* Harper & Row. New York.

HINDS, NORMAN E. A. 1930. *Geology of Kauai and Niihau.* B. P. Bishop Mus. Bull. 71:1–103.

HITCHCOCK, CHARLES H. 1911. *Hawaii and Its Volcanoes.* The Hawaiian Gazette Co., Ltd. Honolulu.

MacDONALD, GORDON A. 1947. *Bibliography of the Geology and Water Resources of the Island of Hawaii.* Hawaii Div. Hydrography Bull. 10:1–191.

MacDONALD, GORDON A., D. A. DAVIS, and D. C. COX. 1960. *Geology and Ground-Water Resources of the Island of Kauai, Hawaii.* Hawaii Div. Hydrography Bull. 13:1–212.

MacDONALD, GORDON A., and D. H. HUBBARD. 1965. *Volcanoes of the National Parks,* ed. 3. Hawaii Natural History Association. Honolulu.

MacDONALD, GORDON A., and W. KYSELKA. 1967. *Anatomy of an Island: A Geological History of Oahu.* B. P. Bishop Mus. Spec. Pub. 55:1–36.

PALMER, HAROLD S. 1927. *Geology of Kaula, Nihoa, Necker, and Gardner Pinnacles and French Frigate Shoal.* Bull. B. P. Bishop Mus. 35:1–35.

————. 1930. *Geology of Molokini*. Occ. Pap. B. P. Bishop Mus. 9(1):1–18.

————. 1936. *Geology of Lehua and Kaula Islands*. Occ. Pap. B. P. Bishop Mus. 12(13):1–36.

SELLING, OLOF H. 1946. *Studies in Hawaiian Pollen Statistics*. Part I. Spec. Publ. B. P. Bishop Mus. 37:1–87; Part II (1947), ibid. 38:1–430; Part III (1948), ibid. 39:1–154.

STEARNS, HAROLD T. 1939. *Geologic Map and Guide of the Island of Oahu, Hawaii*. Hawaii Div. Hydrography Bull. 2:1–75.

————. 1940. *Supplement to the Geology and Water Resources of the Island of Oahu, Hawaii*. Hawaii Div. Hydrography Bull. 5:1–164.

————. 1940. *Geology and Ground-Water Resources of Lanai and Kahoolawe, Hawaii*. With chapters on petrography of Lanai and Kahoolawe, by Gordon A. MacDonald, and geophysical investigations on Lanai, by Joel H. Swartz. Hawaii Div. Hydrography Bull. 6:1–177.

————. 1946. *Geology of the Hawaiian Islands*. Hawaii Div. Hydrography Bull. 8:1–106.

————. 1947. *Geology and Ground-Water Resources of the Island of Niihau, Hawaii*. With a chapter on petrography of Niihau by Gordon A. MacDonald. Hawaii Div. Hydrography Bull. 12:1–51.

————. 1966. *Geology of the State of Hawaii*. Pacific Books. Palo Alto, California.

————. 1966. *Road Guide to Points of Geologic Interest in the Hawaiian Islands*. Pacific Books. Palo Alto, California.

STEARNS, HAROLD T., and W. O. CLARK. 1930. *Geology and Water Resources of the Kau District, Hawaii*. U. S. Dept. Agric. Geolog. Survey Water Supply Paper 616:1–194.

STEARNS, HAROLD T., and GORDON A. MACDONALD. 1942. *Geology and Ground-Water Resources of the Island of Maui, Hawaii*. Hawaii Div. Hydrography Bull. 7:1–344.

STEARNS, HAROLD T., and GORDON A. MACDONALD. 1946. *Geology and Ground-Water Resources of the Island of Hawaii*. Hawaii Div. Hydrography Bull. 9:1–363.

STEARNS, HAROLD T., and GORDON A. MACDONALD. 1947. *Geology and Ground-Water Resources of the Island of Molokai, Hawaii*. Hawaii Div. Hydrography Bull. 11:1–113.

STEARNS, HAROLD T., and KNUTE N. VAKSVIK. 1935. *Geology and Ground-Water Resources of the Island of Oahu, Hawaii*. Hawaii Div. Hydrography Bull. 1:1–479.

STEARNS, NORAH D. 1935. *Annotated Bibliography and Index of Geology and Water Supply of the Island of Oahu, Hawaii*. Hawaii Div. Hydrography Bull. 3:1–74.

STONE, JOHN B. 1926. *The Products and Structure of Kilauea*. B. P. Bishop Mus. Bull. 33:1–59.

WENTWORTH, CHESTER K. 1925. *The Geology of Lanai*. B. P. Bishop Mus. Bull. 24:1–72.

————. 1926. *Pyroclastic Geology of Oahu*. B. P. Bishop Mus. Bull. 30:1–121.

————. 1951. *Geology and Ground-Water Resources of the Honolulu–Pearl Harbor Area, Oahu, Hawaii*. Board of Water Supply, City and County of Honolulu. Honolulu.

Volcano Observatory: Weekly Bulletins of the Hawaii Volcano Observatory were begun with Vol. 1 in 1913. This series was published by the U. S. Department of Agriculture Weather Bureau, and largely written by T. A. Jaggar, Jr. This series of papers was supplanted by *Reports of the Hawaiian Volcano Observatory,* published by the U. S. Geological Survey of the Department of the Interior.

Chapter 2. Climate

ANON. 1966. *Climatological Data: Pacific.* Annual Summary 1965. Vol. 10, no. 13, pp. 147–54. U. S. Dept. of Commerce. Asheville, North Carolina.

BLUMENSTOCK, DAVID I. 1961. *Climates of the States: Hawaii.* Climatology of the United States, no. 60–51. U. S. Dept. of Commerce Weather Bureau. Washington, D.C. 20 pp.

LEOPOLD, L. B., et al. 1955. *On the Rainfall of Hawaii: a Group of Contributions.* Meteor. Monographs 1(3):1–55.

TREWARTHA, GLENN T. 1954. *An Introduction to Climate.* McGraw-Hill. New York.

WOUDT, BESSEL D. van't, and ROBERT W. NELSON. 1963. *Hydrology of the Alakai Swamp, Kauai.* Hawaii Agric. Exper. Stat. Bull. 132:1–30.

Note: a number of points in this chapter were based on conversations with Mr. Saul Price of the U. S. Weather Bureau in Honolulu, as well as unpublished data in this office.

Animals and Plants—General References

BRYAN, WILLIAM A. 1915. *Natural History of Hawaii.* The Hawaiian Gazette Co., Ltd. Honolulu.

CARLQUIST, S. 1965. *Island Life.* Natural History Press. New York.

————. 1966. *The Biota of Long-Distance Dispersal.* I. Principles of dispersal and evolution. Quart. Rev. Biol. 41:247–70.

FOSBERG, F. R. 1961. *Guide to Excursion III, Tenth Pacific Science Congress.* University of Hawaii and Tenth Pacific Science Congress, Honolulu.

GOSLINE, WILLIAM A. 1968 *Considerations Regarding the Evolution of Hawaiian Animals.* Pacific Science 22:267–73.

Insects of Hawaii. University of Hawaii Press, Honolulu. Volumes of this work, begun by Elwood C. Zimmerman, have been continued with contributions by various entomologists. These volumes are still in the process of preparation and appearance.

MAYR, ERNST. 1943. *The Zoogeographic Position of the Hawaiian Islands.* Condor 45(2):45–48.

PERKINS, R. C. L. 1913. *Introduction* (to *Fauna Hawaiiensis*). In, David Sharp, ed., *Fauna Hawaiiensis* (vol. 1:xv–ccxxviii). Cambridge University Press. Cambridge.

RUHLE, GEORGE C. 1959. *A Guide for the Haleakala Section* [Haleakala National Park]. Hawaii Natural History Association.

SHARP, DAVID, ed. 1899–1913. *Fauna Hawaiiensis.* 3 vols., 2163 pp., contributions by various authors. Cambridge University Press. Cambridge.

STONE, BENJAMIN C. 1967. *A Review of the Endemic Genera of Hawaiian Plants.* Botan. Rev. 33:216–59.

USINGER, ROBERT L. 1941. *Problems of Insect Speciation in the Hawaiian Islands.* Amer. Nat. 75:251–63.

ZIMMERMAN, ELWOOD C. 1948. *Insects of Hawaii.* Vol. 1, "Introduction," 206 pp. University of Hawaii Press. Honolulu.

Chapter 3. Dispersal

CARLQUIST, S. 1967. *The Biota of Long-Distance Dispersal.* V. "Plant Dispersal to Pacific Islands." Bull. Torrey Botan. Club 94:129–62.

FALLA, R. A. 1960. *Oceanic Birds as Dispersal Agents.* Proc. Royal Soc. London, B, 152:653–59.

FORBES, CHARLES N. 1912. *New Hawaiian Plants.* III. "Preliminary Observations Concerning the Plant Invasion on Some of the Lava Flows of Mauna Loa, Hawaii." Occ. Pap. B. P. Bishop Mus. 5(1):15–23.

FOSBERG, F. R. 1948. *Derivation of the Flora of the Hawaiian Islands.* In E. C. Zimmerman, *Insects of Hawaii,* Vol. 1, pp. 107–19. University of Hawaii Press. Honolulu.

GLICK, P. A. 1939. *The Distribution of Insects, Spiders and Mites in the Air.* U. S. Dept. of Agriculture Tech. Bull. 673:1–150.

GUPPY, H. B. 1906. *Observations of a Naturalist in the Pacific Between 1896 and 1899.* Vol. II. Plant Dispersal. Macmillan & Co. London.

HENSHAW, H. W. 1910. *Migration of the Pacific Golden Plover to and from the Hawaiian Islands.* The Auk 27:245–62.

McCAUGHEY, V. 1917. *Vegetation of the Hawaiian Lava Flows.* Botan. Gaz. 64:386–420.

NAMIAS, JEROME. 1952. *The Jet Stream.* Sci. Am. 187(10):27–31.

PROCTOR, VERNON W. 1968. *Dispersal of Aquatic Organisms: Viability of Seeds Recovered from the Droppings of Captive Kildeer and Mallard Ducks.* Amer. J. Botan. 55:20–26.

———. 1968. *Long-Distance Dispersal of Seeds by Retention in Digestive Tract of Birds.* Science 160:321–22.

RIDLEY, H. N. 1930. *The Dispersal of Plants Throughout the World.* L. Reeve & Co. Ashford, England.

ST. JOHN, H. 1955. *The Relationship Between the Species of* Erythrina *(Leguminosae) Native to Hawaii and Tahiti.* Pacific Plant Studies 13. Webbia 11:293–99.

SKOTTSBERG, C. 1941. *Plant Succession on Recent Lava Flows in the Island of Hawaii.* Göteborgs Kungl. vetenskap-och-Vitterhets-Samhälles Handlingar ser. b, 1(8):1–32.

STEPHENS, S. G. 1958. *Salt Water Tolerance of Seeds of* Gossypium *Species as a Possible Factor in Seed Dispersal.* Amer. Nat. 92:83–92.

YOSHIMOTO, C. M., J. L. GRESSITT, and C. J. MITCHELL. 1962. *Trapping of Air-Borne Insects in the Pacific Area.* I. Pacific Insects 4:847–58. Other contributions in this series are in Proc. Haw. Ent. Soc. 17:150–55, 1959; Pacific Insects 2:239–43, 1960; Pacific Insects 3:556–58, 1961; Pacific Insects 5:873–83, 1963.

Chapter 4. Problems of Island Existence

CARLQUIST, S. 1966. *The Biota of Long-Distance Dispersal*. IV. "Genetic Systems in the Floras of Oceanic Islands." Evolution 20:433–55.

GILLETT, G. W. 1966. *Hybridization and Its Taxonomic Implications in the* Scaevola gaudichaudiana *Complex of the Hawaiian Islands*. Evolution 20:506–16.

ROCK, J. F. 1917. *The Ohia Lehua Trees of Hawaii*. Terr. Hawaii Board of Agric. and Forestry Botan. Bull. 4:1–76.

SKOTTSBERG, C. 1944. *On the Flower Dimorphism in Hawaiian Rubiaceae*. Arkiv för Botanik 31A:(4):1–28.

WELCH, D'ALTE A. 1938. *Distribution and Variation of* Achatinella mustelina *Mighel in the Waianae Mountains, Oahu*. B. P. Bishop Mus. Bull. 152:1–164.

————. 1942. *Distribution and Variation of the Hawaiian Tree Snail* Achatinella apexfulva *Dixon in the Koolau Range, Oahu*. Smithsonian Institution Misc. Coll. 103(1):1–236.

Chapter 5. Adaptive Radiation

HARDY, D. E. 1965. *Insects of Hawaii*. Vol. 12. "Diptera: Cyclorrhapha. II. Family Drosophilidae." Univ. of Hawaii Press. Honolulu.

ST. JOHN, HAROLD. 1966. *Monograph of* Cyrtandra (*Gesneriaceae*) *on Oahu, Hawaiian Islands*. B. P. Bishop Mus. Bull. 229:1–465.

SPIETH, H. T. 1966. *Courtship Behavior of Endemic Hawaiian* Drosophila. Univ. of Texas Publ. 6615:133–46.

STONE, BENJAMIN C. 1969. *The Genus* Pelea *A. Gray. A Taxonomic Monograph*. Phaerogamarum Monographiae III:1–180. Verlag J. Cramer, Lehre, Germany.

SWEZEY, OTTO. 1954. *Forest Entomology in Hawaii*. Bishop Mus. Spec. Publ. 44:1–266.

USINGER, ROBERT L. 1942. *The Genus* Nysius *and Its Allies in the Hawaiian Islands* (Hemiptera, Lygaeidae, Orsillini). B. P. Bishop Mus. Bull. 173:1–167.

Chapter 6. Arborescence

CARLQUIST, S. 1962. *A Theory of Paedomorphosis in Dicotyledonous Woods*. Phytomorphology 12:30–45.

SHERFF, E. E. 1930. *Revision of the Hawaiian Species of* Euphorbia. Ann. Missouri Botan. Gard. 25:1–94.

SKOTTSBERG, C. 1927. Artemisia, Scaevola, Santalum, *and* Vaccinium *of Hawaii*. B. P. Bishop Mus. Bull. 43:1–89.

————. 1940. *Observations on Hawaiian Violets*. Acta Horti Gotoburgenses 13:451–528.

Chapter 7. Flightlessness in Insects and Birds

For discussions of this topic, see the references by Perkins, Zimmerman, and Carlquist under "Animals and Plants—General References" above. Detailed information on the flightless Hawaiian lacewings is given in the following:

ZIMMERMAN, ELWOOD C. 1957. *Insects of Hawaii*. Vol. 6. "Ephemeroptera—Neuroptera —Trichoptera." University of Hawaii Press. Honolulu.

Chapter 8. Loss of Dispersibility in Plants

CARLQUIST, S. 1966. *The Biota of Long-Distance Dispersal*. II. "Loss of Dispersibility in Pacific Compositae." Evolution 20:30–48.

————. 1967. *The Biota of Long-Distance Dispersal*. III. "Loss of Dispersibility in the Hawaiian Flora." Brittonia 18:310–35.

SHERFF, E. E. 1937. *The Genus* Bidens. Part I. Field Mus. Nat. Hist. Botan. Ser. 16:1–346.

Chapter 9. Loss of Competitiveness, etc.

ARNOLD, HARRY L. 1968. *Poisonous Plants of Hawaii*. Charles E. Tuttle & Co. Rutland, Vermont.

CAUM, E. L. 1933. *The Exotic Birds of Hawaii*. Occ. Pap. B. P. Bishop Mus. 10(9):1–55.

MILLER, G. S., JR. 1924. *The Characters and Probable History of the Hawaiian Rat*. B. P. Bishop Mus. Bull. 14:1–11.

NEAL, MARIE C. 1965. *In Gardens of Hawaii*. B. P. Bishop Mus. Spec. Pub. 50. Bishop Museum Press. Honolulu.

ST. JOHN, H. 1952. *Monograph of the Genus* Isodendrion *(Violaceae)*. Hawaiian Plant Studies 21. Pacific Science 6:213–55.

STONE, B. C. 1967. *A Review of the Endemic Genera of Hawaiian Plants*. Botan. Rev. 33:216–59.

STONE, W. 1917. *The Hawaiian Rat*. Also, Stokes, J. F. G., *Notes on the Hawaiian Rat*. Occ. Pap. B. P. Bishop Mus. 3(4):1–10.

TABRAH, F. L., and B. M. EVELETH. 1966. *Evaluation of the Effectiveness of Ancient Hawaiian Medicines*. Hawaii Med. J. 25:223–30.

Chapter 10. The Land Shells

CAUM, E. L. 1928. *Check List of Hawaiian Land and Fresh Water Mollusca*. B. P. Bishop Mus. Bull. 56:1–79.

COOKE, C. MONTAGUE, JR. 1917. *Some New Species of* Amastra. Occ. Pap. B. P. Bishop Mus. 3(3):1–29.

————. 1921. *Notes on Hawaiian Zonitidae and Succineidae*. Occ. Pap. B. P. Bishop Mus. 7(12):263–77.

————. 1931. *The Land Snail Genus* Carelia. B. P. Bishop Mus. Bull. 85:1–97.

————. 1933. *New Species of Amastridae.* Occ. Pap. B. P. Bishop Mus. 10(6):1–27.

COOKE, C. MONTAGUE, JR., and YOSHIO KONDO. 1960. *Revision of Tornatellinidae and Achatinellidae (Gastropoda, Pulmonata).* B. P. Bishop Mus. Bull. 221:1–303.

GULICK, ADDISON. 1932. *Biological Peculiarities of Oceanic Islands.* Quart. Rev. Biol. 7(4):405–27.

GULICK, J. T. 1905. *Evolution, Racial and Habitudinal.* Carnegie Institute of Washington Publication 25:1–269.

HUBERDICK, BENGT. 1952. *Hawaiian Lymnaeidae.* Occ. Pap. B. P. Bishop Mus. 20(19):207–328.

NEAL, MARIE C. 1934. *Hawaiian Helicinidae.* B. P. Bishop Mus. Bull. 125:1–102.

PILSBRY, H. A. 1921. *The Dispersal and Affinities of Polynesian Land-Snail Faunas.* Proc. First Pan-Pacific Scientific Congress. B. P. Bishop Museum Spec. Pub. 7:147–51.

PILSBRY, H. A., and C. MONTAGUE COOKE, JR. 1908. *Notes on Hawaiian Land Shells.* Occ. Pap. B. P. Bishop Mus. 3(2):1–22.

THWING, E. W. 1907. *Reprint of Original Descriptions of* Achatinella, *with Additional Notes.* Occ. Pap. B. P. Bishop Mus. 3(1):1–196.

Chapter 11. Honeycreepers and Other Birds

AMADON, DEAN. 1950. *The Hawaiian Honeycreepers (Aves, Drepaniidae).* Bull. Amer. Mus. Nat. His. 95:157–262.

BALDWIN, PAUL H. 1953. *Annual Cycle, Environment, and Evolution in the Hawaiian Honeycreepers (Aves, Drepaniidae).* Univ. Calif. Publ. Zool. 52:285–398.

BRYAN, E. H., JR. *Check List and Summary of Hawaiian Birds.* Books About Hawaii. Honolulu.

DUNMIRE, WILLIAM W. 1961. *Birds of the National Parks in Hawaii.* Hawaii Natural History Association. Kilauea, Hawaii.

GRINNELL, JOSEPH. 1911. *The Linnet of the Hawaiian Islands: A Problem in Speciation.* Univ. Calif. Publ. Zool. 7:179–95.

HENSHAW, H. W. 1902. *Birds of the Hawaiian Possessions.* Thos. G. Thrum. Honolulu.

MILLER, ALDEN H. 1937. *Structural Modifications in the Hawaiian Goose* (Nesochen sandvicensis): *A Study in Adaptive Evolution.* Univ. Calif. Publ. Zool. 42:1–80.

MUNRO, GEORGE C. 1960. *Birds of Hawaii.* ed. 2. Bridgeway Press. Rutland, Vermont.

PERKINS, R. C. L. 1903. *Vertebrata.* In David Sharp, ed., *Fauna Hawaiiensis* 1(4):365–466. Cambridge University Press. Cambridge.

RICHARDSON, FRANK, and JOHN BOWLES. 1964. *A Survey of the Birds of Kauai, Hawaii.* B. P. Bishop Mus. Bull. 227:1–51.

ROTHSCHILD, WALTER. 1893–1900. *The Avifauna of Laysan and the Hawaiian Possessions.* R. H. Porter. London.

SPIETH, H. T. 1966. *Hawaiian Honeycreeper,* Vestiaria coccinea *(Forster), Feeding on Lobeliad Flowers,* Clermontia arborescens *(Mann) Hillebrand.* Amer. Nat. 100:470–73.

WILSON, SCOTT B., and A. H. EVANS. 1890–1899. *Aves Hawaiienses: The Birds of the Sandwich Islands.* R. H. Porter. London.

Chapter 12. The Lobelioids

CARLQUIST, S. 1962. Trematolobelia: *Seed Dispersal; Anatomy of Fruit and Seeds.* Pacific Science 16:126–34.

——. 1962. *Ontogeny and Comparative Anatomy of Thorns of Hawaiian Lobeliaceae.* Amer. J. Botan. 49:413–19.

ROCK, JOSEPH F. 1919. *A Monographic Study of the Hawaiian Species of the Tribe Lobelioideae, Family Campanulaceae.* Mem. B. P. Bishop Mus. 7(2):1–394.

——. 1957. *Some New Hawaiian Lobelioids.* Occ. Pap. B. P. Bishop Mus. 22(5): 35–66.

——. *Hawaiian Lobelioids.* Occ. Pap. B. P. Bishop Mus. 23(5):65–75.

ST. JOHN, H. 1935. *Hawaiian* Panicum, Metrosideros, Sanicula, *and* Rollandia. Occ. Pap. B. P. Bishop Mus. 11(13):1–18.

——. 1939. *New Hawaiian Species of* Clermontia, *Including a Revision of the* Clermontia grandiflora *Group.* Hawaiian Plant Studies 6. Occ. Pap. B. P. Bishop Mus. 15(1):1–19.

——. 1939. *New Hawaiian Lobeliaceae.* Hawaiian Plant Studies 7. Occ. Pap. B. P. Bishop Mus. 15(2):21–35.

——. 1940. Ophioglossum, Rollandia, *and* Scaevola. Hawaiian Plant Studies 9. Occ. Pap. B. P. Bishop Mus. 15(28):351–59.

ST. JOHN, H., and E. Y. HOSAKA. 1938. *Notes on Hawaiian Species of* Lobelia. Hawaiian Plant Studies 5. Occ. Pap. B. P. Bishop Mus. 14(8).117–26.

WIMMER, F. E. 1953, 1956. *Campanulaceae—Lobelioideae.* In A. Engler and L. Diels, eds., Das Pflanzenreich 106 (1–260) & 107 (1–813). Akademie-Verlag. Berlin.

Chapter 13. Silverswords and Their Relatives

CARLQUIST, S. 1957. *Leaf Anatomy and Ontogeny in* Argyroxiphium *and* Wilkesia (*Compositae*). Amer. J. Botan. 44:696–705.

——. 1958. *Structure and Ontogeny of Glandular Trichomes of Madinae (Compositae).* Amer. J. Botan. 45:675–82.

——. 1959. *Vegetative Anatomy of* Dubautia, Argyroxiphium *and* Wilkesia (*Compositae*). Pacific Sci. 13:195–210.

——. 1959. *Studies in Madiinae: Anatomy, Cytology, and Evolutionary Relationships.* Aliso 4:171–236.

KECK, DAVID D. 1966. *The Hawaiian Silverswords: Systematics, Affinities, and Phytogeographic Problems of the Genus* Argyroxiphium. Occ. Pap. B. P. Bishop Mus. 11(19):1–38.

ROCK, JOSEPH F., and MARIE C. NEAL. 1957. *A New Variety of Silversword.* Occ. Pap. B. P. Bishop Mus. 22(5):1–3.

SHERFF, E. E. 1935. *Revision of* Tetramolopium, Lipochaeta, Dubautia, *and* Railliardia. B. P. Bishop Mus. Bull. 135:1–136.

Chapters 14–19. Hawaiian Flora, Ecology

BECCARI, ODOARDO. 1921. *A Monographic Study of the Genus* Pritchardia. Mem. B. P. Bishop Mus. 7(1):1–77.

BROTHERUS, V. F. 1927. *Hawaiian Mosses.* B. P. Bishop Mus. Bull. 40:1–37.

CAUM, E. L. 1930. *New Hawaiian Plants.* Occ. Pap. B. P. Bishop Mus. 9(5):1–30.

——. 1933. *Notes on* Pteralyxia. Occ. Pap. B. P. Bishop Mus. 19(8):1–24.

——. 1936. *Notes on the Flora and Fauna of Lehua and Kaula Islands.* Occ. Pap. B. P. Bishop Mus. 11(21):1–17.

COWAN, RICHARD S. 1949. *A Taxonomic Revision of the Genus* Neraudia *(Urticaceae).* Pac. Sci. 3:231–70.

DANSER, B. H. 1937. *A Revision of the Genus* Korthalsella. Bull. Jard. Bot. Buitenzorg 14:115–59.

DEGENER, OTTO. 1930. *Illustrated Guide to the More Common or Noteworthy Ferns and Flowering Plants of Hawaii National Park, with Descriptions of Ancient Hawaiian Customs, and an Introduction to the Geologic History of the Islands.* Honolulu Star Bulletin. Honolulu.

——. 1932 et seq. *Flora Hawaiiensis.* Privately published. (This loose-leaf flora, still very much incomplete, has been published at various dates; six "volumes" of about one hundred pages each have now been issued.)

——. 1945. *Plants of Hawaii National Park.* Honolulu Star Bulletin. Honolulu.

DOTY, MAXWELL S., and DIETER MUELLER-DOMBOIS. 1966. *Atlas for Bioecology Studies in Hawaii Volcanoes National Park.* Hawaii Botan. Sci. Pap. no. 2:1–507.

FAGERLIND, F. 1949. *Some Reflections on the History of the Climate and Vegetation of the Hawaiian Islands.* Svensk Bot. Tidskr. 43:1–81.

FOSBERG, F. R. 1936. *Hawaiian Geraniums.* Occ. Pap. B. P. Bishop Mus. 12(16):1–19.

——. 1937. *The Genus* Gouldia *(Rubiaceae).* B. P. Bishop Mus. Bull. 147:1–82.

——. 1939. *Taxonomy of the Hawaiian Genus* Broussaisia *(Saxifragaceae).* Occ. Pap. B. P. Bishop Mus. 15(4):49–60.

——. 1959. *Upper Limits of Vegetation of Mauna Loa, Hawaii.* Ecology 40: 144–46.

FOSBERG, F. R., and E. Y. HOSAKA. 1938. *An Open Bog on Oahu.* Occ. Pap. B. P. Bishop Mus. 14(1):1–6.

HARTT, CONSTANCE G., and MARIE C. NEAL. 1940. *The Plant Ecology of Mauna Kea, Hawaii.* Ecology 21:237–66.

HILLEBRAND, WILLIAM. 1888. *Flora of the Hawaiian Islands.* Privately published. Heidelberg. Reprinted 1968 by Hafner & Co., New York.

HITCHCOCK, A. S. 1922. *The Grasses of Hawaii.* Mem. B. P. Bishop Mus. 7(2):1–132.

HOSAKA, E. Y. 1937. *Ecological and Floristic Studies in Kipapa Gulch, Oahu.* Occ. Pap. B. P. Bishop Mus. 13:175–232.

——. 1940. *A Revision of the Hawaiian Species of* Myrsine (Suttonia, Rapanea). Occ. Pap. B. P. Bishop Mus. 16(2):25–76.

HUBBARD, D. H., and V. R. BENDER, JR. 1960. *Trailside Plants of Hawaii National Park.* Hawaii Natural History Association. Kilauea.

LAM, H. J. 1954. Nesoluma *and* Planchonella *from the Hawaiian Islands.* (Sapotaceae). Occ. Pap. B. P. Bishop Mus. 21(10):209–12

McCaughey, V. 1918. *The Strand Flora of the Hawaiian Islands.* Bull. Torrey Botan. Club 45:259–77.

Oliver, W. R. B. 1935. *The Genus* Coprosma. B. P. Bishop Mus. Bull. 132:1–207.

Palmer, H. S. 1930. *Geology of Molokini;* with E. L. Caum, *Notes on the Flora of Molokini.* Occ. Pap. B. P. Bishop Mus. 9(1):1–18.

Ripperton, J. C., and E. Y. Hosaka. 1942. *Vegetation Zones of Hawaii.* Hawaii Agric. Exper. Stat. Bull. 89:1–60.

Robyns, W., and S. H. Lamb. 1939. *Preliminary Ecological Survey of the Island of Hawaii.* Bull. Jard. Bot. Bruxelles 9:241–93.

Rock, Joseph F. 1913. *The Indigenous Trees of the Hawaiian Islands.* Privately published. Honolulu.

———. 1916. *The Sandalwoods of Hawaii.* Terr. Hawaii Board of Agric. & For. Bull. 3:1–43.

———. 1919. *The Arborescent Indigenous Legumes of Hawaii.* Terr. Hawaii Board of Agric. & For. Bull. 5:1–53.

Rotar, Peter P. 1968. *Grasses of Hawaii.* Univ. of Hawaii Press.

St. John, Harold. 1931. *Additions to the Flora of Niihau.* Occ. Pap. B. P. Bishop Mus. 9(14):1–11.

———. 1932. *Notes on* Pritchardia. Occ. Pap. B. P. Bishop Mus. 9(19):1–5.

———. 1934. Panicum, Zanthoxylum, Psychotria, *and* Sicyos. Occ. Pap. B. P. Bishop Mus. 10(12):1–7.

———. 1946. *Endemism in the Hawaiian Flora, and a Revision of the Hawaiian Species of* Gunnera (Haloragidaceae). Hawaiian Plant Studies II. Proc. Calif. Acad. Sci., 4th ser., 25:377–420.

———. 1947. *The History, Present Distribution, and Abundance of Sandalwood on Oahu, Hawaiian Islands.* Hawaiian Plant Studies 14. Pac. Sci. 1:5–20.

———. 1959. *Botanical Novelties on the Island of Niihau, Hawaiian Islands.* Hawaiian Plant Studies 25. Pac. Sci. 13:156–90.

St. John, Harold, and J. R. Kuykendall. 1949. *Revision of the Native Hawaiian Species of* Gardenia (Rubiaceae). Hawaiian Plant Studies 15. Brittonia 6:431–49.

Sherff, E. E. 1935. *Revision of* Tetramolopium, Lipochaeta, Dubautia, *and* Railliardia. B. P. Bishop Mus. Bull. 135:1–136.

———. 1935. *Revision of* Haplostachys, Phyllostegia, *and* Stenogyne. B. P. Bishop Mus. Bull. 136:1–101.

———. 1939. *The Genus* Labordia. Hawaiian Euphorbiaceae, Labiatae and Compositae. Field Mus. Botan. Ser. 17(6):447–612.

———. 1943. *Revision of the Hawaiian Members of the Genus* Pittosporum *Banks.* Field Mus. Botan. Ser. 22(10):467–580.

———. 1954. *Revision of the Genus* Cheirodendron *Nutt. ex Seem. for the Hawaiian Islands.* Fieldiana (Botany) 29:1–45.

———. 1955. *Revision of the Hawaiian Members of the Genus* Tetraplasandra *A. Gray.* Fieldiana (Botany) 29:49–142.

Skottsberg, C. 1925. *Juan Fernández and Hawaii: A Phytogeographical Discussion.* B. P. Bishop Mus. Bull. 16:1–47.

———. 1931. *Remarks on the Flora of the High Hawaiian Volcanoes.* Acta Horti Gotoburgensis 6:47–65.

————. 1934. *Astelia* and *Pipturus of Hawaii.* B. P. Bishop Mus. Bull. 117:1–77.

————. 1936. *The Arboreous Nyctaginaceae of Hawaii.* Svensk Bot. Tidskr. 30: 722–43.

————. 1940. *Report on Hawaiian Bogs.* Proc. Sixth Pacific Sci. Congress 4:659–61.

————. 1944. *Vascular Plants from the Hawaiian Islands.* IV. Acta Horti Gotoburgensis. 15:275–531.

STEPHENS, S. G. 1964. *Native Hawaiian Cotton* (Gossypium tomentosum *Nutt.*) Pac. Sci. 18:385–98.

STEVENS, FRANK L. 1925. *Hawaiian Fungi.* B. P. Bishop Mus. Bull. 19:1–189.

WAGNER, WARREN H. 1954. *The Fern Genus* Diellia. Univ. Calif. Publ. Botan. 26: 1–212.

YUNCKER, T. G. 1933. *A Revision of the Hawaiian Species of* Peperomia. B. P. Bishop Mus. Bull. 112:1–131.

Chapters 20–27. The Leeward Islands

BAILEY, ALFRED M. 1952. *Laysan and Black-Footed Albatrosses.* Denver Mus. Nat. Hist. Mus. Pictorial 6:1–79.

————. 1952. *The Hawaiian Monk Seal.* Denver Mus. Nat. Hist. Mus. Pictorial 7:1–30.

————. 1956. *Birds of Midway and Laysan Islands.* Denver Mus. Nat. Hist. Mus. Pictorial 12:1–130.

BRYAN, E. H., JR. 1942. *American Polynesia and the Hawaiian Chain.* Tongg Publishing Co. Honolulu.

————. 1954. *The Hawaiian Chain.* B. P. Bishop Museum. Honolulu.

BRYAN, E. H., JR., and collaborators. 1926. *Insects of Hawaii, Johnston Island, and Wake Island.* B. P. Bishop Mus. Bull. 81:1–41.

CHRISTOPHERSEN, ERLING, and E. L. CAUM. 1931. *Vascular Plants of the Leeward Islands, Hawaii.* B. P. Bishop Mus. Bull. 81:1–41.

EMORY, KENNETH P. 1928. *Archaeology of Nihoa and Necker Islands.* B. P. Bishop Mus. Bull. 53:1–124.

FISHER, WALTER K. 1903. *Notes on the Birds Peculiar to Laysan Island, Hawaiian Group.* The Auk 20:384–97.

FOSBERG, F. R. 1955. *Pacific Forms of* Lepturus R. Br. (Gramineae). Occ. Pap. B. P. Bishop Mus. 21(14):285–94.

GALTSOFF, P. S. 1933. *Pearl and Hermes Reef, Hawaii, Hydrographical and Biological Observations.* B. P. Bishop Mus. Bull. 107:1–49.

KENYON, KARL W., and CLIFFORD H. FISCUS. 1963. *Age Determination in the Hawaiian Monk Seal.* Jour. of Mammalogy 44:280–82.

LAMOUREUX, CHARLES H. 1961. *Botanical Observations on Leeward Hawaiian Atolls.* Atoll Res. Bull. 79:1–10.

————. 1963. *The Flora and Vegetation of Laysan Island.* Atoll Res. Bull. 97:1–14.

PALMER, HAROLD S. 1927. *Geology of Kaula, Nihoa, Necker, and Gardner Islands and French Frigate Shoal.* B. P. Bishop Mus. Bull. 35:1–35.

RICE, DALE W., and KARL W. KENYON. 1962. *Breeding Distribution, History, and Populations of North Pacific Albatrosses.* The Auk. 79:365–86.

RICE, DALE W., and KARL W. KENYON. 1962. *Breeding Cycles and Behavior of Laysan and Black-Footed Albatrosses.* The Auk 79:517–67.

RICHARDSON, FRANK. 1957. *The Breeding Cycles of Hawaiian Sea Birds.* B. P. Bishop Mus. Bull. 218:1–41.

ROTHSCHILD, WALTER. 1893–1903. *The Avifauna of Laysan and the Neighboring Islands.* R. H. Porter. London.

ST. JOHN, HAROLD. 1935. *Additions to the Flora of Midway Islands.* Occ. Pap. B. P. Bishop Mus. 11(14):1–4.

SCHAUINSLAND, H. 1899. *Drei Monate auf einer Korallen-Insel.* Max Nossler. Bremen.

WETMORE, A. 1925. *Bird Life Among Lava Rock and Coral Sand.* Nat. Geog. 48:76–108.

Chapter 30 ❧❧❧ HAWAIIAN NAMES AND WORDS

ALTHOUGH Hawaiian cannot be said to be a spoken language for any but a handful of people, many Hawaiian names and terms have persisted. Among these are the names for animals and plants. Often these names are rough equivalents, sometimes exact ones, of the genus, even species concepts used by modern biologists. For example, "naupaka" is always a name for *Scaevola*. The *Scaevola* which grows on beaches, *S. taccada*, is "naupaka kai." The Hawaiians were students of their environment, and had names for virtually all of the plants and animals.

Hawaiian terms are very useful, often used, as in the case of the lava types (aa, pahoehoe), kipuka (vegetation surrounded by lava flows), puka (crevice, hole in lava), mauka (inland), makai (seaward). Place names are all but universally Hawaiian. Correct pronunciation is important—and very easy, if you do not try to force English pronunciation onto the Hawaiian language. Unlike English, Hawaiian is spelled phonetically.

Vowel sounds are the same as in Spanish or German: a=ah; e=eh; i=ee; o=oh; u=oo. Consonant sounds are obvious, with the exception of w, which one often hears pronounced like v, although this is not invariable.

There are no true diphthongs in Hawaiian; each vowel sound is pronounced. Thus, Napoopoo is pronounced "Nah-poh-oh-poh-oh." When certain vowels follow each other closely, diphthongs tend to result in practice: Kauai is sometimes heard "cow-eye," although properly, it is "kah-oo-ah-ee."

Hawaiian is not strongly accented, and a place name said without any of the syllables accented would probably be recognized easily enough. However, accents do occur, sometimes unexpectedly: the name Haleakala is accented on the last syllable, for example.

INDEX

A

Aa lava flows, 12–14; penetration of, into forested areas, 13–14; isolated pockets of vegetation (kipukas) left by, 13, 14; additions to coastline from, 13, 14; lava blocks rearranged to form fishponds, 13, 14; plant growth in, 111

Acacia kauaiensis, species from Kauai, 287

Acacia koa, the koa tree: dispersal of, to the Islands, 105, 294, 297; "aggressiveness" of, 177; habitat and characteristics of, 285–87

Achatinella snails: diversity in species of, 112, 119, 180; method of feeding developed by, 137; number of species of, 180, 184; grouping of, 181; species by geographical grouping, 182–83; lack of mobility in, 184

Achyranthes splendens, the amaranth, 414, 417

Adaptations of plants and animals: adaptive radiation, 122–33, 156, 190; unique adaptations, 134–38

Adiantum hispidulum, a maidenhair fern, 299

Agates found in the Islands, 48

Age of Hawaiian chain, 3

Air, flotation in. *See* Flotation in air, as means of dispersal

"Alakai Swamp" on Kauai, 345, 350

Albatrosses, 407–8, 410, 426–28; the Laysan, 407, 408, 426; the black-footed, 407, 408, 427; as the "gooneys" on Midway, 427

Alectryon, the mahoe, 167, 168

Aleurites molucana, the kukui tree, 303–4, 433

Aloi Crater, 1962 eruption of, 28; fire fountain produced by, 29; lava lake formed by, 29, 30

Alphitonia ponderosa, a kauwila tree, 287, 290

Alpine zone of the Islands, 358–74; plants of, 358, 359, 361, 362; the four mountains of, 361

Alsinodendron, "false berry" of, 172

Alyxia olivaeformis, the maile vine, 296

Amaranthus brownii, endemic plant of Nihoa, 378

Amastra snails: diversity in, 187; variety of tendencies in species of, 188, 189

American Trust Territory of Micronesian atolls, 425

Amphoradenium ferns: epiphytism of, 336; *Amphoradenium tamariscinum,* 336, 340; *Amphoradenium montanum,* 336, 341; *Amphoradenium tripinnatifidum,* 336, 342; *Amphoradenium haalilioanum,* 336, 342; *Amphoradenium hymenophylloides,* 336, 342; *Amphoradenium sarmentosum,* 336, 343; *Amphoradenium pinnatifidum,* 336, 343; *Amphoradenium hillebrandii,* 341; *Amphoradenium pumilum,* 357

Anas wyvilliana laysanensis, 401

Anas wyvilliana wyvilliana, the koloa (Hawaiian duck), 218, 219, 403

Anoectochilus sandwicensis, an orchid, 324

Anous minutus melanogenys, the whitecap noddy tern, 425

Anous stolidus pileatus, the common noddy tern, 386

Antidesma, the hame: of the wet forest, 303; *Antidesma platyphyllum,* 311

Aragonite found in the Islands, 50

Arborescence of plants on the Islands, 139–57; *Euphorbia,* the akoko, 139–43, 144; *Lepidium,* 143, 145, 157; *Chenopodium,* the aweoweo, 145, 146; *Nototrichum,* the kului, 145, 146, 147; *Charpentiera,* the papala, 145, 147; violets, 148–49; *Plantago,* the plantain weed, 149–50, 151; *Scaevola,* the naupaka, 151–55, 156; lobelioids, 156, 157; *Dubautia,* the silversword, 156; reasons underlying trends toward, 156–57

Argemone glauca, the puakala, 157, 284

Argyroxiphium; the shinshina, 359. *See also* Greenswords; Silverswords

Arnold, Harry L., 173

Artemisia, sagebrush: *Artemisia australis,* 297; as Hawaiian alpine, 358, 361

Ash, unleashed by explosive volcanic eruptions, 39, 40

Asplenium genus of ferns: *Asplenium falcatum,* 331; *Asplenium midus,* epiphyte, 335, 344; *Asplenium trichomanes,* Halaakala alpine, 366

Astelia, the painiu: *Astelia menziesiana,* 97, 110, 323; dioecism of, 119; epiphytism of, 333, 337; *Astelia argyrocoma,* 337; common in Hawaiian bogs, 351; *Astelia nivea,* 351, 355; *Astelia forbesii,* 357

Athyrium fern: *Athyrium microphyllum,* 331; *Athyrium sandwichianum,* 332

Augites found in cinder cones, 48

Auricularia, ear fungus, 332

Avifauna of Laysan and the Neighboring Islands, The (Rothschild), 400

Awaawapuhi Valley on Kauai, rainfall on, 71

B

Bailey, Alfred M., 400

Banza grasshoppers: gigantism of *Banza nihoa,* 138; flightlessness of, 158, 159

Barrier reefs, formation of, 4, 5

Basalt lavas, 4, 13

Batis maritima, coastal plant, 274

Beach plants, dispersal of, 102

Beetles, flightlessness of, 159, 160–61, 162

Bidens, the kokoolau: dispersal of, to the Islands, 93, 94; changes in, causing diminishing of dispersibility, 164, 165; *Bidens molokaiensis,* a coastal kokoolau, 269, 271; growth of, on dry ridge sites, 298; *Bidens waiancensis,* 298

Biennials of Hawaiian flora, 157

Birds: dispersal of, to the Islands, 86; list of, not native to the Islands but observed there as stragglers, 86, 98; attachment to, as means of dispersal, 88–94; fruit eating by, as means of dispersal, 94–101; pollination of plants by, 135–36; flightlessness in Hawaiian birds, 158; of the Islands, 190–221

Birds of Midway and Laysan Islands (Bailey), 400

Bishop Museum, Honolulu, 17, 37, 38, 434; Bishop Museum's Tanager Expedition (1932), 379, 400, 410

Black Point lava strip on flank of Diamond Point, 41

Black sand of beaches of the Islands, 57–58

Blowholes on coasts of the Islands, 58

Bobea elatior, the ahakea of the coffee family, 288

Boerhavia, beach plant: dispersal of, to the Islands, 90, 91; on Pearl and Hermes Reef, 416

Bogs, Hawaiian, 79, 345–58; formation of, 79, 346; scarcity of *Sphagnum* moss in, 347, 358; mud of, 347; sedge and tussocks in, 347, 349, 355, 356; habitat as difficult one, 353

Boiling Pots, near Hilo, basalt lava columns at, 20, 21, 22

Bonin Islands, 1946 submarine eruption in, 11

Booby birds: red-footed booby (*Sula sula rubripes*), 384, 393; blue-faced booby (*Sula dactylatra personata*), 385, 387, 393; brown booby (*Sula leucogaster plotus*), 419, 420

Branta sandwicensis, the nene (Hawaiian goose), 218

Brigham, William T., 10

Brighamia of the lobelioids, 248–49; *Brighamia insignis,* 249

Bromeliads, the pineapple family, 333

Broussaisia, the kanawau: dioecism of, 119, 120; *Broussaisia arguta,* 120; of the wet forest, 303

Buddleia asiatica, a weed, 109

Bulwer's petrel (*Bulweria bulweri*), 378, 380, 416, 421

Buteo solitarius, the io (Hawaiian hawk), 214, 217

C

Calcite found in the Islands, 50

Caldera, in island building: formation of, 4, 5, 7–8, 27; addition of lava over, 4, 5, 27

Callistopteris baldwinii, a fern, 327

Calophyllul inophyllum, the beach tree, 104

Canavalia, the awikiwiki, 169

Canthium odoratum, the walahee, 278

Capparis sandwichiana, the maiapilo, 271

Cassytha filiformis, parasitic laurel, 94, 97

Casuarina tree on Midway, 428

Cauliflory characteristic of tropical trees, 130, 132

Ceodes umbellifera, the papala, 289

Chaetoptila, the kioea (honeyeater), 214, 215

Chain of Craters Road in Hawaii Volcanoes National Park, 26, 28; lava flows into sinks along, in 1969–70 eruptions, 29

Chamaesyce garden weeds, 140

Charpentiera, the papala: "halfway to dioecism," system of, 121; arborescence of, 145, 147; *Charpentiera abovata*, 147

Chasiempis sandwichensis, the elepaio, 213, 214

Cheirodendron, the olapa or lapalapa: of the wet forest, 303; *Cheirodendron trigynum* var. *acuminatum,* the olap, 306; *Cheirodendron platyphyllum,* the lapalapa, 307; epiphytism of, 334, 335; *Cheirodendron fauries* in Wahiawa Bog, 348

Chenopodium, the aweoweo: arborescence of, 145, 146, 147; *Chenopodium oahuense,* 146, 147, 269, 382, 388

"Chinaman's Hat Island." *See* Mokolii Island

Cibotium, the hapuu tree fern: 304; *Cibotium chamissoi,* 304, 328; *Cibotium glaucum,* 328; epiphytism of, 335, 338

Cinder cones, volcanic, 4, 5, 24–26, 32, 34, 35, 45, 46; spatter produced by, 35–37

Ciridops, the ula-ai-hawane (honeycreeper), 198, 209

Cladium angustifolium, sedges: dispersal of, to the Islands, 101; of the wet forest, 324

Claoxylon sandwicense, the poola, 311

Clermontia of the lobelioids, 239–45, 306; dispersal of, to the Islands, 91, 92; differences within species of, 112; hybridization of, 113; diversification in flowers in, 240; *Clermontia micrantha,* 240; *Clermontia lindseyana,* 240, 241; *Clermontia kohalae,* 240, 241; *Clermontia kakeana,* 240, 242; *Clermontia grandiflora,* 240, 242; *Clermontia drepanomorpha,* 240, 242; *Clermontia persicaefolia,* 240, 243; *Clermontia parviflora,* 240, 243, 245, 338; *Clermontia peleana,* 240, 244, 245; *Clermontia clermontioides,* 244, 245; epiphytism of some species, 333, 335, 338

Climate of the Islands, 63–80, 156; temperatures, 64–66; kona storms, 66–67; trade winds and their rainfall, 67–73; "Kona-Coast weather," 74–77; microclimates, 78–80

Coasts, Hawaiian, plants of, 267–74; trees, 267–69; shrubs, 269–72; vining species, 273, 274; sedges and grasses, 273, 274

Cocculus ferrandianus, the huehue, 173, 298

Cochlicopidae family of land shells, 185, 187, 189

Coconut palms, brought to the Islands by Polynesians, 105

Coffee-growing on Kona Coast island of Hawaii, 75

Colors in Hawaiian flora, 97

Colubrina, the kauwila, 169, 281, 285, 294

Competitiveness, loss of, in flora and fauna of the Islands, 176–77

Conservation of flora and fauna on the Islands, problems of, 177–79

Coots of the Island, 218, 220

Coprosma, the pilo: *Coprosma ernodeoides,* 95, 97, 107, 362, 365; *Coprosma stephanocarpa,* 95, 309; dioecism of, 119, 309; odorless leaves of, 175; of the wet forest, 303; *Coprosma longifolia,* 309; *Coprosma ochracea,* 349, 355; as alpine plant, 358, 361, 362; *Coprosma montana,* 362

Corals: coral reefs, 5, 6; coral beaches, 57; coral effects, 60; coral platforms, 60

Cordyline terminalis, the ti (ki), 433

Corvus tropicus, the alala (Hawaiian crow), 214, 217

Crater, volcanic formation of, 4, 7, 8

Crow, colonization of, in the Islands, 190, 214

Cyanea of the lobelioids, 91, 222–36, 306; development of prickles on seedlings of, 175; *Cyanea pilosa,* 223, 224; *Cyanea acuminata,* 224; *Cyanea recta,* 224; *Cyanea aculeatiflora,* 225, 227, 228; *Cyanea atra,* 225, 226; *Cyanea gayana,* 225; *Cyanea marksii,* 225, 226; *Cyanea solonocalyx,* 225, 227; *Cyanea tritomantha,* the aku, 225, 227, 228, 229, 230; *Cyanea grimesiana,* 230, 231; *Cyanea asplenifolia,* 231; *Cyanea shipmanii,* 231, 232; *Cyanea fauriei,* 232, 233; *Cyanea angustifolia,* 233; *Cyanea arborea,* 233, 235; *Cyanea leptostegia,* 233, 234–35

Cyrtandra: dispersal of, to the Islands, 91, 97; speciation of, 127–28; of the wet forest, 304, 306

D

Darwin, Charles, 157

Day length in the Islands, 64

Delissea of the lobelioids, 222–23; *Delissea undulata,* 222, 223

Deschampsia ambigua, a grass, 350, 352

Devastation Walk, produced by Kilauea-iki eruption, 33, 92, 109

"Devil's Throat, The" caldera of Kilauea, 29

Diamond Head Crater on Oahu, 8; as tuff cone, 40–41, 44, 45; calcite crystals found in, 50; plant fossils found in tuffs of, 61

Dianella, the uki, 97; *Dianella sandwicensis,* 299

Dicranopteris, the uluhe fern, 304, 348, 353; *Dicranopteris linearis,* 326

Dictyophorodelphax insect, 126

Dikes and dikelets formed by intrusive lava, 21–23

Dioecism in plants, 119–21; "halfway to dioecism," 119, 121

Diomedea, the albatross: *Diomedea immutabilis* (the Laysan albatross), 407, 408; *Diomedea nigripes* (the black-footed albatross), 407, 408

Diospyros ferrea var. *sandwicensis,* the lama tree, 276, 285

Dispersal mechanisms of plants: changes in, 172, 307; opportunities for amateurs in discoveries about, 172–73

Dispersal of animals and plants to Hawaiian chain, 81–111; by drifting in air, 82–84; by wind, 84, 85–86; by active flight, 86; role of northern hemisphere jet stream in, 87–88; Indo-Malaysia-to-Hawaii pattern of, 88; by becoming attached to birds, 88–94; by fruits eaten by birds, 94–101; by drifting in seawater, 102–5, 387, 419, 423; establishment after arrival, 105–11

Dispersal within the Islands, 122

Dispersibility, loss of, in plants, 163–73; loss of dispersal mechanisms in evolution, 163, 164; through increase in size of seeds or spores, 163, 165, 167, 169, 170; through loss of ability to cling to, or to stick to, birds, 165–67; through loss of ability to float, 169; explanations of various manifestations of, 169, 171–72; in evolution in the wet forest, 307

Diversification within plant and animal groups, 122–33

Dodonaea, the aalii shrub, 283, 358, 362, 365; *Dodonaea viscosa,* 283

Doodia kunthiana, the pamoho, 330

Downthrusts, volcanic, 26; course of streams changed by, 58–59

Dracaena aurea, the halapepe tree, 282

Dragonfly *Anax:* dispersal of, to the Islands, 119; gigantism of *Anax strenuus,* 138

Drepanididae subfamily of honeycreepers, 190, 198

Drepanidis, the mamo honeycreeper, 198, 211

Driest place in the Islands, Kawaihae on Hawaii as, 71, 72

Drifting in seawater, as means of dispersal to the Islands, 102–5, 387, 419, 423; dry forest trees involved in this mode of origin, 294, 297, 300

Drosera, the sundew bog plant, 88, 347, 349, 351; *Drosera anglica,* in Wahiawa Bog, 347

Drosophila fruit flies, 124

Dry forest, Hawaiian, trees and plants of: lower dry forest, 275–85; upper dry forest, 285–300

Drypetes genus of trees and shrubs, 295

Dubautia, 84, 92, 93, 156, 165, 250–61; *Dubautia linearis,* 250, 251; *Dubautia scabra,* 250, 251; *Dubautia ciliolata,* 252, 254, 365, 373; *Dubautia menziesii,* 252, 254, 255, 360, 365, 373; *Dubautia platyphylla,* 253, 255; *Dubautia reticulata,* 254, 255, 257; *Dubautia sherffiana,* 255, 257; *Dubautia plantaginea,* 256, 257, 319; *Dubautia laxa,* 257, 260, 319; *Dubautia knudsenii,* 258, 260; *Dubautia latifolia,* 259, 261; *Dubautia railliardioides,* 260, 261; *Dubautia waialealae,* 261, 352; as wet forest shrubs, 303, 307; as alpine plants, 358, 361, 362; *Dubautia struthioloides,* 365

Dunes formed by coral sand blowing inland, 60

E

"Eel's Eye, The." *See* Makaopuhi Crater

Elaeocarpus bifidus, the kalia tree, 312

Elaphoglossum, the tongue fern, 335, 344

Endemism of flora and fauna of the Islands, 175–76

Endodontidae family of land shells, 188, 189

Epiphytes of the Islands, 333–45

Eragrostis, a grass, 416; *Eragrostis variabilis,* 402, 403

Erosion on the Islands, 50–56; rainfall as agent of, 50; age related to degree of, 50; difference in patterns of, on windward and leeward slopes, 51; and conversion of face into steep, plunging cliffs (pali), 51; action of, on lava beds, 51, 52, 53; isolation of segment of ridge by erosion on all sides, 54, 55; wave action at shoreline, 55–56; erosion plus downthrusts, 58–59

Eruption underseas: as start of volcanic island, 4, 6; lateral cones built up by, 4, 5, 7

Erythrina sandwicensis, the wiliwili tree, 102, 104, 105, 160, 171, 269, 276, 285, 294

Euphorbia, the akoko: arborescence of, 139–43, 144; *Euphorbia degeneri*, 139, 140, 269; *Chamaesyce* type of, 140; *Euphorbia celastroides*, 140–41, 143; *Euphorbia multiformis*, 142; *Euphorbia remyi*, 142, 143, 144; *Euphorbia clusiaefolia*, 143, 144; *Euphorbia rockii*, 143, 144; loss of dispersibility by, 165, 167

Eurya sandwicensis, the anini, 315

Ewa Plain coral platform on Oahu, 60

Exocarpus genus: *Exocarpus sandwicensis*, of ridge and dry forest areas, 295; of alpine zone, 358; *Exocarpus gaudichaudii*, 365, 368

Explosive eruptions from steam formed by rainwater seepage in hot volcanic areas, 38–40

Extinction of flora and fauna on the Islands, 177–79; "decadent" vanishing genera, 177; factors contributing to, 179

F

Fault in ocean floor underlying the Islands, 1

Ferns: dispersal of, to the Islands, 83–84; growth of, on lava and in wet forests, 107, 108; loss of dispersibility by, 163, 165; "aggressiveness" of several, 177; of the wet forest, genera and species of, 304, 306, 326–32; epiphytism of, 335–36

Fertility, lowering of, in flora and fauna of the Islands, 177

Field trips on the Islands, 429–35; car rental for, 429; commercial tours, 429; information and help available, 429; map showing natural or seminatural areas, 430; hiking, 430–31; helicopter charter, 430; small proportion of land left as wilderness, 431; trails following ridges, 432; advantages of going with others instead of alone, 432, 434; plants of interest to visitors, 433; on specific islands, 434–35

Fimbristylis cymosa, a coastal sedge, 273, 274, 402, 403

Finches, the "Laysan finch" (honeycreeper), 400, 403

Fire fountains in craters, 29, 32, 47

Fishponds formed of aa lava blocks on island coasts, 13, 14

Fleshy-fruited plants, dispersal of, 94–98

Flightlessness: in Hawaiian insects, 157–58, 159–61; in Hawaiian birds, 158, 160, 218, 400, 404; reasons for, 161–62; and evolution in the wet forest, 307

Flotation in air, as means of dispersal to the Islands, 82–88; plants that reproduce by spores, 83; ferns, 83–84; small seeds, 84; orchids, 84; insects, 84, 85–86

Flotation in seawater, as means of dispersal to the Islands. *See* Drifting in seawater

Flowering-plant immigrants to the Islands, 84, 94, 102

Food-getting modes of several Hawaiian animals, changes in, 136–37

Forested areas, penetration of: by aa lava flows, 13–14; by pahoehoe lava flows, 15, 17, 18

Forest Entomology in Hawaii (Swezey), 126

Fossils, Pleistocene and terrestrial, 61–62

Fragaria, the strawberry, 359; *Fragaria chiloensis*, 361, 365, 370

French Frigate Shoal of Leeward chain, 5, 389–94; military installation on, 375; physical characteristics of, 389; Disappearing Island in, 389; Whale and Skate islets in lagoon of, 389, 393; birds on, 392, 393–94; plants and animals on, 393; sea turtles on, 394

Freycinetia arborea, the ieie, 335, 336, 337

Frigate birds on French Frigate Shoal, 392

Fringing reefs, formation of, 4, 5

Fruit-eating birds as means of dispersal, 94–101

Fruit flies of the Islands: speciation of, 123, 124–25; of the wet forest, 306

Fulica alai, the Alae keokeo (Hawaiian coot), 220

Fungi of the Islands, 332

G

Gardenia, the nanu, 303; *Gardenia brighamii*, 310; *Gardenia manii*, 310

Gardner Pinnacles of the Leeward chain, 2, 381, 395–97; dikelets on, 23, 396; geology of, as most interesting feature, 395, 396; marine birds on, 395, 397; *Portulaca lutea* as only plant on, 395, 396

Garnets found in the Islands, 48

Geology of Hawaiian Islands, 1–63; volcanoes, 1–47; downthrusts, 26, 58–59; minerals, 47–50; erosion, 50–56; black sand of beaches, 57–58; blowholes, 58; weathering, 59; coral effects, 60; Pleistocene and terrestrial fossils, 61–62; ground water, 62–63

Geranium genus: *Geranium arboreum,* 135, 136, 362; *Geranium humile,* 349, 354, 359; *Geranium tridens,* 362, 363; *Geranium cuneatum,* 362, 365, 368, 371

Gigantism: curious phenomenon of, 137; of insects, 137–38; of lizards, 138; of snails, 188, 189

Gillett, George W., 61, 119

"Gooneys" on Midway, 427

Gossypium sandvicense, the Hawaiian cotton (huluhulu or mao), 104, 105, 269, 272

Gouldia, the manono, 303; *Gouldia terminalis,* 309

Grammitis tenella, fern epiphyte, 343

Grasses: dispersal of, 100, 101; wind pollination of, 121; of Hawaiian coasts, 274

Greenswords (*Argyroxiphium*), 262, 266, 362; Haleakala greensword (*Argyroxiphium virescens*), 265, 266; Puu Kukui greensword (*Argyroxiphium grayanum*), 266, 353, 354

Gressitt, J. Linsey, 84

Grooved lava, 13

Ground water of the Islands, 62–63

Gulick, 184

Gunnera, the apeape, 304; *Gunnera petaloidea,* 321

Gygis alba, the fairy tern, 397, 426

Gypsum crystals found in the Islands, 49, 50

H

Haleakala National Park, 262, 263, 435

Haleakala volcano, 3, 24, 75; dikes in crater of, 22; lava flows and cinder cones in crater of, 24, 25, 26, 47; spatter in crater of, 35, 36; pyroxenes crystals from, 48; erosion on, 50; sharp climate changes within area of, 78–79, 359; as alpine locality, 361; alpine plants of, 362–65

Halemaumau "fire pit" sink within Kilauea caldera, 29, 30, 31, 32; May 1924 explosive eruption at, 39

Hanauma Bay Crater, 45

Hawaii, island of, 1, 2, 3; lava flows on, 9–21; effects of altitude on average temperatures on, 65; field trip on, 434

Hawaiian Islands National Wildlife Refuge, 375

Hawaiian language, 447; phonetic spelling in, 447; vowel and consonant sounds, 447; no true diphthongs in, 447; not strongly accented, 447

Hawaiian monk seal (*Monachus schauinslandi*), 394, 413, 419, 422, 424

Hawaii Visitors Bureau, 429

Hawaii Volcanoes National Park, 10, 21, 434; forms of pahoehoe lava in, 16; calderas in, 28; Kilauea as largest of calderas in, 30; explosive eruptions in, from steam caused by rainwater seepage, 38–40; sulfur formations in, 50; Kau Desert in, 79, 434

Hedyotis, of the coffee family, 303, 310, 358; *Hedyotis fluviatilis,* 310; *Hedyotis centranthoides,* 365, 371

Helicarionidae family of land shells, 189

Heliotropium anomalum, the beach heliotrope, 269, 272

Hemignathus lucidus, the nukupuu, 191, 200

Hemignathus obscurus, the akialoa, 191

Hemignathus procerus, the Kauai akialoa, 191, 202

Hemignathus wilsoni, the akiapolaau, 191, 201

Herbivores, introduction of, on the Islands, 179

Hesperomannia genus: 294; *Hesperomannia arbuscula* subsp. *oahuensis,* 294

Hibiscadelphus genus: adaptation of, to nectar-feeding birds, 135, 136, 293; *Hibiscadelphus hualalaiensis,* 293; dispersal of, to the Islands, 294

Hibiscus genus: *Hibiscus brackenridgei,* 293; *Hibiscus st.-johnii,* 293; dispersal of, to the Islands, 294; *Hibiscus arnottianus,* the kokia keokeo, 315; *Hibiscus kahili,* the kokio, 316

Hicropteris genus of fern, 304; *Hicropteris pinnata,* 327

Hilina Pali near Kilauea, plant growth in lava flows of, 110, 111

Hillebrandia genus of begonia family, 322; *Hillebrandia sandwicensis,* 322

Hilo on island of Hawaii, rainfall and humidity at, 75

Himantopus knudseni, the aeo (Hawaiian stilt), 220

Himatione, the apapane, 198, 207; nest of, 212; *Himatione sanguinea sanguinea,* 404; *Himatione sanguinea freethii,* the Laysan honeyeater, 404

History of formation of Hawaiian chain of islands, 1–3

Honeycreepers, 176, 190–212; adaptive radiation of, 190, 193; possible family relationships of, 190; question as to origin of, 190; two subfamilies of, 190; genera and subgenera of, 193; on island of Laysan ("Laysan finch"), 400, 403

Honeyeaters (Meliphagidae), 214, 216; Laysan honeyeaters, 400, 404

Honolulu: geology of, 40–47; average temperature in, 64; warm and cool sections in, 66; rainfall patterns of, and rainbows, 69

Hoo-ilo season of ancient Hawaiians, 66

Hualalai volcano, 3, 5, 9–10; pahoehoe lava flow near summit of, 16; collapsed lava tube near summit of, 19, 21; and "Kona-Coast weather," 74; as alpine locality, 361; alpine plants of, 365; cinder cones and shrubs of summit of, 367

Humuula Saddle Road on island of Hawaii: 1935 aa lava flow on, 12, 13; pahoehoe lava specimens along, 16; alpine plants seen on, 365

Hybridization of plants and animals, 113–19, 121

Hydromagmatic volcanic explosions, 40

I

Iao Needle on island of Maui, 54, 55

Ilex, the kawau (holly): dioecism of, 119; of the wet forest, 303; *Ilex anomala*, 312

Inbreeding of plants and animals, 111–13; results of, 112, 121; antidotes to, 112; self-pollination of flowers, 119, 121, 134; dispersal within the Islands as aid in preventing of, 122

Indo-Malaysian character of native Hawaiian flora and fauna, 88

Insects: dispersal of, to the Islands, 84, 85–86; speciation of, on the Islands, 123; dietary specialization of, 123, 126; color patterns of, evolved according to plant background, 125–26; pollination of flowers by, 134, 135; gigantism of, 137–38; flightlessness in Hawaiian insects, 157–58, 159–61; plant-eating role of, in the Islands, 175; of the wet forest, 306

Insects of Hawaii (Zimmerman), 158

Ipomoea, the pohuehue, 102, 300; *Ipomoea pes-caprae*, 103, 274, 401; *Ipomoea indica*, 412

Iron in lava, 35

Island existence, problems of, 111–22; inbreeding, 111–13; outbreeding, 112, 113, 119; production of new mutations, 112, 113, 121; hybridization, 113–19, 121; dioecism in plants, 119–21; self-pollination in bisexual plants, 119, 121, 134; events of dispersal within the Islands, 122

Island Life (Carlquist), 158, 250

Island of volcanic origin, stages in origin and changes of, 4–6; Oahu as illustrative of, 6–8

Isodendrion genus of violets, 178

J

Jacquemontia sandwicensis, the pauohiiaka, 273, 274

Jagger, T. A., 39, 40

Jaspers found in the Islands, 48

Jet stream of northern hemisphere, role of, in dispersal to the Islands, 87–88

Joinvillea gaudichaudiana, the ohe, 323

K

Kaau ash and lava cone of Oahu, 46

Kahauloa Crater on Oahu, 45

Kahoolawe, island of, 5; rainfall on, 77; as bomb impact area, 435

Kaimuki vent on Oahu, lava and spatter from eruption of, 42

Kalalau Valley on Kauai: dikes in, 23; erosion of lava beds in, 52; rainfall on, 71

Kalama cinder cone on Oahu, 45

Kalapana, black-sand beach at, 57

Kalaupapa leper colony on Molokai, 47

Kanaele Swamp. *See* Wahiawa Bog

Kaohikaipu Island, as cinder cone, 46

Kapoho on island of Hawaii, 1960 lava flow at, 1, 11, 12; eruption in 1960 at, 34, 35

Kauai, island of, 3, 5; pali on, 51; advanced state of erosion on, 52; hanging valleys on, 53; ponded lavas on summit plateau of, 53, 54, 55; blowhole at Poipu on, 58; downthrust on, 58–59; field trip on, 435

Kau Desert on island of Hawaii, 79, 434

Kaula islet as lateral tuff cone, 47

Kaupo Gap through crater wall of Haleakala, 24, 25

Kau season of ancient Hawaiians, 67

Kauwila, use of term for both *Alphitonia* and *Colubrina* trees, 290

Kawaihae on island of Hawaii, as driest place in the Islands, 71, 72

Kilauea volcano, 3, 5, 9–10; December 1959 eruption of, 10; pahoehoe lava flows in, 14, 15; lava trees in, 15;

lava cavern in, 19; caldera activity at, 26; downthrusts at, 26; fault on south-west rim of, 26, 27; eruptions of, 29; range in size of calderas of, 29, 30; lava lake in caldera of, 30, 31, 32; spatter in vents of, 35; volcanic bomb from, 37; sulfur and sulfur fumes from vents of, 49; alpine plants in, 361, 365

Kilauea-iki caldera, 1959 eruption at, 32, 33, 92, 108–9, 111

Kipukas: formation of, by aa lava flows, 13, 14; on island of Hawaii, 14

Kohala Mountains, of island of Hawaii, 5

Kokia genus: adaptation of, to bird pollinators, 137; *Kokia rockii,* a tree cotton of the dry forest, 281

Koko Crater on Oahu, 45, 46; blowhole along coast road at, 58

Koko Head Crater on Oahu, 45, 46, 47

Koko Head Ridge on Oahu, tuff cones of, 45, 47

Kona Coast of island of Hawaii, 74–75; rainfall and humidity on, 75; coffee-growing on, 75

Kona storms, 66–67

Koolau Gap through crater wall of Haleakala, 24, 25, 359; rainfall on, 78

Koolau Mountains on Oahu, 45; sudden dropoff of eastern half of, 51; rainfall on, 69, 70, 75; trail following ridge in, 432

Koolau volcano on Oahu, 6–7, 8

Korthalsella complanata, the Hawaiian mistletoe, 286

Kure Island of Leeward chain, 1, 2, 375, 425, 427–28; moderately rich flora and fauna of, for an atoll, 428

L

Labordia, the kamakahala, 318; *Labordia baillonii,* 318; *Labordia kaalae,* 318; *Labordia waialealae,* 318

Lacewings, Hawaiian, flightlessness of, 158, 159, 160

Lagenophora mauiensis, bog plant, 349, 354

Laminella genus of land shells, 187

Lanai, island of: sea stack off coast of, 56; wet forest on summit of ridge of, 79; field trips on, 435

Land birds: dispersal of, to the Islands, 86, 190; few groups of, in the Islands, 190

Land shells, 89, 90, 180–89; "Pacific" and "holarctic" relationships of, 189. *See also* Land snails

Land snails, 89, 90, 180–89; lack of uniformity in species of, 112, 119; shifts in habitat of some, 137; plant-eating role of, in the Islands, 175; endemic family groups of, 176; as successful colonists, 180; gigantism of, 188, 189

Latitude of the Islands, 64

Lava beds, erosion of, 51, 52, 53; hanging valleys formed by, 53; resistance of ponded lavas to erosion, 53–54

Lava blocks, from volcanic explosions, 40

Lava boulders, weathering of, 59

Lava caverns, 19, 21

Lava flows: on island of Hawaii, 1, 3, 9–21; submarine eruptions, 11–12; of aa lava, 12–14; "clinkers" and "rivers" of, 13; accretionary lava balls, 13; of pahoehoe lava (liquid), 14–21; colonization of plants in, 106; lichens on, 106, 107; growth of wet forest plants on, 111; growth of weeds on, 111

Lava, intrusive, and dikes, 21–23

Lavas, composition of, 4, 5, 35

"Lava trees," 15, 17

Lava Trees State Park on island of Hawaii, 15

Lava tubes, 18, 19, 21

Laysan Island of Leeward chain, 398–410; raised-atoll plan of, 398; acreage of, 398; overhead aerial view of, 398; central lagoon of, 399; coral reef as tilted shelf on western edge of, 399; birds of, 400, 402, 403; plants of, 400; exploitation of guano deposits on, 400; rabbit plague on, 400, 404, 405; marine birds on, 406–9; as interesting showcase of atoll life, 410

Leeward Islands, 1, 2, 3, 375–428; atolls of, 6; rainfall on, 66; marine birds on, 221, 375; total acreage of, 375; military installations on, 375; minimal commercial value of, 375; poverty of flora and fauna on, 375; constant changing of vegetation on, 410; as Wildlife Refuge, 435

Lehua, formation of island of, 40, 43

Leper colony on Molokai, 47

Lepidium, a shrub of mustard family: arborescence of, 143, 145, 157; *Lepidium serra,* 143, 145; *Lepidium arbuscula,* 143; *Lepidium owaihense,* 416, 418

Leptogryllus crickets, 159

Lepturus repens, an atoll grass, 389, 416, 423

Lichens: on lava flows, 106, 107; epiphytism of, 334

Lily family, 97

Limnaeidae family of land shells, 188, 189

Liparis hawaiiensis, an orchid, 324

Lipochaeta, the nehe: *Lipochaeta integrifolia,* 269, 270; *Lipochaeta lavarum,* 270

Lisianski Island of Leeward chain, 410–13; as upraised atoll with central depression, 410; acreage of, 410; plants and birds of, 410–12; exploitation of guano deposits on, 410; rabbit plague on, 410; overhead aerial view of, 411; Hawaiian monk seals on shores of, 413

"Little Beggar" vent, Kilauea, spatter from, 35

Liverworts, epiphytism of, 334, 335

Lizards, gigantism of, 138

Lobelia of the lobelioids, 88, 91, 245–46; oha, or ohawai, as Hawaiian name for, 245; *Lobelia gaudichaudii* (*Lobelia kauaensis*), 245, 348, 351; *Lobelia tortuosa,* 246; *Lobelia hypoleuca,* 246

Lobelioids, 156, 157, 222–49; *Delissea,* 222, 223; *Cyanea,* 222–36; *Rollandia,* 236–39; *Clermontia,* 239–45; *Lobelia,* 245–46; *Trematolobelia,* 247–48; *Brighamia,* 248–49; in wet ohia forests, 303

Loxops genus of honeycreeper: *Loxops coccinea,* the akepa, 190, 198; *Loxops virens,* the amakihi, 190, 191, 199; *Loxops maculata,* the creeper, 190; *Loxops sagittirostris,* the greater amakihi, 191

Luzula campestris var. *hawaiiensis,* of the wet forest, 322

Lycium carolinianum, the aeae (or ohelo kai), 273, 274

Lycopodium moss: *Lycopodium cernuum,* 325; *Lycopodium venustulum,* 325; *Lycopodium phyllanthum,* 339

Lysimachia, of primrose family: *Lysimachia hillebrandii,* 320; *Lsyimachia rotundifolia,* 320

M

Magma (liquid lava), 5; dikes and dikelets formed by intrusion of, 21–23; in Kilauea volcano, 26

Makaopuhi Crater: 1965 eruption of, 29; formation of steam in, 39

Makuku cone in Nuuanu Valley of Oahu, lava flow from, 46

Mammals on the Islands, absence of, before human occupation, 173

Manana (Rabbit) Island, as tuff cone, 46

Manoa Valley of Honolulu, showers in, and rainbows, 69

Marattia douglasii, the pala fern, 326

Marine birds, 86, 220–21; as means of dispersal of fruits and seeds, 98, 220

Marine bluffs, formation of, 4, 5

Maui, island of, 5, 47; erosion on, 50; hanging valleys on, 53; sea stacks of west coast of, 56; coral sand of isthmus of, 60; field trip on, 435

Mauna Kea volcano, 3, 5; cinder cones on summit of, 24, 26; snow on summit of, 64, 65; annual precipitation on, 69; as alpine locality, 361

Mauna Loa volcano, 3, 5, 8, 9–10; lava flows from Mokuaweoweo caldera of, 10; November 1935 flank eruption of, 11; lava flows from rifts extending from, 11; snow on summit of, 64; annual precipitation on, 69; and "Kona-Coast weather," 74; as alpine locality, 361; alpine plants of, 365

Mechanical devices for attachment of fruits, as factors in dispersal, 91–94

Mecodium recurvum, fern epiphyte, 339

Megalagrion oahuense, damselfly, 137

Messerschmidia argentea, shrub of heliotrope family, 389

Metrosideros: various forms of, 114–18; "aggressiveness" of the ohia, 177. See also Ohia lehua

Mezoneurum kauaiense, the kea or uhiuhi, 280

Microclimates of the Islands, 78–80

Microsorium spectrum, a polypody fern, 332

Midway Islands of Leeward chain, 1, 2, 66, 375, 425–28; development of, as cable station and seaplanes station, 425; use of, as military base, 425; importance of today, 425; birds of, 426–28; moderately rich flora and fauna of, for an atoll, 428

Millerbirds, 214; Nihoa millerbird (*Acrocephalus familiaris kingi*), 378, 379, 380; Laysan millerbird (*Acrocephalus familiaris familiaris*), 400, 406

Minerals of the Islands, 47–50

Mint family, 97; odorlessness of Hawaiian members of, 175

Moho, the oo, of honeyeaters, 214, 216

Mokolii Island, as sea stack, 55, 56

Mokuaweoweo caldera of Mauna Loa volcano, lava flows from, 10

Molluscs. *See* Land shells; Land snails

Molokai, island of, 5; fishponds made of lava blocks along south shore of, 14;

peninsula on north coast of, 47; erosion on, 51; hanging valleys on, 53; sea cliffs on northern coast of, 56; field trip on, 435

Monk seals. *See* Hawaiian monk seals

Moonstones found in the Islands, 48

Morinda citrifolia, the noni, 268

Mosses, epiphytism of, 334, 335, 339

Mt. Kaala on Oahu, rainfall on, 69, 70

Mt. Waialeale on Kauai: as wettest place in the Islands, 67, 71–73, 261, 350; Wailua Falls on, 72; rainfall on, 73; summit bog of, 350, 351

Muscilaginous covering of seeds as factor in dispersal, 89, 90, 167

Mushrooms, Hawaiian, 332

Mutations in plants and animals, 112, 113, 121

Myoporum sandwicense, the naio tree, 275, 285

Myrsine, the kolea: dioecism of, 119; of the wet forest, 303; *Myrsine lessertiana,* 314; *Myrsine sandwicensis,* the kolea laulii, 315; *Myrsine angustifolia* in Wahiawa Bog, 348

N

Nabis bug, speciation of, 123

Nama sandwicensis, beach plant, 157, 272, 274; *Nama sandwicensis* var. *laysanicum,* 409

Na Pali Kona Coast of Kauai, 51, 52, 435

Napau Crater, 1965 eruption of, 29

National Cemetery of the Pacific, 41

Natural bridge formed by lava flow on Koko Crater, Oahu, 17, 18

Naupakas: dispersal of, to the Islands, 119; hybrids of, 119; arborescence of, 151–55, 156. *See also Scaevola*

Necker Island of Leeward chain, 2, 381–88; size of, 381; insects on, 382; shrubs and herbs on, 382, 387, 388; flowering plants on, 382; absence of land birds on, 382–83; highest point of, 382; Shark Bay of, 383; lava beds on, 383; marine birds on, 384–87; human colony on, in remote time, 387

Neowawrea phyllanthoides, a tree from Kona Coast, 295

Nepheline content of lavas, 5

Nephrolepis exaltata ferns, 83

Neraudia melastomaefolia, a wet forest plant, 317

Nertera: epiphytism of, 333; *Nertera granadensis* var. *insularis,* in Wahiawa Bog, 349

Nesoluma polynesicum, the keahi, 280

Nesosydne insect genus, diversification in, 123, 125–26

Nightshade family, 97, 277, 414, 417

Nihoa Island of Leeward chain, 2, 138, 376–80; physical aspects of, 376–77, 378; plants of, 378; marine and land birds of, 378, 380; human colony on, in remote time, 379, 387

Niihau, island of, 5, 40; rainfall on, 77; as private property, 432

Nohonohae cone, on island of Hawaii, "bomb-like" lumps of spatter in, 36

Nothocestrum, the aiea tree, 97, 277, 300

Nototrichum, the kului: arborescence of, 146, 147; *Nototrichum sandwicense,* 146; origin of, 300

Nuuanu pali on Oahu: small dikes at base of, 23; strong updraft on, 69

Nycticorax nycicorax hoactli, the night heron, 220

Nysius bug, speciation of, 123, 126–27

O

Oahu, island of, 5; stages in origin and changes of, 6–8; inward receding of shorelines in, 8; tuff comes of southeastern Oahu, 40, 41–47; lateral craters at eastern end of, 41; quartz crystals found in, 48; pali on, 51, 53, 68; hanging valleys on, 53; blowhole on, 58; Ewa Plain coral platform on, 60; plant fossils in tuff cones of, 61; field trip on, 434

Obsidian of Puuwaawaa crater, 24

Ocean, moderating effect of, on climate of the Islands, 64

Ocean depths of Hawaiian chain, 1–2

Ohia lehua (*Metrosideros*): *Metrosideros polymorpha,* 84, 85, 88, 108, 285, 301; forest of, in Kona District on island of Hawaii, 106; forests of, in wet forests, 301; in Hawaiian bogs, 349, 350, 352, 354, 356

Old World flycatchers in the Islands, 213–14

Olivine crystals found in the Islands, 47–48

Ophioglossum pendulum, the laukahi fern, 339

Orchids: dispersal of, to the Islands, 84; species of, in the Islands, 324, 333

Oreobolus furcatus, a sedge, 264; tussocks of, in Hawaiian bogs, 347, 353, 356

Osmanthus sandwicensis, the olopua tree, 290

Osteomeles, the uulei: *Osteomeles anthyllidifolia,* 296; as Hawaiian alpine, 365

Outbreeding of plants and animals, 112, 113, 119

P

Pacific islands, physical position of Hawaiian chain in relation to, 81

Pacific Ocean currents, location of the Islands with relation to, 105, 106

Pahoehoe lava flows, 14–21, 32, 110; penetration of forested areas by, 15; pahoehoe crusts raised into sheets, 15, 16; "lava trees" resulting from, 15, 17; tree molds resulting from, 15, 17; penetration of, into wood as it turns to charcoal, 17, 18; formation of lava tubes by, 18, 19, 21; formation of lava caverns, 19, 21; contraction of, into basalt columns, 20, 21; plant growth in, 111

Palagonite, solidifying of ash into, 41

Pali (steep, plunging coastal cliffs), 51

Paliku locality in Haleakala Crater, rainfall on, 78–79

Palmeria, the akohekohe, 198, 208

Pandanus umlonutissimus, the hala tree, 102, 267, 268–69

Panicum grasses: dispersal of, to the Islands, 100, 101; tussocks of, in Hawaiian bogs, 349; *Panicum isachnoides,* 356; on Necker, 382; *Panicum torridum,* 388

Papala, use of term for both *Pisonia* and *Charpentiera* trees, 289

Partulina genus of snails, 180, 184–85

Pearl Harbor on Oahu, 8

Pearl and Hermes Reef of Leeward chain, 413–24; coral islets of, 413–14, 422; as atoll with barrier reef, 414; plants of, 414, 416; Southeast Island of, 415, 416, 420, 421, 423; sand bars in, 416; birds of, 416, 419, 420–21; adaptability of plants and animals in atoll life, 416; debris of human occupation on, 416; floating ashore of seeds of *Mucuna* and other legumes, 419, 423; sea turtles and Hawaiian monk seals on shores of, 419, 422, 424; "South North Island" of, 422, 423

Pelea, the alani: dispersal of, to the Islands, 100, 101; *Pelea clusiaefolia,* 101, 130, 313; dioecism of, 119; *Pelea barbigera,* 128, 129; *Pelea orbicularis,* 128, 131; *Pelea waialealae,* 128, 131, 349; *Pelea rotundifolia,* 128; *Pelea oahuensis,*

129; *Pelea anisata* (mokihana), 130, 132; of the wet forest, 303, 306; *Pelea wawreana,* 313

Pele's hair, of volcanic glass, 37, 38

Pele's tears, of volcanic glass, 38

Pellaea ternifolia, the kalamoho laulii, 367

Pennula sandwicensis, the moho (flightless rail), 158, 218, 219

Pepeopae Bog on Molokai, 356, 357

Peperomia, the alaawanui: *Peperomia reflexa,* 299; epiphytism of, 333, 338; *Peperomia leptostachya,* 338

Perennial-plant flora, as supreme type in the Islands, 157

Perkins, R. C. L., 184

Perrottetia sandwicensis, the olomea, 310

Phaeornis thrush: *Phaeornis obscurus,* the omao, 213–14; *Phaeornis palmeri,* the puoiohi, 214, 215

Phaethon rubricauda rothschildi, a tropic bird, 407

Phyllanthus sandwicensis, small shrub of spurge family, 295

Phyllostegia genus, 96, 97, 320; *Phyllostegia racemosa,* 96; *Phyllostegia lantanoides,* 320

Phytolacca brachystachys, Hawaiian pokeweed, 320

Pillow lavas, 4, 11–12, 13

Pipturus, the mamaki: dispersal of, to the Islands, 91; all male and female flowers on same plant, 121; "aggressiveness" of, 177; of the wet forest, 304; *Pipturus albidus,* 316

Pisonia, the papala tree: dispersal of, to the Islands, 90, 92, 294; *Pisonia sandwicensis,* 289; *Pisonia umbellifera,* 289

Pittosporum, the hoawa tree, 99, 100; dioecism of, 119, 120; gigantism of, and loss of dispersibility, 167, 170; *Pittosporum terminalioides,* 291; of the wet forest, 303; *Pittosporum dolosum,* 313

Plagithmysus longhorn beetles, 126

Planchonella trees of the sapota family, 279; *Planchonella sandwicensis,* the aulu, 279

Plantago, the plantain weed: dispersal of, to the Islands, 88–89; arborescence of, 149–50, 151; *Plantago pachyphylla,* 150, 151; *Plantago princeps,* 150, 151, 157; epiphytism of, 333, 338; *Plantago hillebrandii,* 338, 351, 356; *Plantago krajinai,* 351; *Plantago glabrifolia,* 351, 352; *Plantago nubicola,* 351; *Plantago melanochrous,* 351, 354

Plants of the Islands: diversification of, 127–33; adaptations of, to suit available pollinators, 134–36; loss of dispersibility in, 163–73; poisonous, 173; with strongly scented oils, lack of, 173, 175

Plastic striated lava, 13

Platydesma, the pilokea: adaptive radiation of, 132–33; *Platydesma campanulata,* 132, 314; *Platydesma rostrata,* 133; *Platydesma cornuta,* 133

Pleomele aurea, the halapepe tree, 282

Pohakuloa on island of Hawaii, aa lava flow near, 13

Poisonous plants in the Islands, 173

Poisonous Plants of Hawaii (Arnold), 173

Pollination relationships, adaptations found in, 134–36

Polypodium pellucidum, the ae fern, 109, 358, 366

Ponded lavas, 53–54

Porosity of Hawaiian land, 79

Portulaca, the ihi: dispersal of, to the Islands, 102; *Portulaca oleracea,* 103, 274; *Portulaca caumii,* 378; *Portulaca lutea,* 382, 387, 395, 396; on Pearl and Hermes Reef, 416

Porzanula palmeri, the Laysan rail, 158, 218, 405

Predators, in evolution of Hawaiian shell families, 185, 187

Pritchardia, the loulu palm: fossils of, 61; gigantism of, and loss of dispersibility, 167, 169, 170; *Pritchardia macdanielsii,* 302; *Pritchardia martii,* 302; *Pritchardia beccariana,* 303; *Pritchardia remota,* 378, 379; on Laysan Island, 400

Procelsterna caerulea saxatilis, the blue-gray tern, 386

Proctor, Vernon W., 100

Prognathogryllus crickets, 158, 159

Proterhinus beetles, 126

Proterhinus weevils, 137

Pseudonestor xanthophrys, a honeycreeper, 191, 203

Psidium cattleianum, the strawberry guava, 304

Psilotum, the moa: hybridization of, 114; *Psilotum nudum,* 285; epiphytism of, 338; *Psilotum complanatum,* 338

Psittacirostra, the honeycreeper: *Psittacirostra kona,* 191, 206; *Psittacirostra psittacea,* the ou, 191, 204; *Psittacirostra cantans,* 191, 378; *Psittacirostra bailleui,* the palila, 205; *Psittacirostra cantans cantans* (Laysan "finch"), 403, 404

Psittacirostrinae subfamily of honeycreepers, 190–91

Pteralyxia, dry-forest tree: fossils of, 61; *Pteralyxia macrocarpa,* 294

Pterodroma phaeopygia, the uau (sooty-rumped petrel), 221

Pueo, the Hawaiian short-eared owl, 214, 218

Puffinus genus, the shearwater: *Puffinus navitatis,* Christmas Island shearwater, 378, 380; *Puffinus pacificus cuneatus,* the wedge-tailed shearwater, 409, 421

Pumice: of lavas, 4; of Puuwaawaa crater, 24; in Kilauea-iki eruption, 32, 111; production of, by cinder cones, 35; production of, by gas in volcanic glass, 38

Puna District on island of Hawaii, 1955 eruptions in, 34, 35

Punchbowl tuff cone in Oahu, 41, 44, 47

Pupillidae family of land shells, 189

Puu Kukui on island of Maui: erosion on, 50; as second wettest mountain in the Islands, 67, 73; Puu Kukui Bog, 349, 352, 353, 354, 355

Puu Oai cone on island of Maui, 47

Puuwaawaa, lateral cone at base of Hualalai volcano, 24

Pyroxenes found in the Islands, 48

Q

Quartz crystals found in the Islands, 48

R

"Rafting" flotation of plants, as means of dispersal, 102, 104, 105

Rails: flightlessness in Hawaiian and Laysan rails, 158, 160, 218, 400, 404; the Laysan rail, 400, 404–5; attempt to introduce on Lisianski Island, 404, 406; fate of rails introduced from Laysan to Midway, 406

Rainbows in Honolulu, 69

Rainfall of the Islands: as agent of erosion, 50; percolation of rocks by, 59; and kona storms, 66–67; and the trade winds, 67–73; and rain shadows, 70, 71; rainfall maps of the Islands, 76–77; and porosity of Hawaiian land, 79

Rain forests, 301

Rainwater seepage in hot volcanic areas, steam formed by, 38–40

Rauwolfia sandwicensis, the hao, 278, 285

Reynoldsia sandwicensis, the ohe tree, 277, 285

Rhus chinensis var. *semialata,* a nonpoisonous sumac, 174

Rockia sandwicensis, the papala, 289

Rollandia of the lobelioids, 91, 236–39; *Rollandia humboldtiana*, 236; *Rollandia angustifolia*, 236, 237; *Rollandia lanceolata*, 236, 237, 238; *Rollandia calycina*, 238; *Rollandia pinnatifida*, 238–39; *Rollandia st.-johnii*, 239; diversification of color in, 239

Roosevelt, Theodore, 375, 410

Rothschild, Walter, 400

Rubus, the raspberry, loss of thorns by, 174, 175

Rumex, the pawale: dispersal of, to the Islands, 84; growth of, in lava, 110; as Hawaiian alpine, 359; *Rumex giganteus*, 365, 373

S

Sadleria ferns, the amau, 107, 108, 329, 358; *Sadleria cyatheoides*, 107, 108, 304, 329, 364; loss of dispersibility in, 163, 165; "aggressiveness" of, 177; *Sadleria pallida*, 304, 329; *Sadleria squarrosa*, 304, 330

Saldula bugs, change in habitat of, 137

Salt Lake Crater on Oahu: downthrust at, 26; as tuff cone, 45; plant fossils found in tuff beds of, 61

Sandalwoods (iliahi), 95, 97, 279, 358, 361, 400; *Santalum pyrularium*, 95, 97, 291; seaside race of, *Santalum ellipticum* var. *littorale*, 267, 269; *Santalum paniculatum*, 279, 285; *Santalum haleakalae*, 362, 363

Santalum. See Sandalwoods (iliahi)

Sapindus oahuensis, the aulu, 283

Scaevola, the naupaka: adaptation of, to bird pollinators, 135; *Scaevola glabra*, 135, 153–54, 155; arborescence of, 151–55, 156; *Scaevola gaudichaudii*, 151, 153; *Scaevola chamissoniana*, 151, 153; *Scaevola gaudichaudiana*, 152, 153; *Scaevola procera*, 152, 153; *Scaevola mollis*, 153; *Scaevola kilaueae*, 154, 155; *Scaevola coriacea*, 155, 274; *Scaevola kauaiensis*, 155; "aggressiveness" of, 177; *Scaevola taccada*, the beach naupaka (or naupaka kai), 269, 300, 411; as natives of wet forest, 303

Scaptomyza fruit flies, speciation of, 124

Schiedea: "halfway to dioecism" system of, 121; as Hawaiian coastal plant, 269; *Schiedea verticillata*, 378

Schinus terebinthifolius, the Brazilian pepper, 304

Schizaea robusta, the oolii makalii fern, 353, 355

Sea bluffs, formation of, 4, 5

Sea caves formed by erosion at shoreline, 56, 58

Sea cliffs: formation of pali, 51; formed by wave action, 56; erosion of, by trade winds, 56

Sea stacks formed by wave action, 55, 56

Sea turtles, 394, 419, 424

Seawater flotation, as means of dispersal to the Islands. See Drifting in seawater

Sedges: dispersal of, 100, 101; of Hawaiian coasts, 274

Selaginella genus: *Selaginella arbuscula*, of the wet forest, 325; *Selaginella deflexa*, of the bogs, 355

Self-pollination of plants, 119, 121, 134

Semiprecious gems of the Islands, 47

Sesbania, shrub on Necker, 382; *Sesbania tomentosa*, the ohai, 387

Sesuvium herb: *Sesuvium portulacastrum*, 273, 274, 388; on Necker, 382, 387; on Pearl and Hermes Reef, 416

Shore birds: dispersal of, to the Islands, 86; as means of dispersal of seeds and fruits, 98–100, 200; list of regular visitors to the Islands, 99, 220

Sida cordifolia, a dry forest shrub, 284

Sida fallax, the ilima, 269, 284

Silene catchfly, 359, 361; *Silene struthioloides*, 365, 374; *Silene hawaiiensis*, 365, 374

Silverswords (*Argyroxiphium*), 165, 166, 262–65, 362; Haleakala silversword, 262–63; on island of Hawaii, 263–64; *Argyroxiphium sandwicense*, 263, 365; Kau silversword, *Argyroxiphium kauense*, 264, 365; Puu Kukui silversword, *Argyroxiphium caliginii*, 264–65, 307, 349, 352, 353

Sisyrinchium: as Hawaiian alpines, 361, 365; *Sisyrinchium acre*, 370

Smilax sandwicensis, the uhi (or ulehihi), 323

Snails. See Land snails

Snow on summits of Mauna Kea and Mauna Loa, 64, 65

Solanum nelsoni, a nightshade, 414, 417

Sophora chrysophylla, the mamani, 358, 361, 362, 365, 369

South Kona District of island of Hawaii, 1950 aa lava flow in, 13

Spatter, produced by cinder cones, 35–37

Sphaerocionium lanceolatum, fern epiphyte, 339

Sphaeroidal weathering of lava boulders, 59

Sphagnum moss, scarcity of, in Hawaiian bogs, 347, 358

Sphenomeris chusana, a fern, 299

Sphinx moth, adaptation of, to sucking nectar from *Boerhavia* flowers, 134, 416

Spieth, Herman, 198

Steam, formation of, from rainwater seepage in hot volcanic areas, 38–40

Stenogyne diffusa, 365, 367

Stenogyne purpurea, 96, 97

Stereocaulon vulcani, lava lichen, 107, 365, 372

Sterna terns: *Sterna fuscata oahuensis,* the sooty tern, 386; *Sterna lunata,* the grayback tern, 418

Sticherus genus of fern, 304; *Sticherus owyhensis,* 327

Straussia, the kopiko: of the wet forest, 303; *Straussia mariniana,* 308; *Straussia faurioi,* 308

Strongylodon, the kaiwi vine: dispersal of, to the Islands, 294; *Strongylodon lucidus,* 298

Styphelia, the pukiawe: *Styphelia tameiameiae,* 110, 296, 358; "halfway to dioecism" system of, 121; stunting of, in bogs, 349; *Styphelia douglasii,* 353; as alpine, 362, 365

Succineidae family of land shells, 189

Sulfur vents and sulfur banks on the Islands, 49, 50

Sunstones found in the Islands, 48

Swezey, Otto, 126

Syzygium jambos, the mountain apple, 304

T

Tanager Peak of Nihoa Island, 378

Tarweeds of California, as ancestors of Hawaiian silverswords, 250

Teals of Laysan, 218, 400, 401, 402, 403

Temperatures of the Islands, 64–66; relative uniformity of, throughout year, 64; decrease of, with altitude, 65; modifying of, by wind and cloud cover, and by topography, 66

Terns: on Necker, 386; on Gardner Pinnacles, 395, 397; on Pearl and Hermes Reef, 418; on Midway, 425, 426

Tetramolopium humile, alpine plant, 360, 365

Tetramolopium rockii, coastal plant, 269, 271

Tetraplasandra, araliad tree, 96, 167, 169, 303; *Tetraplasandra hawaiiensis,* 96, 167, 288; *Tetraplasandra meiandra,* 96, 305; *Tetraplasandra waialealae,* 167, 305

Thurston Lava Tube in Hawaii Volcanoes National Park, 18, 21

Tobacco plants on Laysan, 400

Tonga, island of, 1967 submarine eruption in, 11

Topography, effects of, on temperatures of the Islands, 66

Tornatellinidae family of land shells: small size of, 184, 185; close relation of *Achatinella* snails to, 185

Touchardia latifolia, the olona, 317

Trade winds: erosion of cliffs by, 56; effects of, on temperatures, 64, 66; and their rainfall, 67–73

Tree molds resulting from lava flows, 15, 17; growth of ferns and seedlings in, 108, 109

Trematolobelia of the lobelioids, 172, 247–48; *Trematolobelia macrostachys,* 247

Tribulus cistoides, a puncture vine, 412, 414, 416, 422

Tuff, from volcanic explosions, 40; tuff cones on Oahu, 40, 41–47; erosion of beds of, 46

Turtles. *See* Sea turtles

U

Uncinia, dispersal of, to the Islands, 93, 94

Urera sandwicensis, the opuhe, 317

Usinger, Robert, 126–27

V

Vaccinium, the ohelo, 91, 94, 97, 107, 318, 359, 361, 365; *Vaccinium calycinum,* 318; stunting of, in bogs, 349; *Vaccinium reticulatum,* 364, 365, 372; *Vaccinium berberidifolium,* 364; *Vaccinium pahalae,* 365

Variability in animal and plant species of the Islands, 113, 119

Vases molded from volcanic glass, 38

Vestiaria coccinea, the iiwi honeycreeper, 198, 210; nest of, 212

Violets, Hawaiian: arborescence of, 148–49; *Viola mauiensis,* 148, 349; *Viola kauaiensis,* 148; *Viola robusta,* 148–49; *Viola tracheliifolia,* 149; *Isodendrion* genus of, 178

Viscidness of fleshy fruits as factor in dispersal, 91

Vittaria elongata, fern epiphyte, 335, 345

Volcanic bombs of fused spatter, 35, 37, 38

Volcanic cone erosion, stage of, in island building, 4, 5

Volcanic dikes and dikelets, 21–23

Volcanic glass, 37, 38

Volcano Observatory in Kilauea, 10, 40

Volcanoes, Hawaiian, 1–47; lava flows, 1, 3, 9–21; sequence of major volcanoes becoming extinct, 3; intrusive lava and dikes, 21–23; cones and craters, 24–26; downthrusts and calderas, 26–38; explosive eruptions–steam, ash, and tuff, 38–40; Honolulu geology, 40–47; lateral craters on the islands, 47

Volcanoes of Kilauea and Mauna Loa on the Island of Hawaii, The (Brigham), 10

W

Wahiawa Bog (Kanaele Swamp) on Kauai, 345–47, 348, 349

Waianae Mountains on Oahu, 45; rainfall on, 69, 70

Waianae volcano on Oahu, 6–7, 8

Waikane Trail, Oahu, fragments from dikes along, 23

Waikiki beach on Oahu, 8

Wailua Falls, pillow lavas at base of, 11

Waimea Canyon on island of Kauai, 58–59

Wallace, A. R., 157

Wasp *Odynerus*, dispersal of, to the Islands, 119

Waterfowl: dispersal of, to the Islands, 86, 218; as means of dispersal of seeds and fruits, 98, 99–100; of the Islands, 218–20

Wave action at shoreline, 55–56

Weathering, on the Islands, 59

Weeds: growth of, on lava flows, 111; introduction of, into forests of the Islands, 179

Wet forest, Hawaiian, 300–32; rain forests in, 301; valleys and gulches in, 301; ohia lehua forests of, 301; trees and plants intermixed with ohias in, 303–4; Indo-Malaysian affinity of species of, 307

Wettest place in the Islands, Mt. Waialeale on Kauai as, 67, 71–73, 261, 350

Wikstroemia, the akia: poisonousness of, 173, 174; *Wikstroemia elongata*, 295; as Hawaiian alpine, 358, 361, 365; *Wikstroemia phillyreaefolia*, 369

Wilkesia, the iliau, 165, 250, 262, 266; *Wilkesia gymnoxiphium*, 266

Wind-blown seeds and insects. *See* Air, flotation in, as means of dispersal to the Islands

Wind pollination of plants, 121, 134, 135

X

Xylosma hawaiiense, the maua, 311

Z

Zanthoxylum (*Fagara*), the heae tree: dispersal of, 100; variations in seed sizes of, and in dispersibility, 167, 169; of upper dry forest areas, 289; *Zanthoxylum* (*Fagara*) *hawaiiense*, 289

Zimmerman, Elwood C., 84, 126, 137, 180

Zonitidae family of land shells, 188, 189